AMPHIBIANS
and
REPTILES
of the
PACIFIC NORTHWEST

AMPHIBIANS
and
REPTILES
of the
PACIFIC NORTHWEST

Ronald A. Nussbaum
Edmund D. Brodie, Jr.
Robert M. Storm

University of Idaho Press
Moscow, Idaho

DEDICATED TO OUR TEACHERS AND FRIENDS PHILIP C. DUMAS, KENNETH L. GORDON,
AND KENNETH M. WALKER, AND TO THE MEMORY OF WALTER W. NUSSBAUM
(21 MARCH 1900-5 MARCH 1982)

University of Idaho Press, Moscow, Idaho 83843
Copyright © 1983 by the University of Idaho.
First published in 1983 as a Northwest Naturalist Book of the
University Press of Idaho.
All rights reserved.
Printed in the United States of America
93   5   4
Library of Congress Catalog Card Number 82-60202
ISBN 0-89301-086-3

TABLE OF CONTENTS

PREFACE

The Pacific Northwest is defined here as the states of Idaho, Oregon, and Washington and the province of British Columbia. There has been no previous attempt to describe the herpetofauna of this region, although the Pacific Northwest is included in a few field guides and books of much broader geographic coverage. Some state and provincial checklists and pamphlets on the amphibians and reptiles of the region exist, but most of them are outdated and superficial.

It is our aim in this book to provide interested amateurs and serious students with a concise guide to the identification of the species of amphibians and reptiles that occur in the Pacific Northwest. We also present a summary of the classification, geographic distribution, and natural history of each species. Though much of the information was gleaned from the literature, we also include a considerable amount of original information from our experiences in the Northwest. To the extent that some of the data on distribution and life history are new, we hope that this book will also be of use to the professional herpetologist.

Our coverage includes all species of amphibians and reptiles that occur naturally in the Pacific Northwest, plus two species (the Bullfrog and Green Frog) that were introduced and seem to be well established. We have not included accounts for the several introduced species of turtles, *Macroclemys temmincki* near Corvallis, Oregon; *Chelydra serpentina* and *Chinemys reevsi* near Vancouver and on Vancouver Island, respectively; and the lizard *Cnemidophorus velox* in Jefferson Co., Oregon: all of questionable futures. Nor have we included accounts of the three marine turtles, *Caretta caretta, Chelonia mydas,* and *Dermochelys coriacea*, that occasionally appear on northwestern beaches.

The formal names used in this book are current as we understand the literature. Readers familiar with the species covered will find few nomenclatural changes from other recent treatments. Only our uses of *Elgaria,* rather than *Gerrhonotus,* and *Spea,* rather than *Scaphiopus,* are likely to be controversial. For uniformity, we use the common names for North American amphibians and reptiles recommended by the *Committee on Common and Scientific Names* of the Society for the Study of Amphibians and Reptiles (Collins, et al., 1978).

References are listed in two parts. The first contains general sources for information on all or many of the species treated in this book. The second contains special literature on one or a few species, as referenced at the end of each species account. We made no attempt to list all available references for each species. A major source of information for some species is the *Catalogue of American Amphibians and Reptiles,* published initially by the *American Society of Ichthyologists and Herpetologists* and presently continued by the *Society for the Study of Amphibians and Reptiles.* The catalogue accounts for Northwestern species are not complete, but new accounts appear each year.

We have tried to use photographs of specimens from the Pacific Northwest, but in a few cases it was necessary to use photographs of individuals from elsewhere. Unless otherwise credited, the photographs are our own.

The range maps were constructed primarily from museum records. Secondary sources included our own field notes and notes from other reliable sources. Some long-standing peculiar locality records were eliminated. Some of these are remarked upon in the appropriate species accounts, as are some sight records in need of verification.

The detailed range maps included in this book would not have been possible without the generous cooperation of many people. Museum curators who provided locality records from collections under their care are Pere Alberch and Jose Rosado (Museum of Comparative Zoology, Harvard University); R. Wayne Campbell (British Columbia Provincial Museum); W. Ronald Heyer and Roy M. Mc-Diarmid (United States National Museum, Smithsonian Institution); Robert F. Inger and Alan Resetar (Field Museum of Natural History); Alan Leviton, John Simmons, and Jens V. Vindum (California Academy of Science); Allan D. Linder (Idaho State University); Charles W. Myers (American Museum of Natural History); Wilmer W. Tanner (Monte L. Bean Life Science Museum, Brigham Young University); Richard L. Wallace (University of Idaho); and John Wright (Los Angeles County Museum). Other individuals provided localities and/or examined our range maps for accuracy. These are Ronald I. Crombie, Stephen P. Cross, Lowell V. Diller, Philip C. Dumas, Earl J. Larrison, James E. Lynch, Jr., Dennis R. Paulson, Robert C. Stebbins, and Siobhan Sullivan. We especially thank R. Wayne Campbell, who contributed substantially to this book by carefully checking our records for British Columbia and by adding numerous localities compiled by him for his own publications.

Lowell Diller, John Larson, Dennis R. Paulson, R. Wayne Van Devender, and Kenneth M. Walker loaned us 35 mm slides for study, some of which are reproduced in the following pages. Gary Breitenbach read the turtle accounts and made helpful suggestions. Margaret van Bolt prepared the base maps and the art work in the key illustrations. She also advised us expertly on the layout of the illustrations. David J. Bay photographed the specimens for the key illustrations. Jan Hodge spent many hours at the computer terminal entering and editing the text.

Many people shared their knowledge of herpetology with us. Ronn Altig provided us with a tadpole key which we used with little modification. Hobart M. Smith advised us on some nomenclatural matters. Lowell Diller and Richard Wallace informed us of significant new localities prior to the appearance of their own publications. Lowell Diller gave us information on reptiles of southwestern Idaho. We are grateful to the following people who provided us with unpublished information: Duane Baxter (Bullfrogs), Robert Lewis and Donald McKenzie (Western Pond Turtles), Matt Rand (Bullfrogs), Richard Ritland (Tailed Frogs), Lyle Wilhelmi (Western Painted and Western Pond Turtles), and Neil Wissing (Bullfrogs).

Milt Williams (Department of Fish and Game, State of Idaho), Charles Bruce (Department of Fish and Wildlife, State of Oregon), Elizabeth Rodrick (Department of Game, State of Washington), and James McCrossan (Ministry of Environment, Fish and Wildlife Branch, Province of British Columbia) informed us of current state and provincial laws and management plans concerning amphibians and reptiles.

This book would not have been possible without the education we received directly, and indirectly through their publications from Ronn Altig, Philip C. Dumas, Denzel E. Ferguson, Henry S. Fitch, Kenneth L. Gordon, James Kezer, Earl J. Larrison, James R. Slater, Robert C. Stebbins, Donald W. Tinkle, and Kenneth M. Walker.

Numerous students and friends contributed substantially to our understanding of the Northwestern herpetofauna by accompanying us on numerous field trips and by sharing their knowledge and ideas with us. Some of them are : Ronn Altig, Joe Beatty, Jeff Briggs, Randy Brown, Glen Clothier, Bob Clover, Tom Darrow, Lowell Diller, Janice Diller, Tony Dorsch, Phil Dumas, Don Dunlap, Denzel Ferguson, John Haertel, Hugh Hanlin, Bob Hollenbeck, Ollie Johnson, Jim Kezer, Bob Livezey, Chris Maser, Don McKenzie, Bob Peacock, Dick Pimentel, Ken Porter, Jim Roberts, Glenn Stewart, Bill Sype, Cindy Tait, and Jim Wernz.

Ronald A. Nussbaum   Edmund D. Brodie, Jr.   Robert M. Storm

INTRODUCTION

There are approximately 42,000 species of vertebrates (animals with backbones) in the world today. Of these, about 20,000 are fishes, 3,300 are amphibians, 6,000 are reptiles, 8,800 are birds and 4,100 are mammals. Of the 9,300 species of amphibians and reptiles found throughout the world, about 460 of them occur in North America north of Mexico, and 62 of these occur in the Pacific Northwest.

The herpetofauna of the Pacific Northwest is relatively poor in number of species compared to more southern parts of North America. For example, the single states of Arizona and Alabama have, respectively, about 115 and 134 species of amphibians and reptiles, or, each has about twice the number found in the entire Pacific Northwest. In large part, these statistics reflect a world-wide tendency for species diversity to decline toward the poles. But, within North America the diversity of amphibians and reptiles also decreases from east to west regardless of latitude, a fact related to the unique historical events that shaped the topography and environments of our continent.

Although the herpetofauna of the Pacific Northwest is not rich in species, it includes some of the most interesting North American forms. Examples are the voiceless Tailed Frog, *Ascaphus truei,* which is notorious for the presence of a copulatory organ in males; the Pacific Giant Salamander, *Dicamptodon ensatus,* remarkable for its large size, voracious predatory habits, and ability to vocalize; and the gentle Rubber Boa, *Charina bottae,* one of only two North American snakes belonging to the largely tropical family Boidae.

Collectively, the amphibians and reptiles of the Pacific Northwest offer a wealth of opportunities for discovery that has scarcely been tapped. It is unlikely that many species remain to be discovered in the Pacific Northwest, but a new salamander was discovered as late as 1970, and there are vast tracts of land in the region that are virtually unexplored by herpetologists. Therefore it would not be too surprising if one or two new forms (plethodontid salamanders seem the most likely candidates) turned up in remote areas, such as in the mountains of northern Idaho or northeastern Oregon. Our information on the geographic distribution of some Northwestern species is sketchy, and considerable field work is needed to define the limits of their distributions. The life history and ecology of most species are inadequately known, and knowledge of geographic variation in life history traits is virtually nonexistent. In all of these areas of study, it is possible for the amateur naturalist and beginning student to contribute significantly to our understanding of the herpetofauna of the Pacific Northwest. An enthusiastic interest in amphibians and reptiles, an ability to keep detailed and accurate field notes, and a willingness to seek out and communicate with professional herpetologists are all that is required.

COLLECTING AND OBSERVING AMPHIBIANS AND REPTILES

LAWS — Many people are unaware that most species of North American amphibians and reptiles are legally protected, at least over some portion of their geographic ranges. At present, none of the species covered in this book receives blanket protection from U.S. federal or Canadian law, but it is illegal to collect or disturb amphibians and reptiles in National Parks and other wildlife preserves.

In Idaho, the only species presently protected by state law is the Bullfrog, which is considered to be a game animal.

The state of Oregon also protects the Bullfrog, by classifying it as a "game fish." Oregon protects an additional ten species of amphibians and reptiles that are considered to be rare or threatened. A scientific collecting permit, issued by the Oregon Department of Fish and Wildlife, is required to legally collect or otherwise disturb these "protected" species. The ten species are the Black Salamander, Larch Mountain Salamander, Oregon Slender Salamander, Siskiyou Mountains Salamander, Tailed Frog, Spotted Frog, Mojave Black-collared Lizard, Longnose Leopard Lizard, Sharptail Snake, and the Short-horned Lizard. In addition, Oregon prohibits the sale or exchange of any amphibian or reptile taken within the state boundaries without a permit.

The state of Washington protects the Bullfrog as a "game species" and turtles (Painted Turtle and Western Pond Turtle) as "protected wildlife." Additional species are being considered for protection by the Washington Department of Game.

British Columbia presently does not protect amphibians and reptiles, but a new wildlife act is being prepared by the Ministry of Environment. The new management plan for amphibians and reptiles in British Columbia may include limits on harvesting for commercial and recreational purposes and legal standards for care of captive specimens.

Two marine turtles, the Green Turtle *(Chelonia mydas)* and the Leatherback *(Dermochelys coriacea)*, occasionally appear on ocean beaches in the Pacific Northwest. Both species are protected by federal (U.S.) and state (Oregon, Washington) laws. A third species of marine turtle, the Loggerhead *(Caretta caretta)*, very rarely wanders as far

COUNTY MAP

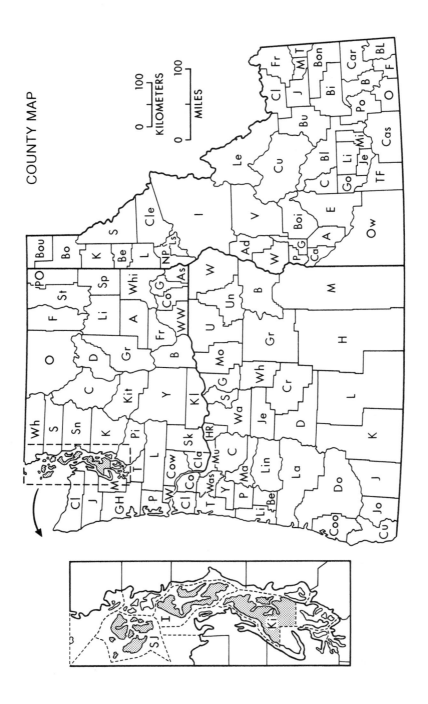

COUNTIES

IDAHO		OREGON		WASHINGTON	
Ada	A	Baker	B	Adams	A
Adams	Ad	Benton	Be	Asotin	As
Bannock	B	Clackamas	C	Benton	B
Bear Lake	BL	Clatsop	Cl	Chelan	C
Benewah	Be	Columbia	Co	Clallam	Cl
Bingham	Bi	Coos	Coo	Clark	Cla
Blaine	Bl	Crook	Cr	Columbia	Co
Boise	Boi	Curry	Cu	Cowlitz	Cow
Bonner	Bo	Deschutes	D	Douglas	D
Bonneville	Bon	Douglas	Do	Ferry	F
Boundary	Bou	Gilliam	G	Franklin	Fr
Butte	Bu	Grant	Gr	Garfield	G
Camas	C	Harney	H	Grant	Gr
Canyon	Ca	Hood River	HR	Grays Harbor	GH
Caribou	Car	Jackson	J	Island	I
Cassia	Cas	Jefferson	Je	Jefferson	J
Clark	Cl	Josephine	Jo	King	K
Clearwater	Cle	Klamath	K	Kitsap	Ki
Custer	Cu	Lake	L	Kittitas	Kit
Elmore	E	Lane	La	Klickitat	Kl
Franklin	F	Lincoln	Li	Lewis	L
Fremont	Fr	Linn	Lin	Lincoln	Li
Gem	G	Malheur	M	Mason	M
Gooding	Go	Marion	Ma	Okanogan	O
Idaho	I	Morrow	Mo	Pacific	P
Jefferson	J	Multnomah	Mu	Pend Oreille	PO
Jerome	Je	Polk	P	Pierce	Pi
Kootenai	K	Sherman	S	San Juan	SJ
Latah	L	Tillamook	T	Skagit	S
Lewis	Ls	Umatilla	U	Skamania	Sk
Lincoln	Li	Union	Un	Snohomish	Sn
Madison	M	Wallowa	W	Spokane	Sp
Minidoka	Mi	Wasco	Wa	Stevens	St
Nez Perce	NP	Washington	Was	Thurston	T
Oneida	O	Wheeler	Wh	Wahkiakum	W
Owyhee	Ow	Yamhill	Y	Walla Walla	WW
Payette	P			Whatcom	Wh
Power	Po			Whitman	Whi
Shoshone	S			Yakima	Y
Teton	T				
Twin Falls	TF				
Valley	V				
Washington	W				

north as the Oregon and Washington beaches. The Loggerhead is protected by U.S. federal law.

State and federal laws restrict the indiscriminant introduction of exotic species, which may become pests. Release of unwanted pets or deliberate attempts to introduce new species of amphibians or reptiles into the Pacific Northwest therefore may be illegal.

COLLECTING. - A wide variety of collecting techniques is used for amphibians and reptiles. The best method depends on the species desired, time of year, time of day, and the immediate weather conditions.

Some species, mainly lizards, snakes, and turtles, are active on the surface only during the day. Other species, mainly amphibians, are surface-active on warm humid nights shortly after or during rain storms. Day-active (diurnal) species vary their activity according to the weather. On hot sunny days, they are active during mid-morning and late afternoon, spending the hot part of the day hiding in cool retreats. All species are more active and conspicuous during the mating season (spring) than later in the summer. During the hot part of the summer, some species, such as the Western Whiptail and the Western Spadefoot Toad, may become completely inactive (aestivate), and some diurnal species may become partially nocturnal. Amphibians and reptiles hibernate during the winter and usually cannot be collected during that season, although we occasionally have dug individuals from their hibernacula. Active or basking individuals usually can be caught by hand, but some quickly run for cover, and special collecting techniques are needed to improve the capture rate (see below).

When amphibians and reptiles are inactive in their refuges, they must be exposed by removing their cover. Turning boards, logs, sheets of metal, and other surface debris is a standard method for collecting inactive or hiding amphibians and reptiles. Short-handled, three- or four-pronged rakes, or specially designed sticks with L-shaped tips ("hooks") are useful tools for turning surface objects. Hooks can also be used for pinning snakes, which often try to escape when exposed. Abandoned buildings, saw mills, and dump sites are excellent places to find amphibians and reptiles by turning surface litter. Where there is no cover, amphibians and reptiles must either move elsewhere or retreat to underground refuges that are inaccessible to humans. Therefore, it is often profitable to set out "refugial traps" such as boards, pieces of tin, and other flat objects in likely habitats to increase the surface cover.

Inactive specimens may be dug from subsurface refugia in leaf litter, soil, and talus with hoes, rakes, and picks. Some seek refuge inside rotten logs and stumps, under loose bark on fallen or standing trees, and in cracks under exfoliating slabs of rocks. A wrecking bar is a useful tool for removing loose pieces of rock, and a pick or hook can be used to break open logs and stumps and to remove bark.

Most species are collected most easily during the mating season when individuals are concentrated at breeding ponds or den sites. During this time, individuals are locally more numerous, more active and visible, and less wary of the collector.

Special techniques include "night-collecting," "road-hunting" or "road-running," "shooting," "rubber-banding," "noosing," "dip-netting," "seining," "drift-fencing," and "trapping." Night-collecting with the use of a flashlight or preferably a headlamp, is often the most productive method for terrestrial salamanders and frogs which may be spotted by their eyeshines. Warm rainy nights are best for these amphibians. They should be looked for along streams, on the forest floor, and on moss-covered talus (especially near waterfalls). Road-hunting can be done day or night. Drive slowly along roads in likely habitat and watch for herps crossing the road. Again, warm rainy nights are best for amphibians, and warm dry nights and daytime are best for reptiles. Road-hunting should be done only when or where traffic is light, otherwise the road-hunter risks an accident and arrest for creating a road hazard. Active snakes and lizards may be shot with a .22 caliber pistol or rifle using bird shot, but specimens are usually killed and good only for museum specimens. Lizards may be stunned with a heavy rubber band shot from a rubber band gun or off the thumb. Rubber-banding also may kill specimens. Lizards may be caught with a small noose of monofilament or thin copper wire on the end of a stick or fishing pole. This noose is placed slowly around the neck and tightened by a quick upward jerk of the hand. This seldom harms the lizard. Dip nets may be used to catch frogs and salamanders in the water, and fine-mesh fish seines may be used to catch tadpoles and salamander larvae and even terrestrial salamanders during the breeding season when they are aquatic. Tea strainers are sometimes useful for catching tadpoles in shallow water. Drift fences, constructed of hardware cloth or long strips of plastic fastened to stakes are useful for catching many terrestrial species (Storm and Pimentel 1954). The fence is usually no higher than one meter, with an apron of fencing material at the base, which is covered with soil to prevent animals from going under the fence. Elaborate fences may have ∧ - shaped strips of metal along the top to prevent animals from climbing over. Fences can be made portable by simply rolling up the fence with the stakes left attached. Specimens that encounter the fence will turn left or right until they encounter a trap, which is either a pit-fall trap or a funnel trap. Pit-falls are usually cans buried adjacent to the fence with the opening flush with the surface of the ground. The cans should have holes in the bottoms for rainwater to escape. Many larger herps, especially snakes, are able to escape from pit-fall traps (depending on the size of the pit), and funnel traps are better for these. Funnel traps are boxes of various materials, shapes, and sizes with funnel openings on either end. The inner end of the funnel is the smaller end. Specimens "funneled" into the trap usually cannot find the small opening by which they entered to escape. Both pit-fall and funnel traps should have some cover, such as a heavy cloth, inside for animals to hide under. Drift fences can be used to completely encircle a small pond to catch incoming and outgoing frogs and salamanders during the breeding season, or they can be arranged linearly along any likely migratory route. Funnel traps (often baited with meat or carrion) can be used to catch tadpoles and salamander larvae in aquatic habitats. A variety of aquatic traps has been designed for catching turtles, including basking traps and large submerged funnel traps. Basking traps are partially submerged baskets with steep sloping sides. The sides are made of smooth sheet metal too slick for the turtle to climb up. The traps are placed at likely basking sites in such a way that turtles can climb onto the upper edges to bask. When they fall in, perhaps attracted by odorous bait, they can't escape. Funnel traps for aquatic turtles are usually constructed of netting draped around metal hoops.

Collectors need containers for the catch. Finely sewn cloth bags are the best all-purpose containers. Deep bags that can be tied tightly at the tops are best. Large frogs, snakes, and lizards can be kept temporarily in cloth bags; keep in mind that the bag must be kept moist for frogs. Small frogs and salamanders, and even small lizards, should be placed in bottles with screen-top lids or plastic freezer cartons with tiny holes in the tops. Moist paper towels, moss, or leaves should be placed inside. Avoid overcrowding in containers and avoid overheating. Most Northwestern amphibians are comfortable between 4° and 18° C and may die at higher temperatures. It is best to place the containers in a large styrofoam box or cooler. In the summer, a bit of ice can be added to the cooler.

OBSERVING AMPHIBIANS AND REPTILES. - Amphibians and reptiles are secretive animals, not as easily observed as birds and some other groups. Often, it is necessary to observe their activities in aquaria or terraria. During the breeding season, many species can be observed at their breeding sites with binoculars. At night, breeding activities of frogs and salamanders are often curtailed by the beam of a light, but a rheostat on a headlamp allows the observer to dim the light to a level that does not disturb the animals. In captivity, a dim, red, night light, which does not disturb the animals, can be used to observe courtship activities in aquaria and terraria.

CARE IN CAPTIVITY. - Many species of amphibians and reptiles are amenable to captivity and make excellent pets or laboratory animals. Others, however, do not survive for long in captivity. In the latter category are the highly active and nervous diurnal snakes, such as racers and whipsnakes, that often will not accept food in captivity, and species with special food requirements, such as ant-eating horned lizards.

In general, metamorphosed amphibians should be kept in aquaria or terraria with moist substrate, usually sand or mixed soil. Water should be present in one end of the cage, contained in a way that the salamanders or frogs can easily crawl in or out. A tilted aquarium with shallow water at one end and soil at the other is convenient, or, a water dish can be buried in the soil so that the top is flush with the soil surface. Cover, such as moss, leaves, rocks, chips of wood or bark, or moist paper towels, should be placed on the substrate so that the animals can hide if they choose. Treefrogs may be provided with dead twigs or living house plants for climbing. To prevent escape, the aquarium should be covered carefully with a screened lid or plate of glass, as amphibians are adept at climbing vertical walls using their moist skin for adhesion.

All Northwestern species of amphibians will eat in captivity. Initially, they should be offered living (moving) food such as earthworms, crickets, mealworms, maggots, and flies. Many species can be trained to accept inanimate food such as strips of beef heart, liver, and fish. Metamorphosed amphibians are carnivorous and will not eat vegetables or fruit. Tadpoles, however, are largely herbivorous and can be fed boiled lettuce or pellets of commercial rabbit food placed in the water. Larval salamanders are carnivorous and are maintained easily on earthworms, tubifex worms, and other aquatic invertebrates. Larval salamanders readily eat small bits of beef or fish. Hatchling larval salamanders must be started on small aquatic invertebrates (zooplankton). Care must be taken to avoid fouling of the water by uneaten food.

Northwestern species of amphibians, both larval and metamorphosed stages, should be maintained at temperatures between 12° and 20°, with 15° C being ideal. Amphibians can be stored for long periods at near freezing temperatures in a refrigerator, without feeding. Above 22° C, Northwestern amphibians are uncomfortably warm, and most species will die at temperatures above 26° C.

Many amphibians, especially larval salamanders, are cannibalistic. To prevent cannibalism, one should avoid overcrowding, provide adequate cover, and keep together animals of about equal sizes.

Snakes and lizards should be kept in terraria provided with an overhead light (60 to 100 watt incandescent bulb) to provide heat. The light bulb should be positioned at one end of the terrarium so that a heat gradient exists. The captive reptile can then position itself at the site of preferred temperature. The light should be turned off at night. A variety of substrates can be used. Sand with small basking rocks is excellent for lizards. Loose sand or soil should be provided for snakes. Flat surface objects such as pieces of bark provide excellent cover for both snakes and lizards. Commercial, absorbent substrate is available in most pet stores.

Most lizards feed on small insects. Crickets and mealworms are commercially available, and a wide variety of insects can be caught locally. Small garter snakes will eat earthworms, small fish, and tadpoles. Larger garter snakes will eat night crawlers, frogs, and larger fish. Kingsnakes and Gopher Snakes readily accept small rodents, which are constricted before they are eaten. Rubber Boas also constrict and eat small rodents, but these snakes occasionally are reluctant to eat in captivity. The other Northwestern snakes are difficult to maintain and normally should not be kept. Although the Western Rattlesnake will sometimes feed on rodents in cages, they are dangerous and should not be kept in private residences. Lizards and snakes should be provided with water in a shallow dish. Snakes are notorious for their ability to escape from cages, and every precaution must be taken to prevent escape. Tightly-fitting covers with no cracks are required, and the covers should be clamped in place or heavily weighted, otherwise large snakes may push the covers away and escape.

Turtles may be kept in aquaria with water that is deep enough to cover their bodies. They also need basking sites such as sand, rocks, or other solid objects. They will readily feed on pieces of beef or fish placed in the water, and they can be trained to take food from fingers or forceps.

Amphibians and reptiles are subject to various ectoparasitic and internal diseases. Pet stores offer pamphlets on treatment of their common diseases, and some veterinarians will treat them.

Checklist of the Amphibians and Reptiles of the Pacific Northwest

Species	Common name	State and/or province	Distributional status	Page
	Class – Amphibia			39
	Order – Caudata – Salamanders			40
Ambystomatidae	Mole Salamanders			46
Ambystoma gracile	Northwestern Salamander	O,W,BC	typical	47
Ambystoma macrodactylum	Long-toed Salamander	I,O,W,BC	typical	51
Ambystoma tigrinum	Tiger Salamander	I,O,W,BC	peripheral	55
Dicamptodon copei	Cope's Giant Salamander	O,W	endemic	59
Dicamptodon ensatus	Pacific Giant Salamander	I,O,W,BC	typical	63
Rhyacotriton olympicus	Olympic Salamander	O,W	typical	68
Plethodontidae	Lungless Salamanders			73
Aneides ferreus	Clouded Salamander	O,BC	typical	74
Aneides flavipunctatus	Black Salamander	O	peripheral	77
Batrachoseps attenuatus	California Slender Salamander	O	peripheral	81
Batrachoseps wrighti	Oregon Slender Salamander	O	endemic	84
Ensatina eschscholtzi	Ensatina	O,W,BC	typical	87
Plethodon dunni	Dunn's Salamander	O,W	typical	91
Plethodon elongatus	Del Norte Salamander	O	typical	95
Plethodon larselli	Larch Mountain Salamander	O,W	endemic	99
Plethodon stormi	Siskiyou Mountains Salamander	O	typical	102
Plethodon vandykei	Van Dyke's Salamander	I,W	typical	104
Plethodon vehiculum	Western Redback Salamander	O,W,BC	endemic	107

20

21

Species	Common name	State and/or province	Distributional Status	Page
	Suborder - Ophidia (Serpentes) - Snakes			
Boidae	Boas			255
Charina bottae	Rubber Boa	I,O,W,BC	typical	256
Colubridae	Colubrids			259
Coluber constrictor	Racer	I,O,W,BC	peripheral	260
Contia tenuis	Sharptail Snake	O,W,BC	peripheral	263
Diadophis punctatus	Ringneck Snake	I,O,W	peripheral	265
Hypsiglena torquata	Night Snake	I,O,W,BC	peripheral	269
Lampropeltis getulus	Common Kingsnake	O	peripheral	272
Lampropeltis zonata	California Mountain Kingsnake	O,W	peripheral	275
Masticophis taeniatus	Striped Whipsnake	I,O,W	peripheral	277
Opheodrys vernalis	Smooth Green Snake	I	peripheral	280
Pituophis melanoleucus	Gopher Snake	I,O,W,BC	peripheral	281
Rhinocheilus lecontei	Longnose Snake	I	peripheral	286
Sonora semiannulata	Western Ground Snake	I,O	peripheral	289
Thamnophis couchi	Western Aquatic Garter Snake	O	peripheral	291
Thamnophis elegans	Western Terrestrial Garter Snake	I,O,W,BC	peripheral	294
Thamnophis ordinoides	Northwestern Garter Snake	O,W,BC	typical	297
Thamnophis sirtalis	Common Garter Snake	I,O,W,BC	peripheral	299
Viperidae	Pit Vipers			303
Crotalus viridis	Western Rattlesnake	I,O,W,BC	peripheral	305

22

COMPOSITION AND ORIGIN OF THE HERPETOFAUNA

The checklist on pages 19-22 summarizes aspects of the Northwestern herpetofauna. To bring the herpetofauna into perspective, it is helpful to assign each species to one of four distributional categories. The four categories are: (1) ENDEMIC - species restricted to the Pacific Northwest, (2) TYPICAL - species that range outside of the Pacific Northwest, but with 50% or more of their entire range within the Pacific Northwest, (3) PERIPHERAL - species with more than 50% of their range outside of the Pacific Northwest, and (4) INTRODUCED - species introduced to the Pacific Northwest by man. The following summary is revealing.

	ENDEMIC SPECIES	TYPICAL SPECIES	PERIPHERAL SPECIES	INTRODUCED SPECIES	TOTAL
AMPHIBIA					
Salamanders	4	11	3	0	18
Frogs	0	6	6	2	14
REPTILIA					
Turtles	0	0	2	0	2
Lizards	0	2	9	0	11
Snakes	0	2	15	0	17
TOTAL	4	21	35	2	62

The region has only four endemic species (6.5% of the herpetofauna), all of which are salamanders. About 66% of the amphibians are endemic or typical, but only about 13% of the reptiles are typical of the Pacific Northwest. It is clear from these data that the amphibian component of the herpetofauna is far more distinctive than is the reptilian component. The reason for this is quite clear. By-and-large, amphibians are adapted to live in moist, cool, forested environments, which, in western North America, are best developed in the Pacific Northwest. Furthermore, the humid forests of the Northwest are relatively isolated from other such environments to the east and south. This isolation has been conducive to local speciation and has prevented the spread of local forms to other parts of North America.

Somewhat the opposite situation occurs for reptiles. They, in general, are adapted to live in warm, dry, open environments such as the foothills and deserts. These environments are extensive in the American Southwest, but are less extensive in the Pacific Northwest.

The deserts and basins of the Pacific Northwest are continuous with those of the Southwest so that there are no geographic barriers to prevent intermingling of the xeric faunas of the two regions. It is not surprising, therefore, to find that the Northwestern reptilian fauna is largely derived from broad-ranging species that are more typical of the southwestern herpetofauna.

During the last glacial maximum (Pinedale Glaciation, 25,000 to 10,000 years ago), xeric habitats were even more restricted in the Pacific Northwest than they are today. Therefore it seems reasonable to presume that many of the reptiles that are peripheral in the Pacific Northwest are recent arrivals, having expanded their ranges northward in the wake of retreating continental and mountain glaciers.

Salamanders (18 species) are the dominant component of the northwestern herpetofauna with 83.3% endemic or typical species. The ambystomatid genera *Dicamptodon* (two species) and *Rhyacotriton* (one species) are the most unusual salamanders of this region in that they have no close relatives anywhere else in the world. The salamander genus *Plethodon,* with six Northwestern species, is the only group of amphibians and reptiles that has undergone even a mild adaptive radiation in the region. The two plethodontid genera, *Batrachoseps* and *Ensatina,* and the salamandrid genus *Taricha* are endemic to western North America, but all three genera have related species and/or subspecies to the south in California. The genera *Aneides* and *Plethodon* are also represented in New Mexico and the eastern United States, and *Ambystoma,* with three Northwestern species, is far more diversified in eastern North America and Mexico.

Frogs (14 species) are less diverse than snakes (17 species) in the Northwest, but frogs have a higher percentage (42.8%) of typical species than snakes (11.8%). The Tailed Frog, *Ascaphus truei,* is by far the most distinctive Northwestern anuran. Its nearest living relatives, frogs of the genus *Leiopelma* (three species), are restricted to the islands of New Zealand half a world away. The typical Northwestern species of *Rana (aurora, cascadae, pretiosa)* form a closely related group that may have evolved from a common ancestor in the Pacific Northwest. The Pacific Treefrog, *Hyla regilla,* is a distinctively western species of a genus that is far more diverse in the neotropics and in eastern North America. With the exception of the Western Toad, *Bufo boreas,* the remaining anurans are either introduced *(Rana catesbeiana, R. clamitans)* or appear to be relatively recent invaders *(Bufo woodhousei, Pseudacris triseriata, Spea intermontana, Rana boylei, R. pipiens, R. sylvatica).*

Neither of the two turtles found in the Pacific Northwest is typical of this region. The Painted Turtle, *Chrysemys picta*, is mainly an eastern and midwestern form, and the Western Pond Turtle, *Clemmys marmorata*, has a broader range to the south in California, Nevada, and Mexico.

Only two of the 11 species of Northwestern lizards are typical of this region, and both of them, the Northern Alligator Lizard *(Elgaria coerulea)* and the Western Skink *(Eumeces skiltonianus)*, have extensive ranges to the south. Of the remaining nine, seven *(Elgaria multicarinata, Crotaphytus bicinctores, Gambelia wislizenii, Phrynosoma platyrhinos, Sceloporus occidentalis, Uta stansburiana, Cnemidophorus tigris)* are southwestern forms, and two *(Phrynosoma douglassi, Sceloporus graciosus)* are found throughout much of western North America.

Of the 17 species of snakes that occur in the Pacific Northwest, only two, the Rubber Boa *(Charina bottae)* and the Northwestern Garter Snake *(Thamnophis ordinoides)* are typical as defined above. Of the remaining 15 species, eight *(Contia tenuis, Hypsiglena torquata, Lampropeltis getulus, L. zonata, Masticophis taeniatus, Rhinocheilus lecontei, Sonora semiannulata, Thamnophis couchi)* are invaders from the Southwest, two *(Thamnophis elegans, Crotalus viridis)* are found throughout much of western North America, and five *(Coluber constrictor, Diadophis punctatus, Opheodrys vernalis, Pituophis melanoleucus, Thamnophis sirtalis)* are wide-ranging in North America. Only two genera, *Lampropeltis* and *Thamnophis*, have more than a single species in the Northwest. Clearly, the Pacific Northwest has not been a region of adaptive radiation for snakes.

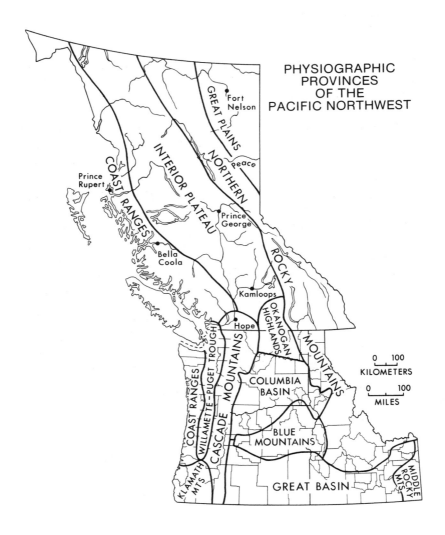

PHYSIOGRAPHIC
PROVINCES
OF THE
PACIFIC NORTHWEST

GREAT PLAINS

Fort
Nelson

NORTHERN

Peace

INTERIOR PLATEAU

COAST RANGES

Prince
Rupert

Prince
George

Bella
Coola

ROCKY

Kamloops

OKANOGAN HIGHLANDS

Hope

MOUNTAINS

COAST RANGES

WILLAMETTE-PUGET TROUGH

CASCADE MOUNTAINS

COLUMBIA
BASIN

0   100
KILOMETERS

0   100
MILES

BLUE
MOUNTAINS

KLAMATH MTS

GREAT BASIN

MIDDLE ROCKY MTS

26

PHYSIOGRAPHIC PROVINCES

Each species is adapted to a particular set of environmental variables that restrict its geographic distribution. In order to understand the distributional patterns of the northwestern herpetofauna, it is necessary to have in mind a broad overview of the present day physiography of the region. An historical perspective is also helpful, but that is the subject of the next section.

The major geographic features of the Pacific Northwest are mountain ranges running mainly in a north-south direction and intervening basins or valleys. Ameliorated by the Pacific Ocean, the Coastal Mountains have the most equable climate in the Pacific Northwest, with cooler summer temperatures and warmer winter temperatures than occur anywhere in the interior. The coastal region also receives the highest annual precipitation of any region in the Northwest, and, as a result, the Coastal Mountains are blanketed by moist coniferous forests.

As moisture-laden air masses from the Pacific Ocean move eastward and rise over the Coastal Mountains, they lose much of their moisture due to expansion so that interior regions receive much less precipitation. Lowland areas to the east of mountain ranges, such as the Willamette-Puget Trough, the Columbia Basin, the Great Basin, and the Alvord Desert (east of Steens Mountain in southeastern Oregon) lie in "rain shadows" and are characterized by xeric vegetation.

For our purposes, we recognize 12 physiographic provinces in the Pacific Northwest, although many other divisions and subdivisions have been named.

KLAMATH MOUNTAINS PROVINCE. - This region of southwestern Oregon is set apart from adjoining provinces by the extreme complexity and old age (pre-Cenozoic) of the rock strata. This province contains the oldest rocks found in Oregon. Elevations range from sea level to 2,280 m. The climate is a relatively mild coastal type (more severe in the eastern part of the province), and the vegetation is dominated by conifers. Biologically, the region forms a "suture-zone" (Remington, 1966) between northern and southern (Californian) faunas and floras. The redwood forests of California barely extend into Oregon in this province, and a salamander *(Batrachoseps attenuatus)* that is characteristic of the redwood environment also finds

27

its northern limit here. Herpetologically, this is an exciting region because several subspecies' boundaries (zones of intergradation) occur here, and the province has a few endemic species *(Plethodon stormi)* and subspecies *(Ensatina eschscholtzi picta).*

COAST RANGES PROVINCE. - The southern boundary of the Coast Ranges Province is the Middle Fork of the Coquille River in southwestern Oregon. In Oregon and Washington, this province is bordered on the east by the Willamette-Puget Trough, and in British Columbia by the Interior Plateau. The Olympic Peninsula in northwestern Washington and the Western System (including the coastal fringe, Vancouver Island, Queen Charlotte Islands) of British Columbia are often set apart, but are here included in the Coast Ranges Province. Elevations range from sea level to 4,663 m, with the highest peaks to the north in British Columbia. The climate is equable and maritime, with cooler climates to the north. The province is the wettest in the Pacific Northwest with as much as 6,350 mm of precipitation/year in some places. Humid coniferous forests characterize the province, and dense mossy rain forests occur on the Olympic Peninsula. This province boasts the highest species diversity of amphibians in the Northwest, with 17 of 32 (53%) species of Northwestern amphibians occurring there. The diversity of amphibians within the Coast Ranges Province decreases dramatically, however, to the north in British Columbia.

WILLAMETTE-PUGET TROUGH PROVINCE. - This province extends northward from the vicinity of Cottage Grove, Oregon across the Columbia River to Puget Sound. Elevations in this lowland range from sea level at Puget Sound up to about 150 m to the south. There are scattered, low, oak-covered hills in the valley, but the valley floor, once savanna-grassland, has now largely fallen to agriculture. There are fewer amphibians but more reptiles in this province, compared to the Coast Ranges Province to the west. The valley forms a barrier for some species, which occur on either side of it in the Coast and/or Cascade Mountains but not in the valley itself. Examples are the Cascade Frog *(Rana cascadae),* the Western Red-back Salamander (*Plethodon vehiculum)* and the Oregon Slender Salamander *(Batrachoseps wrighti).* A few species, such as the Southern Alligator Lizard *(Elgaria multicarinata)* and the Western Rattlesnake *(Crotalus viridis)* occur in the Willamette-Puget Trough, but not in the bordering mountain provinces.

CASCADE MOUNTAINS PROVINCE. - This province, often subdivided, extends northward from southwestern Oregon, where it joins the Klamath and Coastal Mountains, to extreme southern

British Columbia where it abuts the Interior Plateau and the Coast ranges, and the Okanogan Highlands. The province is delimited to the west by the Willamette-Puget Trough and to the east by the Columbia and Great Basins. The Cascade Mountains were shaped partly by volcanism, with the snow-capped volcanic peaks of (from north to south) Mount Baker, Mount Rainier, Mount Adams, Mount St. Helens, Mount Hood, Mount Jefferson, and the Three Sisters dominating the skyline. Elevations range up to 4,392 m (Mount Rainier). Somewhat removed from the marine influence, the climate of the Cascades is more extreme than that of the Coast Ranges. Elevation plays an important role in determining the climate, with relatively mild climates on the lower western slopes and permanent snowfields on the higher peaks. The vegetation is largely coniferous forest, varying from relatively wet fir forests on the western slopes to dry pine-oak and juniper forests on the eastern slopes. There are more species of amphibians than reptiles in the Cascades, with two endemic species, the Oregon Slender Salamander *(Batrachoseps wrighti)* and the Larch Mountain Salamander *(Plethodon larselli)*. The major effect of the Cascades on the herpetofauna of the Pacific Northwest is that these mountains form a western barrier for the lowland desert forms (mainly reptiles) of the interior Columbia and Great Basins.

COLUMBIA BASIN PROVINCE. - This large interior basin occupies most of southeastern Washington, part of northcentral Oregon, and a small portion of west-central Idaho in the vicinity of Lewiston. To the south it is narrowly continuous with the Great Basin Province along the Deschutes River. The topography of this region was determined mainly by volcanic activity dating from the Miocene Epoch. Massive lava flows ranging up to 1,500 m in thickness underly almost all of the Columbia Basin Province. The terrain is flat to hilly with some steep canyons and basaltic buttes, and with some scabland topography. Elevations range from 150 to about 650 m. The climate has a distinctive interior flavor with cold winters and hot summers. Lying to the lee of both the Coast and Cascade Ranges, the Columbia Basin receives little precipitation, resulting in a shrub-grassland vegetation. This province has more species of reptiles (18) than amphibians (9). None of the species that occur here is endemic; most of them are seemingly recent invaders from the south.

GREAT BASIN PROVINCE. - The Great Basin, or Basin and Range Province as it is often called, includes the Harney High Lava Plains, the Malheur-Owyhee Upland, and the Snake River Plains of southeastern Oregon and southern Idaho. This is a region dominated by lava plains, basaltic buttes, and relatively small fault block ranges of mountains, Steens Mountain outstanding among the latter. The climate is much like that described above for the Columbia Basin Province. Vegetation is largely shrub (sagebrush) with juniper and pine in the wetter areas. Reptiles dominate the herpetofauna of this province, and there are no endemic forms. The composition of the herpetofauna of this region is much like that of the Columbia Basin to the north.

BLUE MOUNTAINS PROVINCE. - This province, lying in northeastern Oregon, extreme southeastern Washington, and extreme west-central Idaho, includes the Seven Devils, Elkhorn, Greenhorn, Strawberry, Wallowa, Blue, and Ochoco Ranges. Geologically, the Blue Mountains Province is very complex. The older (Paleozoic) rocks of the province consist of limestones, schists, shales, and others; and some of the younger rocks are of volcanic origin. Elevations range from about 700 to 2,900 m, and the slopes are steep with finely-dissected valleys. The province has an interior climate with winter and summer extremes well below 0° and above 25° C, respectively. Precipitation is much higher than that of the bordering Columbia and Great Basins, and the highest peaks receive as much as 1,000 mm of precipitation per year. Precipitation is high enough to support coniferous forests ranging in character from relatively dry pine forests to wetter fir forests. The Blue Mountains have fewer species of amphibians than do the Coastal and Cascade Mountains to the west, but only slightly fewer than the Northern Rocky Mountains to the east in Idaho. In fact, this is the first montane province we have encountered that has fewer amphibians (six species) than reptiles (nine species). This pattern, fewer species of amphibians in the eastern than in the western mountain ranges of the Pacific Northwest, is largely explained by harsher and drier interior climates and perhaps partly by historical events related to glaciation.

NORTHERN ROCKY MOUNTAINS PROVINCE. - This province extends as a narrow band across the length of British Columbia, east of the Interior Plateau; occupies most of northern and central Idaho; and extends into Montana where it is bordered to the east by the Great Plains. The Northern Rocky Mountains are complex, consisting of deformed sedimentary and metamorphic rocks and intruded granites. Elevations range from about 750 to 3,850 m in Idaho and up to 3,950 m in British Columbia. The climate is highly variable, being much colder in the north where the growing seasons are shorter. Generally, the climate is very cold in the winter with long uninterrupted periods of freezing temperatures, and warm to hot in the summer. Precipitation ranges from about 500 to 2,500 mm per year. Most of the region is wet enough to support coniferous forests, ranging from relatively dry ponderosa pine to wet hemlock-fir forests. The province has only five salamanders, one of them possibly introduced, and eight frogs (two introduced), so that only 34.4% of the native amphibians of the Pacific Northwest are found in this large montane province. Only 11 of the 30 (36.7%) Northwestern reptiles are known to occur here.

MIDDLE ROCKY MOUNTAINS. - This province is barely represented in the Pacific Northwest, entering only in extreme southeastern Idaho. It includes the Bear River Range, which is continuous with the Wasatch Mountains to the south in Utah. Elevations here range from 1,800 to 3,000 m. The climate is harsh with long freezing winters, hot summers and relatively low (about 500 mm) annual precipitation. The higher peaks have coniferous forests, but the lower slopes and valleys are populated with low shrubs, mainly sagebrush. Only four species of amphibians and 11 species of reptiles occur in this region. This is the only province in the Pacific Northwest where the Smooth Green Snake, *Opheodrys vernalis,* has been reported.

OKANOGAN HIGHLANDS PROVINCE. - This province bridges the gap between the northern Cascades and the Northern Rocky Mountains in north-central Washington and southern British Columbia. The region is characterized by broad-topped mountains and relatively gentle slopes. Elevations range up to 2,400 m. Four major rivers, including the Okanogan and Columbia Rivers, flow southward through this Province in broad low valleys. The climate is. typically interior with cold winters and hot summers. Precipitation is relatively high on the upper slopes where coniferous forests occur and relatively low in the river valleys. The sagebrush-scrub vegetation of the Columbia Basin extends far up the Okanogan River Valley into British Columbia, and some reptiles characteristic of the southern Basin Provinces, such as the Western Rattlesnake, the Night Snake, and the Short-horned Lizard, also find their northern limits in this valley. Relatively few species of amphibians and reptiles are known from the Okanogan Highlands, but the region is poorly explored herpetologically.

INTERIOR PLATEAU PROVINCE. - This province occupies much of central British Columbia north of the Okanogan Highlands. It is bordered on the west by the Coast Ranges and on the east by the Northern Rocky Mountains. This is an area of high plateaus and mountains with harsh climates and relatively short growing seasons. The vegetation is dominated by coniferous forests, including balsam fir, Douglas fir, hemlock, and spruce. The herpetofauna of this

Province is poor in species, including only six species of amphibians and five of reptiles. Most of these are restricted to the southern end of the province where relatively mild climates occur.

GREAT PLAINS PROVINCE. - The Great Plains enter the picture only in a small part of northeastern British Columbia. The climate here is harsh with a very limited growing season. This is reflected by the herpetofauna, which includes only seven species.

HISTORICAL DEVELOPMENT
OF THE HERPETOFAUNA

There are very few fossil amphibians and reptiles known from the Pacific Northwest. Therefore it is necessary to infer the development of the herpetofauna in very broad terms based on the knowledge of fossil floras and glaciation in the Northwest. Numerous fossil floras have been described from the region, and Detling (1968), H. P. Hansen (1947), Heusser (1960, 1965), MacGinitie (1958), Nussbaum (1976) and others summarized the paleoecological implications of these floras.

The terrestrial environments of the Pacific Northwest prior to Middle Cretaceous time are largely unknown. During Middle to Upper Cretaceous times (100 to 65 MYBP = million years before present), most of the Pacific Northwest was occupied by tropical to subtropical forests (Neotropical Geoflora) similar in many respects to forests found today in Panama and northern South America. The northern temperate forests (Arcto-Cretaceo-Tertiary Geoflora) at that time occupied a circumglobal position north of latitude 55°. The tropical herpetofauna of the Northwest at that time is unknown but surely it bore no resemblance to our modern herpetofauna.

At the close of the Cretaceous Period and the beginning of the Cenozoic Era, orogenic (mountain forming) activity pushed the Rocky Mountains up to moderately high elevations, and epeirogenic (broad upwarping) forces caused the retreat of the Cretaceous epicontinental seas from the Great Plains. The rising land masses and the absence of the ameliorating influence of continental seas created harsher climates that drove the tropical floras southward. Simultaneously, the northern temperate forests moved south, so that during the Paleocene Epoch (65 to 55 MYBP) an ecotone between tropical and temperate forests extended across what is now southern Montana, Idaho, and southern Washington. The Arcto-Cretaceo-Tertiary Geoflora that occupied the northern half of the Pacific Northwest during Paleocene time contained fossil redwoods and fossil trackways of a large salamander thought to be closely related to the Pacific Giant Salamander (Peabody, 1954). This is the earliest evidence of a precursor to a modern element of the Northwest herpetofauna in the fossil record.

During the Eocene Epoch (55 to 35 MYBP) erosion occurred at a faster rate than orogeny, and a low rolling terrain was produced in western North America. The fossil floras of Eocene age indicate that the cooling trend that began during the Paleocene was reversed, and tropical floras reinvaded the Pacific Northwest. These tropical forests extended as far north as latitude 50°, or to an area somewhat north of the Canadian-U.S. boundary. There is no direct evidence of the nature of the Eocene herpetofauna of the Pacific Northwest, but it was presumably tropical in complexion with temperate forms occurring only in northern British Columbia.

Orogenic activity increased during the Oligocene Epoch (35 to 25 MYBP), and the resulting cooler climates once again brought the temperate forests southward to occupy most of the Pacific Northwest. This cooling trend has continued from the Oligocene to Recent times with minor fluctuations.

There is abundant evidence that from Oligocene to Upper Miocene times (12 MYBP), a rather homogeneous, temperate, summer-wet forest, characterized by the presence of redwoods, occupied most of the Pacific Northwest. The modern redwood forest of coastal California is thought to be a relict of the once widespread forest type. Such an environment would have been well-suited for temperate salamanders and frogs, and it seems likely that the ancestors of our endemic and typical amphibians were widespread across the Pacific Northwest during these times. A fossil salamander, *Taricha oligocenica,* closely related to the recent Roughskin Newt, was associated with the fossil redwood forests of Oregon (van Frank, 1955). Tihen (1974) described another fossil newt, *Taricha miocenica,* from the Lower Miocene of southeastern Montana, a region where this genus does not occur today.

During the transition from late Miocene to early Pliocene time (14 to 10 MYBP), an orogenic maximum pushed the Cascades high enough to create an effective rain shadow, and epeirogenic activity uplifted the region to the east of the Cascades. Redwoods and other temperate forest species were eliminated from the Columbia and Great Basins, and farther to the east in the Rocky Mountains the climate became much harsher because of the loss of the ameliorating effect of moist air masses from the Pacific Ocean. At this time the topography of the Pacific Northwest began to take on modern appearances. The new elevational extremes resulted in distinct lifezones, as seen today. Xeric elements of the southwestern Madro-Tertiary Geoflora expanded northward into the interior basins and valleys of the Pacific Northwest, presumably accompanied by desert-adapted reptiles related to our modern forms.

Orogeny continued in the Pacific Northwest past the Pliocene-

Pleistocene boundary (two MYBP) right up to Recent times and is probably continuing. During the early Pleistocene, mountain building accentuated the basin and range topography of the Pacific Northwest and further restricted the distributions of montane-forest species.

Over the past 100,000 years, at least four major and one minor glacial episodes occurred in the Pacific Northwest, with corresponding interglacial periods. Analysis of fossil pollens from peat bogs indicate that the effects of these glaciations was cyclical. In general, the glacial maxima pushed faunas and floras southward and lowered lifezones, and the interglacial periods allowed the biota to regain lost ground.

During the last glacial maximum (Pinedale Glaciation), which occurred 25,000 to 10,000 years ago, continental ice covered all of British Columbia, northern Washington, and the panhandle of Idaho. Mountain glaciers occurred in the high Cascades of Oregon, the Blue Mountains, Steens Mountain, and the Northern Rocky Mountains of Idaho. Fossil pollens indicate that the glacial borders were occupied by lodgepole pine parkland and boreal forests of hemlock, spruce, and fir occurred in the mountains below the mountain glaciers. Much of southeastern Washington, southcentral Oregon, and all of the Willamette Valley was flooded by glacial lakes. The Columbia Basin was covered by ice, lakes, and lodgepole pine parkland. The sagebrush deserts of the Great Basin of Oregon and Idaho did not exist. Instead, this region was occupied by ponderosa pine forests and grasslands. At this time, the herpetofauna must have been reduced to a few montane species of amphibians and even fewer reptiles.

After the retreat of Pinedale glaciers, the desert component of our modern herpetofauna reinvaded the interior valleys of the Pacific Northwest. A period of maximum drought called the Altithermal or Hypsithermal Interval occurred 6,600 to 4,000 years ago. During that time xeric environments extended further north and higher up the slopes than today. This period probably witnessed the maximum development of a desert-adapted (Madro-Tertiary) herpetofaunal component in the Pacific Northwest. At the same time, humid-montane environments and associated amphibians and reptiles were restricted to smaller ranges at higher elevations in Idaho, Oregon, and Washington.

The deglaciated environments of northern Washington and Idaho, and all of British Columbia, are depauperate as far as amphibians and reptiles are concerned. This may be in part because not enough time has passed for reinvasion of these regions, but it also reflects the cold, harsh environments that presently exist in these northern latitudes.

HERPETOLOGY

Herpetology is the study of amphibians and reptiles. The existence of a science called herpetology is somewhat anomalous and is mainly the result of historical accident. Influential 17th and 18th century biologists had trouble distinguishing between amphibians and reptiles and often lumped them together. They were viewed rather disdainfully as cold-blooded, abhorrent, crawling ("herpeton" is Greek for a creeping thing) forms of life hardly worthy of serious study. By the time amphibians and reptiles were recognized clearly as two distinctive groups, it was too late, the tradition of herpetology was established firmly and it is likely to remain so. However, a conscious effort should be made to remember that amphibians and reptiles are very different kinds of animals. Amphibians really have as much in common with their ancestors the fishes as they do with their descendants the reptiles; and reptiles are in many ways more similar to birds than to amphibians.

NOMENCLATURE

Biologists classify organisms using a hierarchial system that hopefully reflects degrees of genetic relatedness. The fundamental category is the "species." All species treated in this book reproduce sexually. Biologists define sexual species as groups of individuals similar enough genetically to breed and produce normal viable offspring. Each such group (species) is reproductively isolated from other such groups. Similar species are grouped together into a "genus," similar genera are grouped into a "family," similar families into an "order," similar orders into a "class," similar classes into a "phylum," and similar phyla into a "kingdom." Some groups are so distinctive that they stand alone in the next higher category. Such groups are said to be "monotypic." Categories usually are subdivided with appropriate prefixes such as "super-," "sub-," "infra-," and so forth, as in "superclass" and "suborder." As an example, our Western Toad would be classified as follows.

Kingdom - Animalia
Phylum - Chordata
Subphylum - Vertebrata
Superclass - Tetrapoda
Class - Amphibia
Order - Anura
Family - Bufonidae
Genus - *Bufo*
Species - *Bufo boreas*

The Latin names of species are binomial (two-part names) in that both the generic and the specific name must be given to identify the species. This is because the specific, or second name in the binomial, may be used for many different species, but only once in a particular genus.

Within kingdoms, generic names (and names of all higher categories) can be used only once. The binomial name for a species is typically followed by the last name (s) of the person (s) who described the species. The describer's name (s) is placed in parentheses if the generic name has changed since the original description of the species.

The morphological, physiological, behavioral, and life history characteristics of a species usually differ to various degrees from place to place. If individuals from a particular area are distinctive enough, they may be classified as a "subspecies." Subspecies, then, are geographic varieties or races of a species. It is important to understand that, by definition, only one subspecies of a given species can occur at a single locality.

There are many problems with the subspecies concept. Among them is the fact that characteristics tend to vary independently across space, so that a species could be subdivided into subspecies in different ways depending on which characters are chosen to define subspecies. Another problem is intergradation. Often boundaries between subspecies are not sharp, so that it is difficult to define the geographic limits of subspecies. In some cases, the zone of intergradation is so large that one could argue that the intergrade populations also should be given subspecific status. Yet another problem is that of microgeographic variation. Many species, when closely studied, are found to vary considerably over very short geographic distances, to the extent that attempts to name subspecies become ludicrous. We have not found the subspecies concept, at least in formal nomenclature, to be useful. Although geographic variation is real, indeed pervasive, many attempts to formally name subspecies often seem to obscure the reality. For that reason, we have de-emphasized the use of subspecific names in this book.

CLASS AMPHIBIA

The term "amphibian" is from the Greek "amphi" meaning double and "bios" meaning life and refers to the two-phase or biphasic life cycle, which is a basic attribute of amphibians. The first phase of the amphibian life cycle is the aquatic larva, or tadpole, that metamorphoses into the terrestrial form or second phase of the life cycle. Some species have repressed one or the other of the life stages, but the primitive or ancestral pattern included both stages.

Another important characteristic of amphibians is the presence, in common with fishes, of an anamniotic embryo that lacks extra embryonic membranes (amnion and chorion). The amphibian embryo, like that of fishes, requires water or damp substrate for development. In contrast, reptiles (also birds and mammals) have amniotic embryos; the embryo develops inside a pool of amniotic fluid contained by a special membrane, the amnion. These self-contained eggs freed the reptiles and higher vertebrates from dependency on water or moist environments for nest sites.

Amphibians differ from fishes most obviously by having limbs, rather than fins, which are used for terrestrial locomotion. Amphibians differ from reptiles in numerous ways, but the most obvious difference is in the nature of the skin. Amphibians have thin, highly vascularized, glandular skin that must be kept moist, and which feels moist or clammy to the touch. Reptiles, on the other hand, have thicker, dry skin containing numerous horny scales.

Amphibians evolved from fishes during the Devonian Period of earth history about 350 million years ago. Amphibians had their heyday during the Permian Period, or the "Age of Amphibians," about 250 million years ago when as many as three subclasses and six orders of amphibians existed. Only three orders in a single subclass survive today. These are the tropical, limbless, and secretive caecilians (Gymnophiona), salamanders and newts (Caudata), and frogs and toads (Anura). Only the latter two orders occur in North America north of Mexico.

SALAMANDERS
ORDER CAUDATA

Salamanders are the tailed, or caudate, amphibians. They differ from frogs in having carnivorous larvae with true teeth and fully developed fore and hind limbs. Frog tadpoles are mainly herbivorous, without true teeth, and have no limbs until they are nearly ready to metamorphose. Salamanders have neither a middle ear cavity nor a tympanum (ear drum), and they have true teeth in the lower jaw *(Siren* excepted), whereas most frogs have a middle ear cavity and tympanum and lack lower jaw teeth. Of course frogs are without tails and have long hind limbs for jumping or swimming.

Salamanders are more often confused with lizards, which are reptiles, than with frogs, because the two have similar body forms. Lizards, however, have dry scaly skin, external ear openings (with a few exceptions) and sharp claws on the tips of their toes. Lizards are day active in warm dry habitats and salamanders are night active in cool moist places.

Primitive salamanders, like the Hellbender of the eastern United States, have external fertilization like frogs. Advanced salamanders, including all Northwestern species, have internal fertilization, which is accomplished with a spermatophore. After courtship, males deposit one to several spermatophores (consisting of clear gelatinous base and a milky white sperm cap) on the substrate, either in water or on land depending on the species. A willing female then picks up one or a few of the sperm caps in her cloaca by placing her vent over the sperm cap, leaving the gelatinous base on the substrate. The spermatozoa are stored for a short period in a special organ called a spermatheca in the roof of the cloaca. Eggs are fertilized in the oviducts or in the cloaca as they pass out of the genital tract past the spermatheca. In most species of salamanders, sexually mature males have more swollen vents than females, and the cloaca of males are lined with papillae, which are not present in females. Females have small folds or pleats lining the inner cloacal walls that run to the lips of the vent. These anatomical differences are related to sexual differences in the reproductive function of the cloaca.

Salamanders lay their eggs in water or in moist places on land. Some species that lay eggs on land have direct development with no larval stage. Hatchlings have the form of miniature terrestrial adults.

A few Old World salamanders give birth to living young. Some other species that lay their eggs in water have larvae that fail to metamorphose, and they become sexually mature and reproduce as larvae. This "paedogenetic" or "neotenic" condition may be either obligate or facultative within populations or species.

Salamanders are carnivores. Their food consists largely of invertebrates that must be swallowed whole, as salamanders do not have cutting or crushing teeth. They find their prey by olfaction and vision. Salamanders are eaten by fishes, snakes, small mammals, birds, and other salamanders.

Although salamanders are seldom seen, they are often very abundant. They are overlooked because of their nocturnal and secretive habits.

World-wide, there are 8 families, 59 genera, and about 452 species of salamanders. They are largely a holarctic (north temperate) group, but one tribe has invaded the New World tropics. At the family and generic levels, North America is the center of salamander diversity. Seven of the eight families and 27 of the 59 genera occur in the United States.

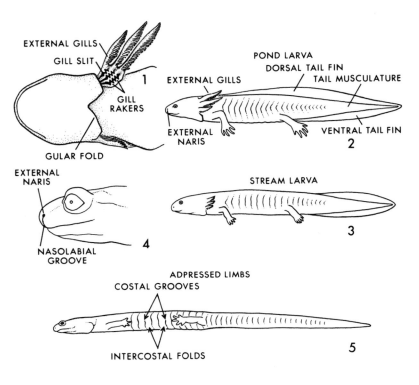

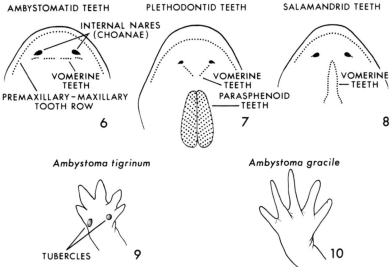

I. Key Illustrations - Salamanders

KEY TO THE SALAMANDERS OF THE PACIFIC NORTHWEST

1A. External gills and gill slits present (1) (larval) 2

1B. External gills and gill slits absent (metamorphosed) 8

2A. Dorsal fin begins above or behind hind limbs (3); gills short (3) . . 3

2B. Dorsal fin begins far forward of hind limbs (2); gills long (2) 5

3A. Eye large, horizontal diameter greater than distance from anterior corner of eye to tip of snout; back and sides with scattered black dots or spots; tail fin not mottled or barred; no light stripe behind eye; less than 44 mm snout-vent length ... Olympic Salamander, *Rhyacotriton olympicus*

3B. Eye small, horizontal diameter less than distance from anterior corner of eye to tip of snout; back and sides without black dots or spots; tail fin usually with light and dark mottling, especially on the tip; light eye-stripe may be present; large size, usually more than 44 mm snout-vent length *(Dicamptodon)* 4

4A. Head width more than 1/5 snout-vent length; adpressed limbs usually meet or overlap ... Pacific Giant Salamander, *Dicamptodon ensatus*

4B. Head width less than 1/5 snout-vent length; adpressed limbs do not meet ... Cope's Giant Salamander, *Dicamptodon copei*

5A. Back and sides blotched or mottled; maxillary teeth present; more than eight gill rakers on anterior side of third gill arch *(Ambystoma)* . . . 6

5B. Back with one or two rows of light spots; maxillary teeth absent; fewer than eight gill rakers ... Roughskin Newt, *Taricha granulosa*

6A. Parotoid glands and glandular ridge at base of upper tail fin evident ... Northwestern Salamander, *Ambystoma gracile*

6B. Glandular areas not evident 7

7A. More than 13 (14-24) gill rakers on anterior face of third gill arch; often greater than 80 mm total length ... Tiger Salamander, *Ambystoma tigrinum*

7B. Fewer than 13 (9-12) gill rakers ... Long-toed Salamander, *Ambystoma macrodactylum*

8A. Nasolabial groove running vertically from nostril to mouth (4) (may require magnification to see); parasphenoid teeth present (7) (Plethodontidae) 10

8B. No nasolabial groove; no parasphenoid teeth (6, 8) 9

43

9A. Costal grooves and intercostal folds absent or indistinct; vomerine teeth in two longitudinal rows, diverging posteriorly (8) ... Roughskin Newt, *Taricha granulosa*

9B. Costal grooves and intercostal folds distinct; vomerine teeth in transverse rows behind choanae (6) (Ambystomatidae) 20

10A. Body elongate and worm-like; limbs short; four toes on hind feet *(Batrachoseps)* 11

10B. Body more robust; limbs longer; five toes on hind feet 12

11A. 4.5-7.5 intercostal folds between adpressed limbs; 16 or 17 costal grooves; belly with large white flecks ... Oregon Slender Salamander, *Batrachoseps wrighti*

11B. 10-12 intercostal folds between adpressed limbs; 18-22 costal grooves; belly with fine, white stippling ... California Slender Salamander, *Batrachoseps attenuatus*

12A. Tail with ring-like constriction at base ... Ensatina, *Ensatina eschscholtzi*

12B. Tail without basal constriction 13

13A. Outermost toe on hind feet much shorter than adjacent toe; digits rounded on ends or pointed; may have a dorsal stripe *(Plethodon)* 14

13B. Outermost toe on hind feet nearly as long as adjacent toe; digits square-tipped or slightly expanded on the tips; no dorsal stripe *(Aneides)* 19

14A. Outer toe on hind feet short, with only one phalanx .... Larch Mountain Salamander, *Plethodon larselli*

14B. Outer toe on hind feet longer, with two phalanges 15

15A. Parotoid glands present; usually 14 costal grooves ... Van Dyke's Salamander, *Plethodon vandykei*

15B. Parotoid glands absent; usually 15 or more costal grooves 16

16A. 17-18 costal grooves; short toes; little or no iridophore flecking on the iris of the eye 17

16B. 15-16 costal grooves; long toes; iridophore flecking heavy on the iris of the eye, especially above the pupil 18

17A. Usually 18 costal grooves; 5.5-8.5 intercostal folds between adpressed limbs ... Del Norte Salamander, *Plethodon elongatus*

17B. Usually 17 costal grooves; 3-6 intercostal folds between adpressed limbs ... Siskiyou Mountains Salamander, *Plethodon stormi*

18A. Dorsal stripe variable in color, extends to tip of tail; stripe not encroached upon along the margins by the ground color, and flecks of stripe color not present along upper sides of body; usually 16 costal grooves ... Western Redback Salamander, *Plethodon vehiculum*

18B. Olive dorsal stripe extends onto tail but not to tip; stripe appears eroded along the edges with an interdigitating of stripe and ground color, flecks and blotches of stripe color present along upper sides of body; usually 15 costal grooves ... Dunn's Salamander, *Plethodon dunni*

19A. Limbs long; when adpressed, tips of toes overlap by 1.5 intercostal folds or are separated by no more than 1.5 intercostal folds ... Clouded Salamander, *Aneides ferreus*
19B. Limbs shorter, 3-5 intercostal folds between adpressed limbs ... Black Salamander, *Aneides flavipunctatus*

20A. Eye large, horizontal diameter usually greater than distance from anterior corner of eye to tip of snout; males with squarish vent region; seldom over 100 mm total length ... Olympic Salamander, *Rhyacotriton olympicus*
20B. Eye smaller, horizontal diameter less than distance from anterior corner of eye to tip of snout; usually much longer than 100 mm total length 21
21A. Prominent parotoid glands and glandular ridge on top of tail ... Northwestern Salamander, *Ambystoma gracile*
21B. No parotoid glands or glandular ridge on tail 22

22A. Longest toe on hind foot longer than sole of hind foot; middorsal stripe or series of blotches ... Long-toed Salamander, *Ambystoma macrodactylum*
22B. Longest toe of hind foot shorter than sole of hind foot; dorsum without stripe 23

23A. A pair of tubercles on the underside of the feet (9) ... Tiger Salamander, *Ambystoma tigrinum*
23B. No tubercles (10) *(Dicamptodon)* 24

24A. Head width more than 1/5 snout-vent length; adpressed limbs usually meet or overlap ... Pacific Giant Salamander, *Dicamptodon ensatus*
24B. Head width less than 1/5 snout-vent length; adpressed limbs do not meet ... Cope's Giant Salamander, *Dicamptodon copei*

MOLE SALAMANDERS
FAMILY AMBYSTOMATIDAE

Mole Salamanders form a distinctive group of relatively primitive salamanders. All species have a larval stage, and there is a tendency toward paedogenesis. With one exception, all larval salamanders in the Pacific Northwest belong to this family. The exception is the larva of the Roughskin Newt of the family Salamandridae. Among other differences, the larval newt differs from all larval ambystomatids in lacking maxillary teeth, which are present in the latter. The metamorphosed ambystomatids of the Pacific Northwest can readily be identified to family by their transverse vomerine tooth rows, lack of parasphenoid teeth, and lack of nasolabial grooves.

The Ambystomatidae is strictly a North American family, ranging from southern Alaska and Canada southward to the southern Mexican Plateau. The family has four genera and 33 species, of which three genera and six species occur in the Pacific Northwest. Two genera, *Dicamptodon* and *Rhyacotriton,* are restricted to the Pacific Northwest and have no close relatives anywhere else in the world.

TRUE MOLE SALAMANDERS
GENUS *AMBYSTOMA*

This is the most diverse (26± species) and widespread genus of the family. Species of this genus all have small eggs and pond-adapted larvae with long gills, well-developed tail fins that extend far forward on the back, and high or deep bodies. Most species, including all of those in the Northwest, have very brief reproductive seasons in the early spring, during which time adults migrate to ponds to court and deposit eggs. Two eastern U.S. species lay their eggs on land in depressions that are eventually covered by water from rain. One of these eastern forms has maternal attendance of the terrestrial nest, but no other members of this genus have parental care. Unlike newts, adult *Ambystoma* breed and return to land quickly (within a few days). They do not acquire an "aquatic morphology" for a prolonged stay in the ponds and lakes, as do the newts. Males have longer tails and longer and stouter hind limbs than females.

46

NORTHWESTERN SALAMANDER
AMBYSTOMA GRACILE (BAIRD)

The Northwestern Salamander is recognized by the presence of conspicuous parotoid glands behind the eyes and a dorsal glandular ridge along the top of the tail, in both larvae and metamorphosed individuals. In larvae, the glandular ridge on the tail is divided by the dorsal caudal fin. Larvae are olive to deep brown dorsally with scattered dark spots. A single row of light lateral-line spots is usually visible low on each side. The venter is light gray, darkening with age. Hatchlings are difficult to distinguish from hatchlings of Long-toed Salamanders, but differ from hatchling Tiger Salamanders in that the latter lack balancers. Recently-metamorphosed juveniles, sometimes found crossing roads on rainy nights, usually have dark gill stubs and have an olive-brown coloration that is intermediate between that of larvae and older transformed animals. Older terrestrial adults from Oregon and Washington have a deep rich brown coloration dorsally and are lighter or grayish brown below. In parts of British Columbia and Alaska, the dorsal brown color is interrupted with small whitish-yellow spots or blotches. Close examination of terrestrial adults from all areas reveals numerous tiny light spots over the dorsolateral surfaces. These are the openings of the poison or granular glands. They are densest on the parotoid glands, on the glandular ridge of the tail, and along the dorsolateral regions of the trunk. Paedogenetic larvae range in size from about 65.0 to 105.0 mm SVL, with the largest individuals being females. Metamorphosed adult males grow to a maximum size of about 93 mm SVL, 228 mm TL; and the larger females to about 107 mm SVL, 248 mm TL.

HABITAT. Northwestern Salamanders occur from sea level up to about 3,100 m elevation in humid coniferous forests and subalpine forests. The terrestrial forms are seldom seen except when they cross roads and trails on warm rainy nights during spring and fall months. They may be observed at night in ponds and lakes during the brief mating season in the spring. Otherwise, they are infrequently found under logs and bark in forest and forest edge habitats. They spend most of their summers and winters in underground retreats such as rodent burrows. Larvae lie hidden in the mud or under leaves, logs, and other cover on lake and pond bottoms during the day, but emerge at night to feed. They can be caught with minnow traps and fish seines. Scuba diving has proved to be an effective means of studying the larvae in mountain lakes.

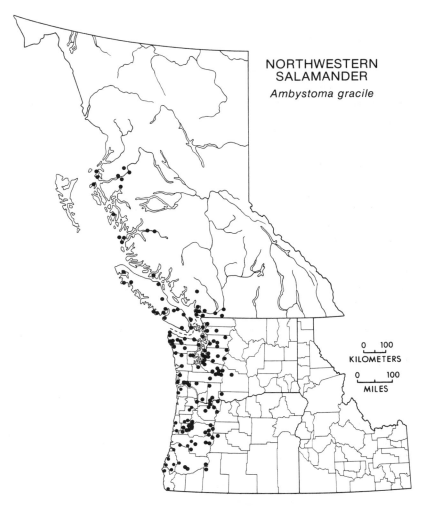

NORTHWESTERN
SALAMANDER

Ambystoma gracile

0   100
KILOMETERS

0   100
MILES

VARIATION. Variation has not been studied extensively, but two subspecies are currently recognized. The Brown Salamander, *Ambystoma gracile gracile,* is uniformly brown dorsally, has three phalanges in the 4th toe, has large parotoid glands, and has four groups of vomerine teeth in a transverse row. In the Northwest, this subspecies is found throughout western Oregon and western Washington, on Vancouver Island, and in southwestern mainland British Columbia as far north as Seymour Inlet, across from the northern tip of Vancouver Island. It also occurs in northwestern California. The British Columbia Salamander, *A. g. decorticatum,* has scattered yellowish-white dots on the dark, dorsal ground color, four phalanges in the 4th toe, smaller parotoid glands, and two groups of vomerine teeth in a transverse series. This subspecies is found in southwestern British Columbia from near Seymour Inlet northward to the southwestern tip of Alaska.

LIFE HISTORY. Breeding sites are mainly ponds and lakes, but also slow parts of streams. The time and duration of the breeding season vary considerably, largely in response to changing altitude and latitude. In southern coastal parts of its range, the Northwestern Salamander may breed as early as late January or February, but in northern, high lakes, where ice may remain until July, breeding may commence as late as August. The duration of the breeding season varies from less than one week to nearly two months, depending on the abruptness of the onset of warm spring weather, and presumably also on the proportion of terrestrial versus neotenic adults in the breeding population. Adults may arrive at breeding sites when snow and ice are still present. Terrestrial males arrive first and remain in the ponds until the breeding season ends, but terrestrial females leave soon after depositing their eggs.

Courtship has not been fully described, and there are two conflicting reports. The first report involved transformed males courting sexually mature larval females. The courtship included a sequence in which the male captured the female from above by clasping her around the body behind her fore limbs with his hind limbs. This embrace is similar to that of southeastern U.S. newts of the genus *Notophthalmus* (Salamandridae) and is unlike that of any other ambystomatid. Another observer described courtship rather more completely, based on several pairs of transformed males and females. The male nudged and butted the female and finally captured her from above, but with his fore limbs around her body behind her fore limbs. The male also clasped with his hind limbs, but the hind limb clasp was either around the posterior abdomen or around the pinioned hind limbs of the female. According to the second observer, the male rubs his chin over the female's snout and his cloaca across the top of the female's tail before dismounting to deposit a spermatophore. This four-limbed embrace executed by male *Ambystoma gracile* is unique in the genus, as other male *Ambystoma (A. laterale, A. jeffersonianum, A. macrodactylum)* clasp only with the fore limbs. However, some salamandrids have a four-limbed embrace.

Eggs are deposited in single, firm, globular, gelatinous masses 80 to 150 mm in diameter, attached to vegetation 0.5 to 1.0 m below the surface. Ova are 1.5 to 2.5 mm in diameter with light brown dorsal poles and cream-colored ventral poles. The innermost jelly layers are often green because of the presence of symbiotic algae, the intensity of green increasing with time. Clutch size varies between populations, but usually falls in the range of 40 to 270 eggs. The embryonic period is 30 to 60 days depending on egg size and temperature. Hatchlings are about 14 to 15 mm TL. Metamorphosis usually occurs in the second year of larval life at about 50 mm SVL, or the larvae may become paedogenetic in their second or third years. Paedogenes reproduce every year at low elevations but may skip a year at high elevations.

Larvae eat many different kinds of aquatic invertebrates, mainly zooplankton. The food of terrestrial forms is unstudied, but it is expected to include a wide variety of terrestrial invertebrates. Trout and aquatic beetle larvae prey on larval Northwestern Salamanders.

Terrestrial individuals have a characteristic defensive posture when disturbed. They stand up on their legs, lower their heads, and lean toward the disturbance. They also lash their tails at predators. When disturbed, they exude copious, white, poisonous and noxious secretions onto the skin, especially in the parotoid and dorsal tail regions where poison glands are concentrated. They also make a series of ticking sounds when disturbed, which may serve as a threat in aggressive intraspecific encounters or as a warning to predators.

REMARKS. Geographic variation needs to be studied to determine the relationships of the various northern and southern populations. We are not convinced that these populations represent a single species. Factors affecting paedogenesis are largely unknown, and the social life of this salamander is unstudied.

REFERENCES. Brodie and Gibson (1969), H. A. Brown (1976), Eagleson (1976), Efford and Mathias (1969), Efford and Tsumura (1973), Henderson (1973), Knudson (1960), L.E. Licht (1969a, 1973, 1975a), Neish (1971), Snyder (1956), Sprules (1974).

LONG-TOED SALAMANDER
AMBYSTOMA MACRODACTYLUM BAIRD

1. Long-toed Salamander *(Ambystoma macrodactylum columbianum)*, Deschutes Co., Oregon.

The Long-toed Salamander is the smallest, commonest, and most widespread species of *Ambystoma* in the Pacific Northwest. Metamorphosed individuals are dark gray to almost black with a yellow, tan, or olive-green dorsal stripe. The stripe has uneven borders, and it is sometimes broken up into blotches. The sides have white speckling of various densities, and the venter is grayish brown to grayish black. Males have longer vent openings that are lined with villus papillae and are usually swollen from the presence of glands that secrete the base and stalk of the spermatophore. Females have shorter vent openings that are not swollen and lack papillae. Males have longer limbs and tails than females. Larvae are usually shorter than 80 mm TL, but exceptional individuals grow to 90 mm TL. Maximum adult size is about 160 mm TL (85 mm SVL).

HABITAT. This species lives in a greater variety of habitats than any other salamander in the Northwest. It occurs in semiarid sagebrush deserts, dry woodlands, humid forests, alpine meadows, and all kinds of intermediate habitats. It is often abundant, even in disturbed agricultural areas. It ranges from sea level to about 3,000 m elevation. Terrestrial individuals are seldom seen outside of the breeding season as they lead a subterranean life during hot, dry, or

51

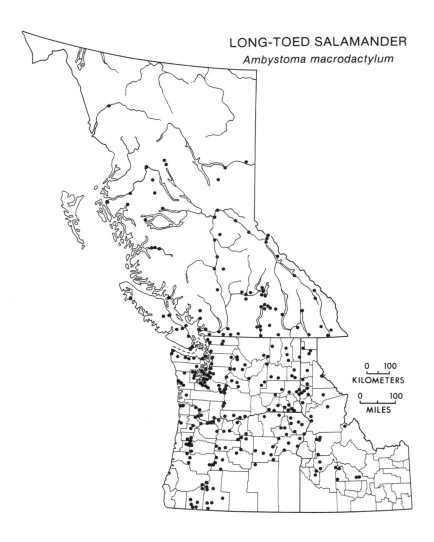

LONG-TOED SALAMANDER
Ambystoma macrodactylum

0   100
KILOMETERS

0   100
MILES

freezing weather. In the early spring, adults can be seen at night in ponds and lakes, often in considerable numbers. They can also be found under pond-side debris at that time of year. Recently metamorphosed juveniles can be found in late summer and autumn in mud and under debris beside drying ponds. Larvae are often numerous in small semipermanent and permanent ponds and lakes.

VARIATION. Five subspecies are recognized, four of which occur in the Pacific Northwest: (1) Western Long-toed Salamander, *Ambystoma macrodactylum macrodactylum* - dorsal stripe continuous on body with nearly parallel edges, but stripe may be indistinct or absent in some individuals; dorsal stripe broken into diffuse flecks on head, snout, and eyelids, or may be nearly absent on head; stripe color dull, nearly matching ground color in some individuals; numerous white flecks on sides, often fused into larger flecks; found west of the Cascade Mountains northward from the Calapooya Divide in Oregon through western Washington and into extreme southwestern British Columbia including Vancouver Island and other small islands: (2) Eastern Long-toed Salamander, *A.m. columbianum* - like the Western Long-toed Salamander, but stripe broken into distinct, not diffuse, spots on the head, snout, and eyelids; stripe bright yellow or tan and distinct from ground color; lateral white flecks not fused into larger flecks; distributed throughout Oregon west of the Willamette Valley and northeast of the Calapooya Divide and the Klamath Drainage, in Washington east of the Willamette-Puget Trough, in Idaho east to the Bitterroot Mountains, and through central and coastal (except extreme southwestern coast) British Columbia north to southeastern Alaska: (3) Northern Long-toed Salamander, *A. m. krausei*- dorsal stripe continuous on body with parallel edges; stripe continuous onto snout and usually expanded between eyes, eyelids with large patch of stripe color; stripe usually narrow and yellow; range includes the Bitterroot Mountains of northwestern Idaho and most of western Montana, southeastern British Columbia east of the Selkirk Mountains and extreme southwestern Alberta: (4) Southern Long-toed Salamander, *A. m. sigillatum* - dorsal stripe interrupted on body forming irregular spots, or at least the stripe is deeply scalloped; dots or flecks of stripe pigment on head; found in western Oregon south of the Calapooya Divide, including the southern Cascades southward from Crater Lake, the Klamath Drainage, the Klamath-Siskiyou Mountains, and southward in the Sierra-Nevada of California to Calaveras Co.

LIFE HISTORY. The Long-toed Salamander has a highly variable life history commensurate with the wide range of habitats that it occupies. In areas with mild coastal climates such as the Willamette Valley, adults migrate to the breeding ponds as early as October, and the breeding season may last through April. Where the climate is harsher, the breeding migration does not occur until early spring, usually from late February to early April, depending on local conditions. Males always arrive first, often when there is still snow on the ground and some ice left on the ponds. This is usually the first amphibian to breed in the spring in the Northwest. Males stay longer in the ponds than females. The duration of the breeding season varies with local conditions. It is long where climates are mild, but may be as short as one to three weeks in the interior where seasons are abrupt.

Courtship involves pushing and head rubbing and a dorsal capture of the female by the male. The male, in a dorsal position, clasps the female behind her fore limbs with his fore limbs and eventually releases her to put down spermatophores. A single male may deposit up to 15 spermatophores in five hours.

The method of egg-laying is variable. In some places eggs are deposited singly, attached to vegetation in shallow water, and in other places clusters of 5 to 100 eggs are deposited in shallow to deep water, either attached to vegetation or the under surface of logs. Eggs also may be placed loosely on the bottom. The egg clusters of this species are not known to harbor the green symbiotic algae found in egg masses of the Northwestern Salamander.

Ova are 2.0 to 2.5 mm in diameter with dark dorsal and white ventral poles. Clutch size increases with female body size and ranges from 85 to 411 eggs per clutch. Clutch frequency is unknown, but is expected to vary, with females laying every year where growing seasons are long and with skipped years where growing seasons are short. The length of the embryonic period in nature is not reported, but eggs of this size should hatch in two to four weeks in nature. Eggs in our laboratory hatched in 22 days at 13.8° C and in 41 days at 9.6° C. Hatchlings range in size from 9.6 to 14.6 mm TL. The larval period is as short as 50 days in some temporary pools, but may last for 14 months in permanent ponds and lakes at high elevations. Metamorphosis occurs at sizes ranging from 48 to 90 mm TL (30 to 46 mm SVL). Paedogenesis is unknown in this species. Terrestrial forms in some populations become sexually mature as small as 48 mm SVL. Some individuals are thought to mature during their third year of life, but this needs to be verified.

Larvae eat zooplankton, immature insects, aquatic snails, and occasionally they are cannibalistic. Terrestrial Long-toed Salamanders eat spiders, lepidopteran larvae, crickets, earthworms, flies, snails and slugs, aphids, collembolans, fly and beetle larvae, amphipods, and a variety of other invertebrates, both terrestrial and aquatic. Predators of larvae are unknown, but probably include aquatic insects and garter snakes. Garter snakes and Bullfrogs are known to eat adult Long-toed Salamanders.

REFERENCES. Alvarado (1967), Anderson (1967, 1968), Ferguson (1961), Kezer and Farner (1955), Knudsen (1960), Storm and Pimentel (1954).

TIGER SALAMANDER
AMBYSTOMA TIGRINUM (GREEN)

2. Tiger Salamander *(Ambystoma tigrinum melanostictum)*, Latah Co., Idaho.

The Tiger Salamander is the most widely distributed of all North American salamanders. Its range includes the subtropical environments of the southeastern U.S. and Mexico, the Great Plains, the Rocky Mountains, and large parts of the Great Basin Desert. Recently, however, herpetologists have begun to suspect that the Tiger Salamander is a composite of several species with much smaller ranges and narrower ecological tolerances.

Terrestrial Tiger Salamanders have broadly rounded snouts, ridiculously small, protruding eyes, and a pair of tubercles on the bottoms of their feet. Unlike Northwestern Salamanders, they lack parotoid glands and obvious glandular tail ridges, and they lack the dorsal stripe of the Long-toed Salamander. In the Pacific Northwest, terrestrial Tiger Salamanders have a dark ground color with whitish or light yellow to olive blotches on the dorsolateral surfaces. The blotches and ground color grade into one another forming a fuzzy marbled pattern. Some are nearly patternless with a few scattered black dots. Larvae lack the thickened parotoid skin and tail ridges of larval Northwestern Salamanders, and they have more gill rakers (more than 16) on the anterior surface of the third gill arch than do larval Long-toed Salamanders (fewer than 14). Hatchling Tiger Salamanders lack

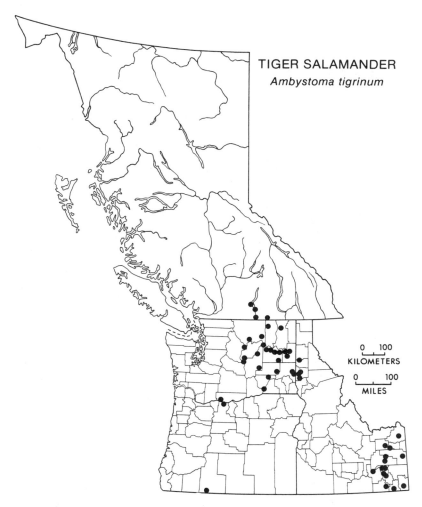

TIGER SALAMANDER
Ambystoma tigrinum

balancers, which are present on the hatchlings of Northwestern and Long-toed Salamanders.

Tiger Salamanders are sometimes said to be the largest members of their family. Appropriately, the very largest seem to be from Texas where a record larva (173 mm SVL) and a record metamorphosed form (169 mm SVL) were collected. However, these lengths are exceeded by larval and terrestrial Pacific Giant Salamanders.

HABITAT. In our region, terrestrial Tiger Salamanders rarely are found, although larvae are sometimes abundant in certain ponds and lakes. Medical Lake, in Spokane Co., Washington, once supported a commercial bait fishery for larval Tiger Salamanders. Most records are from the Columbia Basin of eastern Washington and the Great Basin of southeastern Idaho. There were no certain records for Oregon until specimens were collected in 1972, south of Klamath Falls near the California border. In the Pacific Northwest, Tiger Salamanders have been collected from 90 to 1,400 m elevation. There are no high montane records for Tiger Salamanders in this region. Larvae, or "water dogs," can be found in farm ponds or lakes in grassland or sagebrush plains, and terrestrial Tiger Salamanders can be found crossing roads on wet nights or emerging from rodent burrows. In our area, they are seldom found under surface cover as they lead a largely subterranean life.

VARIATION. Seven subspecies are recognized. To date, only one, the Blotched Tiger Salamander *(Ambystoma tigrinum melanostictum),* had been reported from the Pacific Northwest. Here, we record the presence of a second subspecies, the Arizona Tiger Salamander *(A. t. nebulosum),* in our region. Terrestrial adults from Klamath Co., Oregon, western Washington, and Latah Co., Idaho are assignable to *A.t. melanostictum.* They have faint, middorsal marbling with little contrast between the dark ground color and lighter olive to yellow blotches. The sides of the body and tail, however, have strongly contrasting ground color and light blotches, bars, or spots. The lateral, light-colored areas often form vertical bars or vertical rows of spots between the costal grooves. The throat, belly, and ventral surfaces of the limbs and tail are boldly marked with yellowish bars and blotches. Specimens from Franklin Co., Idaho, in the collections of the Museum of Zoology, The University of Michigan, are very differently colored. They are olive gray above with a few scattered black spots, and the sides and ventral surfaces are nearly devoid of light marking. These specimens fit the description of the Arizona Tiger Salamander. Their presence in southeastern Idaho at the northern limits of the Great Basin is not surprising as this subspecies is common to the south in Utah in similar habitats. Emmett Reid Dunn, in 1940, predicted the presence of Arizona Tiger Salamanders in southeastern Idaho.

LIFE HISTORY. Almost nothing is known about the life history of Tiger Salamanders in the Pacific Northwest. Courting terrestrial adults were seen on 22 April 1967 in a pond near Moscow, Idaho. They had arrived at the pond about one week after the arrival of Long-toed Salamanders. A paedogenetic larva captured 5 April 1935 in a lake near Chelan, Washington deposited eggs the same day in a container, and eggs have been found during April in Medical Lake,

Washington. Courtship of this species does not involve clasping of the female by the male. Instead, the male pushes the female away from the courting "crowd" with his snout, so that courtship can be completed without interference from other males.

Eggs are deposited singly or in small clumps, normally attached to vegetation. There are no reports of egg clusters invaded with green symbiotic algae in the Northwest. Ova are dark brown dorsally and white ventrally, and average about 2.0 mm in diameter. Clutch size and clutch frequency are unknown for this species in our area, but large females from elsewhere contain as many as 7,700 mature ovarian eggs. Eggs hatch in two to four weeks, and hatchlings are about 15 mm TL. Larvae may metamorphose after their first, second, or third summers, usually at sizes between 55 and 110 mm SVL. Larvae may become sexually mature at sizes larger than about 80 mm SVL. In some Texas populations with long growing seasons and rapid growth, larvae may mature in one year.

Hatchlings feed mainly on zooplankton, switching to a more varied diet of aquatic invertebrates as they grow larger. Larvae everywhere are occasionally cannibalistic, but specialized cannibalistic individuals with large heads, slit-like eyes, and fang-like teeth occur in some larval populations in Arizona, Colorado, Nebraska, Oklahoma, and Texas. Cannibals are clearly adapted to feed on normal larvae, and they can ingest individuals of their own length. Cannibals develop from normal larvae and do not represent a distinct species. Elsewhere, cannibalistic morphs are known in some tadpole populations of Spadefoot Toads (see account for the Great Basin Spadefoot). Terrestrial Tiger Salamanders eat most kinds of terrestrial invertebrates, and occasionally eat small vertebrates.

Terrestrial Tiger Salamanders are sometimes found piled up in burrows. This "piling up" behavior is thought to have survival value by reducing the surface area of individuals exposed to evaporation during dry weather, and in this manner preventing rapid loss of body water and perhaps death. This behavior also has been observed in Long-toed Salamanders.

REMARKS. Any new information on the life history, ecology, geographic variation, and distribution of Tiger Salamanders in the Pacific Northwest would be a welcome addition to the herpetological literature. Tiger Salamander larvae are often sold for bass bait and hence are transported commercially. The chances of accidental and deliberate introductions are therefore high, and new locality records should be viewed cautiously. The two locality records along the

Columbia River in Klickitat Co., Washington and Wasco Co., Oregon are old records (1936 and 1890, respectively), which have not been verified. The recently discovered population in Klamath Co., Oregon may have originated from an introduction. The systematics of Tiger Salamanders is in great doubt.

REFERENCES. Alvarado (1967), Dunn (1940), Rose and Armentrout (1976).

GIANT SALAMANDERS
GENUS *DICAMPTODON*

The two species of this genus are considered to be more primitive than species assigned to *Ambystoma*. These are large stream-adapted salamanders with large white eggs, hidden nest sites, and parental (maternal) care.

COPE'S GIANT SALAMANDER
DICAMPTODON COPEI NUSSBAUM

3. Cope's Giant Salamander *(Dicamptodon copei)*, Cowlitz Co., Washington.

This species is a smaller relative of the Pacific Giant Salamander. It becomes sexually mature in the larval form at relatively small size, and rarely metamorphoses in nature. The largest Cope's Giant Salamander is always smaller than the smallest neotenic Pacific Giant Salamander from the same community. Aside from this difference, Cope's Giant Salamanders differ from larvae of the Pacific Giant Salamander in having: (1) more slender body proportions, (2) a smaller head, (3) shorter limbs, (4) a lower tail fin, (5) fewer teeth on all rows, (6) fewer gill rakers per gill arch, and (7) a more mature skin, at equivalent body

59

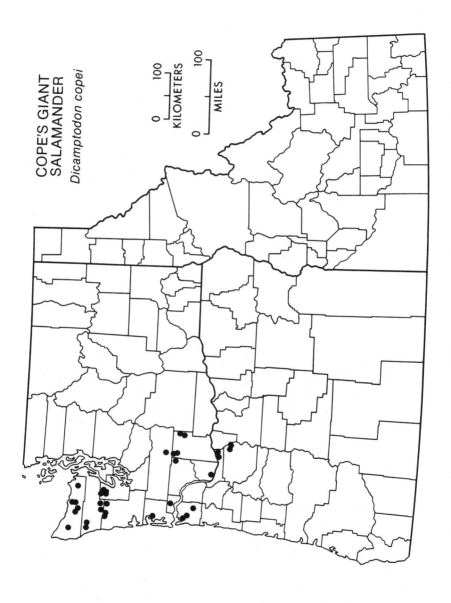

COPE'S GIANT
SALAMANDER
Dicamptodon copei

sizes that contains numerous, enlarged granular or poison glands, often in clumps that appear as light patches on the dorsolateral surfaces. Cope's Giant Salamander also differs in coloration, having less mottling on the tail fin, darker ventral coloration, and faint or missing eye stripes.

Cope's Giant Salamander seldom is longer than 195 mm TL (113 mm SVL), but there is some geographic variation in size. The largest individuals occur in the Mount Adams-Mount St. Helens region of Washington.

HABITAT. These salamanders normally are restricted to streams and seepages in moist coniferous forests with water temperatures that usually range from 8° to 14° C, and are seldom higher than 18° C. They occasionally occur in clear, cold mountain lakes and ponds. The elevational range is from sea level up to about 1,350 m. They can be found under stones, slabs of bark, or other cover in streams. After and during heavy rainfall, individuals can be found at night, out of the streams, crawling among the wet rocks and vegetation at streamside. On one rainy autumn night in the Columbia River Gorge, larvae were observed on cliff faces beside a waterfall as high as three meters above the base of the cliff. They were outside of the spray zone of the waterfall on rock that was wet from rain. Larval Pacific Giant Salamanders also venture onto land, but, we think, more rarely than do Cope's Giant Salamanders. The propensity for larvae to travel on land has important implications regarding dispersal.

VARIATION. There is some slight geographic variation in average and maximum size, size at maturity, limb length, tooth counts, gill raker counts, and other features. Individuals from the Columbia River Gorge are darker dorsally and ventrally than those from other areas. Larvae from different populations also vary in their sensitivity to artificially administered metamorphogenic agents such as thyroxine and powdered beef thyroid gland. No regular pattern of geographic variation is known in this species, and no subspecies have been named.

LIFE HISTORY. Cope's Giant Salamander apparently does not have a well-defined breeding season, as eggs in many different stages of development can be found on a single day. Presumably, courting and egg-laying occur throughout the spring, summer, and fall months, perhaps with peaks of activity in the spring and fall.

Females deposit their entire clutches in hidden nest chambers under stones, cutbanks, and logs. Eggs are attached singly to the roof and sides of the nest chamber. The water temperature at nine nest sites ranged from 9.0° to 12.3° C. The female parent remains in the nest un-

4. Cope's Giant Salamander *(Dicamptodon copei)*, above; paedogenetic adult. Pacific Giant Salamander *(Dicamptodon ensatus)*, below; larva from same locality Cowlitz Co., Washington.

til the eggs hatch. Guarding females will readily bite an intruding hand and apparently will attack interlopers of their own kind. Usually, there are a few individuals near the nest, some of them with eggs in their stomachs and often with bite marks on their bodies and tails. Guarding females are themselves frequently battle-scarred. Every nest observed so far contained only a partial clutch. Up to 96% of the eggs of some clutches had been removed as determined by counting eggless jelly pedicels attached to the roofs and walls of the nest chambers.

Clutch size varies as a function of female body size, both within and between populations. Clutch size ranges from 25 to 115 eggs, with an average of about 50 eggs per clutch. Clutch frequency is unknown, but females probably cannot oviposit more often than once every two years because of the energetic cost of parental care.

Deposited ova are white and average 5.5 mm in diameter, exclusive of the jelly capsules. At 8.0° C in the laboratory, 240 days were required for development from blastula to initial feeding stages. Hatchlings begin to feed at 34 mm TL. The growth rate of larvae and age at maturity are unknown. Larvae of both sexes mature at about the same size within a given population. Size at maturity varies from 65 to 77 mm SVL among populations. The two sexes apparently do not differ greatly in average or maximum size, although the few largest known individuals are females.

Cope's Giant Salamanders feed on almost all available aquatic organisms small enough to be ingested. Immature insects form the bulk of the diet, but fish eggs, small fish, eggs and tadpoles of the Tailed Frog *(Ascaphus truei),* and smaller larvae of their own kind and of the Pacific Giant Salamander are also eaten. In turn they are preyed upon by Common Garter Snakes, larger larvae of the Pacific Giant Salamander, and Water Shrews *(Sorex palustris).*

REMARKS. Much remains to be learned about the life history of this form. In particular, the frequency of its metamorphosis in nature is unknown and should be studied. Only two naturally occurring terrestrial individuals are known. One was collected years ago on the Olympic Peninsula, and the other more recently by Robert C. Stebbins at the north end of Spirit Lake, a region since obliterated by the eruption of Mount St. Helens.

REFERENCES. Antonelli et al. (1972), Nussbaum (1970, 1976).

PACIFIC GIANT SALAMANDER
DICAMPTODON ENSATUS
(ESCHSCHOLTZ)

The Pacific Giant Salamander is the largest salamander in the Pacific Northwest, and it may be the largest terrestrial salamander in the world. Paedogenetic larvae grow up to 351 mm TL (205 mm SVL), and metamorphosed adults reach sizes of at least 170 mm SVL and 340 mm TL. Some Tiger Salamanders may be slightly longer than the longest Pacific Giant Salamanders, but Tiger Salamanders have a proportionately longer tail than Pacific Giant Salamanders, which adds length but little bulk. The heaviest terrestrial salamanders are likely to be Pacific Giant Salamanders. Transformed Pacific Giant Salamanders are recognized easily by their marbled dorsal pattern. They have a dark brown or almost black ground color with lighter tan or coppery marbling, often brightest on the head. Sometimes the marbling is faint or restricted to the head, and, rarely, it is absent. Larvae are recognized by their dark dorsal color, light stripes behind the eyes, short gills, and mottled dorsal tail fin (faded to unicolor on large paedogenetic individuals) that extends anteriorly to a point nearly opposite the vent. The larvae are likely to be confused only with those of Cope's Giant Salamander, which have smaller heads and shorter limbs.

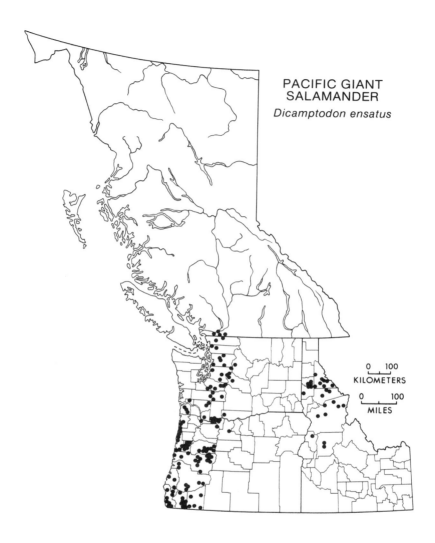

PACIFIC GIANT
SALAMANDER
Dicamptodon ensatus

0   100
KILOMETERS
0   100
MILES

HABITAT. Transformed individuals are seldom seen even though they are quite common in proper habitat. They are largely restricted to moist coniferous forests where they can be found under logs and bark, under stones in streams (during the breeding season), or walking along fully exposed on the forest floor during warm rainy weather. They are most often seen at night during wet periods on roads in the beams of headlights. Larvae are far more commonly encountered than are the

64

terrestrial forms. Larvae are often numerous in mountain streams, and are occasionally caught on hook-and-line by fishermen. Although mountain streams are the usual habitat of larvae, they also occur in clear mountain lakes and ponds. They can be observed at night in pools or slow moving parts of streams with the use of a powerful flashlight when they emerge from their hiding places under stones and submerged logs to feed along the bottom. Pacific Giant Salamanders occur from sea level up to 2,160 m in elevation.

VARIATION. The color of the larvae of this species usually varies to match the color of the local substrate. In regions where the stream bottoms are covered with uniform darkly colored rocks, such as basalt, the backs of larvae are darkly colored with no mottling. In the Trinity-Siskiyou Mountains of northwestern California and southwestern Oregon, larvae are lighter with a marbled or speckled pattern that matches the spotted pattern of the granitic and metamorphic rocks in the streams. Larvae from Idaho tend to be darker than those from more coastal regions. The color of the terrestrial forms varies considerably. In the redwood belt of California they have a reddish-brown dorsal ground color with brighter coppery coarse-grained marbling and whitish venters with some marbling on the chin, throat, and underside of the legs. To the north in Oregon, Washington, and British Columbia, they have darker ground color, both dorsally and ventrally, with medium-coarse dorsal marbling that does not extend onto the throat and underside of the limbs. In these regions, some individuals are nearly patternless. The darkest individuals with the finest-grained dorsal marbling occur in the Northern Rocky Mountains of Idaho. Occasional patternless individuals are also found in Idaho. Subspecies have not been named.

LIFE HISTORY. These salamanders have a complex and highly variable pattern of life history. Some individuals do not metamorphose but grow to adult size and reproduce in the larval form. At some localities it appears that all larvae metamorphose and only terrestrial adults reproduce, whereas at other localities a high percentage of the breeding population is paedogenetic. Factors responsible for this variation are largely unknown, but at sites where the larval habitats (streams) occasionally dry out, metamorphosis is the rule.

Breeding occurs during both spring and fall. Courtships observed in aquaria and field observations suggest that courtship normally takes place deep in hidden water-filled nest chambers beneath logs and stones or in crevices. Males deposit up to 16 spermatophores that average 7.6 mm high by 5.7 mm maximum basal diameter. Females pick up one to a few of the sperm caps with their cloacas, and deposit their entire clutch of 135 to 200 eggs (larger females deposit more eggs) in the nest chamber. The eggs are attached singly, side-by-side, usually on the roof of the nest chamber. The ovum is about 6.5 mm in diameter, pure white, and surrounded by six clear jelly layers. The outermost three jelly layers form a pedicel that firmly attaches each egg to the substrate. The female stays in the nest until the eggs hatch and the young abandon the nest chamber, a period as long as 200 days. The function of maternal care is not fully understood, but prevention of egg cannibalism seems to be one function. Large larvae and terrestrial adults seem to be attracted to nest sites, and these peripheral individuals often have eggs or embryos in their stomachs. They also normally have bite marks on them, attesting to the ferocity with which attending females guard their clutches.

Recently-hatched larvae average about 34 mm TL. These hatchlings have considerable yolk remaining in their guts, and they need not feed for two to three months until all of the yolk is used up, at which time they have grown to about 47 mm TL. Larvae grow from 1 to 12 mm TL per month during the warm season, depending on locality and conditions. They may metamorphose over a wide range of sizes, again depending on locality and conditions. The usual larval period is 18 to 24 months. After that time the tissues become progressively unresponsive to thyroxine (hormone that triggers metamorphosis), and the larvae are on their way to becoming paedogenetic.

Sexual maturity, in both larval and terrestrial forms usually occurs at sizes greater than 115 mm SVL, although there are some populations in which individuals mature as small as 85 mm SVL. There is no significant difference in the size of males and females. Clutch frequency is unknown for this species, but considering that brooding females spend at least seven months in their nest chambers without feeding (stomachs of brooding females are always empty with the occasional exception of a few, presumably spoiled, eggs), it is not likely that they can oviposit more frequently than once every two years.

Larval Pacific Giant Salamanders feed on a wide variety of aquatic invertebrates including immature stages of stone flies, caddis flies, and may flies, and the larger ones eat fish, tadpoles, and smaller individuals of their own kind. In turn they are preyed upon by fishes, garter snakes, Water Shrews (*Sorex palustris*), River Otters, and, surprisingly, even weasels. Terrestrial Pacific Giant Salamanders are famous for their voracious feeding habits. They eat many kinds of terrestrial invertebrates, but most interestingly, they also eat small snakes, shrews, mice, and salamanders; even feathers have been identified in their feces (terrestrial Pacific Giant Salamanders have been found as high as two m up in trees).

These salamanders have a variety of defensive mechanisms that includes noxious and toxic skin secretions, warning postures, and biting. Their defensive posture consists of arching their body and holding themselves high off the ground on the tips of their toes. From this position they can lash the tail, coated with repulsive skin secretions, toward the would-be predator. They will not hesitate to bite a human hand, and when the bite is accompanied by body twisting or spinning (also used to overcome struggling prey), it can be painful. The terrestrial forms have a most unusual defensive behavior. They emit a rattling or growling sound accompanied by sideways snapping with the jaws and lashing with the tail. These salamanders are thought to have a "true" voice, and an audiospectrogram of the sound has been published. Interestingly, the propensity to vocalize and the defensive postures seem to vary geographically. Individuals from the coastal redwood belt of California are far more likely to vocalize when disturbed than are those from the Pacific Northwest.

REMARKS. This fascinating species presents numerous interesting problems. Many aspects of the life history are unknown, and factors that determine the proportion of paedogenetic individuals in a given population largely are unstudied. Individuals held in aquaria and terraria are territorial, and bite marks on non-captive individuals suggests that territoriality is part of the sociobiology of the species.

It has been suggested that populations in Idaho constitute a distinct species, based on biochemical differences. We find the evidence unconvincing and prefer to maintain the Idaho form as *Dicamptodon ensatus* until unequivocal evidence is presented.

REFERENCES. Antonelli et al. (1972), Maslin (1950), Nussbaum (1969a, 1970, 1976), Nussbaum and Clothier (1973), Nussbaum and Maser (1969).

OLYMPIC SALAMANDERS
GENUS *RHYACOTRITON*

A relatively primitive genus, *Rhyacotriton* seems to be most closely related to *Dicamptodon*. Olympic Salamanders are small stream- or brook-adapted forms. The genus is monotypic.

OLYMPIC SALAMANDER
RHYACOTRITON OLYMPICUS (GAIGE)

5. Olympic Salamander *(Rhyacotriton olympicus),* Multnomah Co., Oregon.

The Olympic Salamander is the smallest of our six species of ambystomatid salamanders. Males seldom exceed 52 mm SVL (94 mm TL), and the larger females are rarely longer than 56 mm SVL (97 mm TL). The stream-dwelling larvae range in size from 14 to 44 mm SVL and are recognized easily by their large eyes that have a horizontal diameter equal to or greater than the distance from the anterior corner of the eye to the tip of the snout. Like all stream-adapted larval salamanders, they have very short gills, depressed bodies, and a low short caudal fin. The dorsal caudal fin of larval Olympic Salamanders does not extend anteriorly past the vent. The dorsal ground color of larvae is tannish-brown, and the ventral color is cream to light yellow, the yellow increasing in intensity with age. There are small black dots scattered over the dorsum and venter. These are the only

Northwestern salamander larvae with as few as 0 to 3 gill rakers per gill arch.

Metamorphosed individuals also have eyes that are larger than the snout length. They are similar to larvae in coloration, but the dorsum is slightly darker, the venter is brighter yellow, and the skin has a more opaque cast because of the thicker and tougher epidermis. Males have prominent swollen glands on either side of the vent, which gives the vent region a "squared-off" appearance.

HABITAT. Larvae occur in small mountain streams, spring heads, and seepages from sea level up to about 1,200 m in elevation. They can be found by digging through loose gravel in stream beds. Metamorphosed individuals are found in humid coniferous forests, seldom far from lotic (flowing) waters. Small cold (8° to 12° C in summer) streams with water seeping through moss-covered gravel are preferred habitats. Large roaring streams apparently are avoided. Typical habitats include the splash zones of rocky, tumbling brooks in shady canyons and the spray zones of waterfalls. They often occur side-by-side with larvae under stones in streams. Adults occasionally are found under surface objects a few meters from water after heavy rains, but they are the most aquatic of our metamorphosed salamanders and should be expected only in saturated stream-side talus and in streams. Experiments have shown that transformed Olympic Salamanders are among the most sensitive of all terrestrial northwestern salamanders to loss of body water and will die quickly in a desiccating environment. They can tolerate a body water loss of only 19.4% of initial body weight, compared to 29.0 to 39.2% for other species.

VARIATION. Within our area, two subspecies have been named, which are separated by a broad zone of intergradation. Adults of the Northern Olympic Salamander *(Rhyacotriton olympicus olympicus)* are plain brown dorsally with few if any black spots. In life small, white spots can be seen on the sides. The ventral surfaces are bright yellow to yellow-orange with few black spots. This northern subspecies occurs in western Washington and in the Coast Mountains of extreme northwestern Oregon. Adults of the Southern Olympic Salamander *(R. o. variegatus)* are olive-tan to olive-brown dorsally and are heavily spotted or mottled with black. The white spots on the sides are less conspicuous. The venter is lighter yellow or olive-yellow with dense black spotting or mottling. Larvae of the northern and southern subspecies are similar in color, although the southern larvae are more heavily spotted ventrally. Individuals of intermediate color occur in the zone of intergradation, which includes the central Coast Moun-

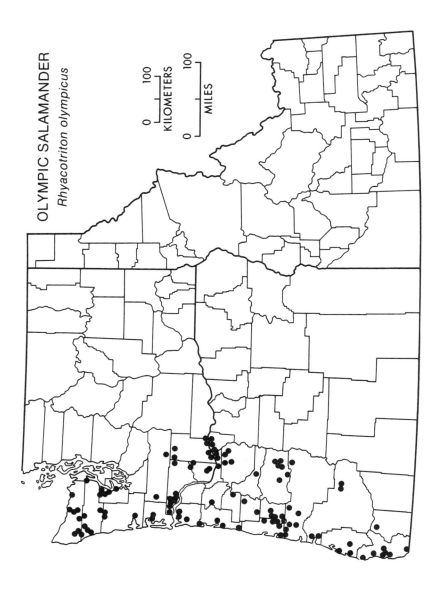

OLYMPIC SALAMANDER
Rhyacotriton olympicus

KILOMETERS
0   100

MILES
0   100

6. Olympic Salamander *(Rhyacotriton olympicus)*, Lincoln Co., Oregon; venter of adult male, note vent lobes.

tains of Oregon and the Cascade Mountains of northern Oregon and extreme southern Washington. The southern subspecies is found in southwestern Oregon and northwestern California.

LIFE HISTORY. Apparently, the Olympic Salamander has a prolonged courting season, as sperm caps of spermatophores have been found in the vents of females almost every month of the active season. Courtship and sperm transfer are thought to occur on land or in the splash zone, but this is uncertain. Eggs may be laid almost any time, but apparently most often during May. Only two nests have been reported. These nests contained far more eggs (32 and 75) than the complement of single females indicating communal nesting. There were no attending adults at either nest, suggesting lack of parental care. A larval Pacific Giant Salamander found within 30 cm of one of the nests had two eggs of the Olympic Salamander in its stomach. The nests were well-hidden deep in narrow cracks in rock. The eggs were lying loosely in the cracks with cold (8.3° and 9.1° C) water flowing slowly around them. The eggs are deposited singly and are surrounded by six jelly layers of various thicknesses. The outer jelly layers do not form a pedicel for attachment to the substrate, and the eggs do not adhere to each other nor to the substrate. The ova are large (3.6 to 4.5 mm in diameter) and pure white in color.

Clutch size increases with female body size and varies by locality. In the Columbia River Gorge, females had fewer mature ovarian eggs (average = 8.0) than did females in the Coast Range west of Corvallis,

Oregon (average = 9.9) in spite of the fact that females in the Columbia River Gorge are of larger average size. Clutch frequency is thought to be one clutch per year per female.

Eggs maintained in the laboratory at 8° C in the dark hatched after 210 to 290 days, and the yolk was absorbed and feeding became necessary after 295 to 360 days. This is the longest embryonic period reported for oviparous (egg-laying) salamanders, but the results need to be checked under natural conditions.

Larvae grow at rates of 0.30 to 0.70 mm SVL/month, and the larval period is thought to be about 3.5 years. Metamorphosis occurs at sizes between 30 and 44 mm SVL, depending on local conditions. Larvae never become sexually mature, and it appears that 1.0 to 1.5 years of additional growth after metamorphosis occurs before individuals become sexually active. Individuals of both sexes are immature at sizes smaller than 40 mm SVL, but the minimum mature size is larger than 40 mm SVL at some localities.

Recapture studies indicate that larval movement is slight, but that there is more movement upstream than downstream. Larval density can be very high (up to 12.9 larvae/m²) in some habitats.

Larvae feed opportunistically on aquatic invertebrates including flatworms, annelids, snails, arachnids, crustaceans, and over 20 families of insects. Larval food habits vary considerably between localities and reflect differences in available food. For example, during May at one site in the Coast Range of Oregon, snails were the dominant food (40% by volume) in the stomachs of 65 larvae. At the same time at a site in the Columbia River Gorge, immature caddis flies, including their cases, were prevalent (32% by volume) in the stomachs of 58 larvae. Metamorphosed Olympic Salamanders eat aquatic and semi-aquatic invertebrates commensurate with their body size. Larval and adult beetles, flies, stone flies, snails, millipedes, amphipods, and earthworms are included in the adult diet.

Enemies of Olympic Salamanders have not been reported, but giant salamanders *(Dicamptodon)* and garter snakes are likely to prey on both larvae and adults. Large larvae and adults of this species exhibit a defensive behavior in response to predator attack. The body is coiled with the tail elevated and undulated slowly. This exposes the bright yellow underside of the tail and may serve to direct the predator's attack to the tail, the skin of which is well supplied with poison glands. The skin secretions of this species taste like garlic and cause nausea; it is effective in repulsing shrews and probably some other predators.

REFERENCES. Nussbaum (1969b), Nussbaum and Tait (1977), Ray (1958), Stebbins and Lowe (1951).

LUNGLESS SALAMANDERS
FAMILY PLETHODONTIDAE

The family Plethodontidae is the most diverse family of salamanders, with about 27 genera and 215 species. The family is almost exclusively New World, but one genus *(Hydromantes)* mysteriously occurs both in California and southern Europe. The most primitive species, with aquatic larvae, occur in eastern North America, centered in the Appalachian Mountains. Advanced species lacking larval stages also occur in eastern and western North America, with a hiatus in the Great Plains. The most specialized species, also without larval stages, occur in the subtropical to tropical environments of Mexico, Central America, and northern South America. This neotropical group has radiated into a variety of niches and includes burrowing, terrestrial, and arboreal forms. Neotropical plethodontids are the only salamanders that have successfully invaded the tropical environment, and there is a bewildering variety of them with new species being discovered every year.

Plethodontids have internal fertilization via spermatophores. All plethodontids deposit large white eggs in hidden nests, and the female guards the clutch. Nest sites are aquatic or semi-aquatic in the primitive species having larvae, and terrestrial in forms that have direct development (no larval stage). Some species are paedogenetic, and some of the paedogenes are adapted to life in subterranean waters. These latter species have pigmentless skin, and some are without eyes. The common ancestor of plethodontids is thought to have been a mountain brook form because the most primitive species living today utilize that habitat and because characteristics such as lunglessness are best explained as stream adaptations.

Plethodontids are distinctive in that adults of all species are lungless, have nasolabial grooves and parasphenoid teeth, and lack pterygoid bones. In the Pacific Northwest we have four genera and 11 species.

73

CLIMBING SALAMANDERS
GENUS *ANEIDES*

Aneides is restricted to North America. One species occurs in the eastern United States, another is found on isolated mountain tops in New Mexico, and three western species occur along the Pacific Border from British Columbia southward to northern Baja California. Only two species are found in the Pacific Northwest. *Aneides* differs from the related genera *Plethodon* and *Ensatina* in having fused premaxillae; long, stout premaxillary teeth in adults that project from the mouth even when it is closed; long, toothless posterior processes on the maxillae; and feet that are adapted for climbing. *Aneides* females deposit eggs in hidden terrestrial nests and guard their eggs. Development is direct. Members of this genus defend themselves against predators by posturing and waving their tails. The glands along the tail release a secretion that irritates the mouth and eyes of predators. Some species, including *A. ferreus* in the Northwest, may squeak and bite when attacked by predators.

CLOUDED SALAMANDER
ANEIDES FERREUS COPE

7. Clouded Salamander *(Aneides ferreus)*, Curry Co., Oregon.

Among Northwestern salamanders, the Clouded Salamander is our best climber. Adults are slender with long limbs that may overlap when adpressed. They differ from other Northwestern plethodontids except the Black Salamander in having a very long outer (fifth) toe on the hind foot which is nearly as long as the toe next to it. Clouded

74

Salamanders have longer limbs than Black Salamanders, and they have a dusky gray ventral surface, whereas the Black Salamander has a black venter. Adult Clouded Salamanders have toes with expanded, nearly squared-off tips, and Black Salamanders have rounded toe tips. The dorsal ground color of hatchlings is a deep chocolate brown, and they have a brassy dorsal stripe beginning on the neck and extending to the tip of the tail, the brassy color intensifying on the tail. The head is dark brown above with a brassy triangle between the eyes. The proximal segment of each limb is brassy above. Juveniles gradually acquire the more subdued adult color, with a brownish dorsum clouded with pale gray or ash and with scattered brassy flecks, the juvenile brassy stripe having largely disappeared. In life the venter is grayish with light flecks, but in preservative the venter may appear lighter gray or even buffy tan without light flecks. Adult males have powerful jaw muscles, giving their heads a more triangular shape than the heads of adult females. Mature females are slightly larger than mature males. Maximum sizes of females and males are 65 mm and 63 mm SVL, respectively.

HABITAT. Clouded Salamanders are largely forest salamanders, but they occur in forest edge habitats, and they are often very abundant in forest clearings caused by fire. They occur from sea level up to about 1,500 m. They can be found under loose bark on the ground, between the loose bark and wood on fallen trees, in rotten logs, and in cracks on cliff faces. They have been found as high as 6.5 m in trees.

VARIATION. There is little geographic variation in this species, and subspecies are not recognized. There is sometimes striking variation in color pattern between nearby populations in which the "brassy" clouding is pale yellow in one population and reddish in the other. The significance of this variation in color pattern is unclear. Occasionally individuals are found with reduced melanism resulting in a color pattern of large light and dark blotches.

LIFE HISTORY. Courtship and egg laying occur in the spring, but the egg laying period probably extends into early summer. Eggs (5.0 mm diameter exclusive of jelly layers) are deposited in cavities in rotten logs or in crevices in rock. Eggs are individually suspended from the roof of the nest chamber by pedicels of the outer jelly membranes. The pedicels are twisted about each other as they converge on a common point of attachment. Clutch size varies from 8 to 18. Presumably the female guards the eggs. Adult males, however, have also been found with females in the nests. Eggs hatch after about 60 days, usually in the autumn. Hatchlings are about 26 mm TL, and they begin to feed two weeks after hatching. In Oregon, males are thought to mature

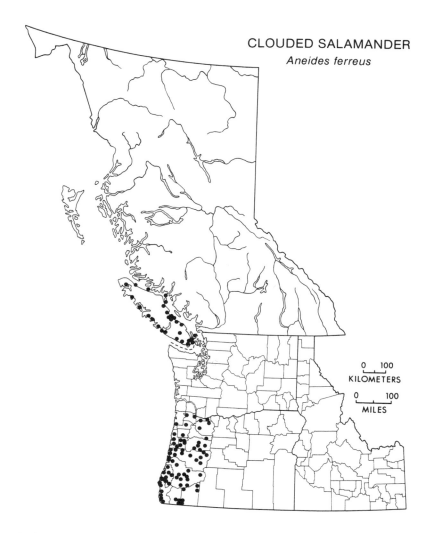

CLOUDED SALAMANDER
Aneides ferreus

0   100
KILOMETERS
0   100
MILES

during their second year after they attain 36 mm SVL. Females apparently mature in their third year at sizes greater than 55 mm SVL. Males can mate every year, but females probably produce eggs every other year.

These salamanders feed opportunistically on small forest floor arthropods. In Oregon, 57% of the stomachs of one sample of 63 Clouded Salamanders contained ants. Adult beetles, isopods, spiders, and mites were also common in the stomachs. Similar food, mainly ants, is eaten by Clouded Salamanders on Vancouver Island, B.C.

Clouded Salamanders are alert and agile climbers. They may use their prehensile tails to aid in climbing. When held in the hand, they will often focus on a nearby object and leap from the hand to the object, clinging with great tenacity, even to vertical surfaces. In laboratory tests, Clouded Salamanders of different ages selected different habitats. Juveniles always selected bark litter over rock; subadults chose bark litter only at higher temperatures, otherwise they preferred rock; and adults exhibited no preference between bark and rock litter.

REMARKS. Clouded Salamanders have not been recorded in Washington or mainland British Columbia. Therefore, their occurrence on Vancouver Island seems anomalous. They should be looked for in the Coast and Olympic Mountains of Washington.

REFERENCES. McKenzie and Storm (1970, 1971), Stelmock and Harestad (1979), Storm (1947), Storm and Aller (1947).

BLACK SALAMANDER
ANEIDES FLAVIPUNCTATUS (STRAUCH)

8. Black Salamander *(Aneides flavipunctatus),* Siskiyou Co., California.

The Black Salamander barely enters the Pacific Northwest in the Siskiyou Mountains of southern Oregon. It is otherwise restricted to northwestern California. The name is somewhat misleading as it is descriptive of individuals from California that are black or black with small light-colored spots. In Oregon, Black Salamanders have a dark dorsal ground color that is frosted over with olive green. Hatchlings and juveniles are brighter, almost metallic, green than the adults.

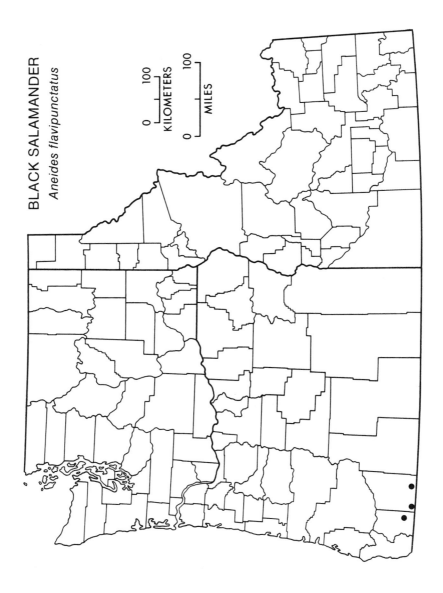

BLACK SALAMANDER
Aneides flavipunctatus

Juveniles are nearly uniformly greenish, but adults have lighter flecks and spots, which are sparse dorsolaterally and midventrally, but dense ventrolaterally. The venter is dark slate-gray, even in preservative, in contrast to the lighter gray to buffy venter of Clouded Salamanders. Black Salamanders have shorter limbs, with 3 to 5 intercostal folds between adpressed limbs, than Clouded Salamanders, and more rounded toe tips than the latter species. Males have larger jaw muscles, hence more triangular-shaped heads, than females. Females attain larger size (76.3 mm SVL, 136.9 mm TL) than males (71.4 mm SVL, 132.2 mm TL). Males have relatively longer tails than females.

HABITAT. Black Salamanders are found in coniferous forests, mixed deciduous-coniferous forests, and open hillsides, from sea level up to at least 1,700 m elevation. They are usually found on the ground under surface litter such as rocks and bark, often near streams as they seem to prefer wetter substrate than other species of *Aneides*.

VARIATION. Two subspecies are recognized. The form that occurs in Oregon presently is assigned to *Aneides flavipunctatus flavipunctatus,* the Speckled Black Salamander, but it does not fit the description of this subspecies very well. Eventually it may be assigned to a new subspecies.

LIFE HISTORY. Nothing is known about these salamanders in Oregon. A female guarding her clutch of 15 eggs was found on 15 July 1895 in Santa Clara Co., California. The nest was about 380 mm below the surface in a cavity in the soil. Ova were about 6.0 mm in diameter and surrounded by thin gelatinous layers. The outermost layer was drawn into a peduncle or pedicel on one side, which served to attach the eggs to a common basal mass of jelly. This base was in turn attached to the substrate. Near Hilts, Siskiyou Co., California, only about three km from the Oregon border, females mature at about 56 mm SVL or 102 mm TL, and males at 50 mm SVL and 89 mm TL. A sample of 21 gravid females from this site had 6 to 13 (average = 9.3) large ovarian eggs, with little or no relationship between clutch size and female size.

Black Salamanders eat terrestrial arthropods, gastropods, and worms. Near Hilts, the diet in February was mostly small black beetles.

Although Black Salamanders are seldom found above ground level, they are agile and show good climbing ability in captivity and, like the Clouded Salamander, they are good jumpers. Their tails are prehensile and are used in locomotion, especially jumping.

REMARKS. The Black Salamander probably has a wider distribution in southwestern Oregon than present records indicate. At Hilts, these salamanders occur on relatively open hillsides with scattered junipers. Salamanders were collected there in early February and March when the soil was wet, but were not found later in the spring when the area was too dry, resembling lizard rather than salamander habitat. These observations indicate that winter and early spring may be the best time to search the rocky open hillsides of southwestern Oregon for this species.

REFERENCES. Lynch (1981), Myers and Maslin (1948), Van Denburgh (1895).

SLENDER SALAMANDERS
GENUS *BATRACHOSEPS*

Slender Salamanders, or "worm salamanders," are distributed along the Pacific border states from Oregon southward to Baja California. There are specimens purported to be from southeastern Alaska and Colima, Jalisco, Mexico, but these are old records, possibly in error. There is also an old, unconfirmed report of *Batrachoseps* from southern Baja California. These salamanders are small and elongate with short limbs. They have distinct costal grooves and intercostal folds that continue onto the tail giving the animals an annulated appearance that emphasizes their superficial similarity to earthworms. They are specialized for tail autotomy (loss) and regeneration as an antipredator device. The tail may be lost at any segment. Slender Salamanders are the only Northwestern forms with four, as opposed to five, toes on the hind feet. Of the nine species of *Batrachoseps*, two occur in the Pacific Northwest (Oregon). Some recently described species are relict forms associated with springs and streams in the deserts of southern California.

CALIFORNIA SLENDER SALAMANDER
BATRACHOSEPS ATTENUATUS
(ESCHSCHOLTZ)

9. California Slender Salamander *(Batrachoseps attenuatus)*, Curry Co., Oregon.

This worm-like species has a dark brown to black ground color with a reddish-brown, brown, buff, or yellowish dorsal stripe. The stripe may be faint or absent in some old adults. The venter is slate gray, usually with fine, white stippling. There are 18 to 22 costal grooves. The limbs are very short and when the limbs are adpressed there are 10 to 12 intercostal folds between the tips of the toes. Juveniles are similar to adults but have relatively longer limbs and shorter tails. The tail of adults is longer than the head and body length. There is no obvious sexual dimorphism. Maximum total length is about 138 mm.

HABITAT. The California Slender Salamander is confined to relatively low elevations in the humid coastal regions. It is especially abundant in the redwood belt, but it also occurs in open areas. During wet weather, individuals can be found under all kinds of surface debris and in rotten logs. During dry weather, these salamanders retreat to burrows.

VARIATION. Some north-south variation in body and limb proportions has been reported for this species in California. Variation

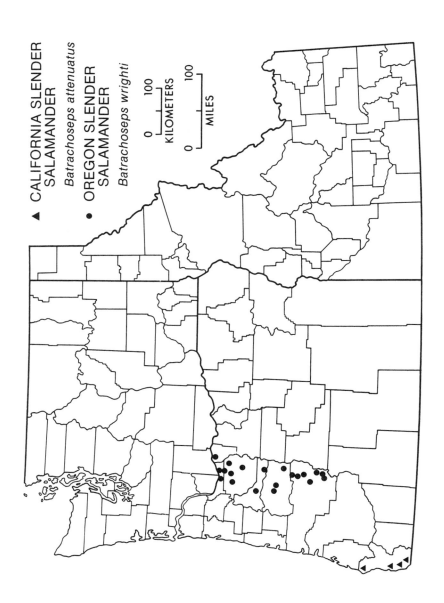

CALIFORNIA SLENDER
SALAMANDER
Batrachoseps attenuatus

OREGON SLENDER
SALAMANDER
Batrachoseps wrighti

KILOMETERS

MILES

0   100

0   100

has not been studied seriously in Oregon, but specimens from Curry Co. seem to have a duller grayish stripe compared to the brighter reddish stripe of most northern California specimens. No subspecies are recognized.

LIFE HISTORY. This species has not been studied in Oregon. In the region of San Francisco Bay, females lay eggs at the onset of the autumn rains, usually in October, and continue to lay through December. Females deposit 4 to 21 (average about 12) eggs in hidden nests. The nests are under bark (or other litter) on the ground or in cavities in rotten logs or soil. Several females often deposit eggs in the same nest. Eggs (3 to 4 mm diameter) are laid in strings of jelly that are usually twisted into a clump. Females usually abandon their eggs, which is unusual for a plethodontid salamander. Eggs hatch in the spring, and hatchlings are 16 to 17 mm TL. Data on size at maturity are not available, but males and females are thought to mature between the ages of 2.5 and 3.5 years. Females usually oviposit once a year, which is probably more frequent than would be possible if females brooded their eggs.

Small terrestrial invertebrates are eaten by these salamanders. Earthworms, collembolans, aphids, larval and adult beetles, millipedes, amphipods, and insects occur in their stomachs.

This species is often found in pairs, the two individuals being very close together under the same surface object. When disturbed, California Slender Salamanders coil up and lie quietly. Upon further disturbance they rapidly uncoil and coil in the opposite direction several times, thereby propelling themselves away from danger. When touched, grabbed, or bitten on the tail, they drop the tail at any segment. The tail is rapidly regrown at about 1.3 to 2.6 mm/month. Tail loss is thought to have high survival value in predator encounters. Up to 48% of the individuals in a population may have regenerating tails, which is suggestive of the efficacy of tail loss in survival. It has been shown that individuals of both sexes that are regenerating tails in natural populations may have delayed maturity and reduced fecundity.

Although California Slender Salamanders spend much of their time in burrows, they apparently cannot form their own burrows. Instead, they rely on the burrows of other animals and on natural openings in the soil. Populations are often very dense, ranging up to one individual per 1.5 m². They have remarkably small home ranges with a radius of about 1.7 m. Some seaside populations exposed to sea spray have individuals with remarkably high tolerance to salt. They may survive indefinitely in solutions of up to 30% sea water.

REFERENCES. Brame and Murray (1968), Brodie et al. (1974b), Hendrickson (1954), Hubbard (1903), P. Licht et al. (1975), Maiorana (1976, 1977), Maslin (1939).

OREGON SLENDER SALAMANDER
BATRACHOSEPS WRIGHTI (BISHOP)

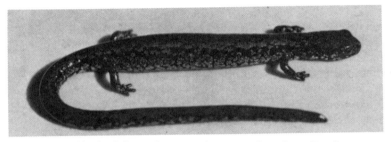

10. Oregon Slender Salamander *(Batrachoseps wrighti),* Lane Co., Oregon.

11. Oregon Slender Salamander *(Batrachoseps wrighti),* Lane Co.

The Oregon Slender Salamander is one of our endemic species. It is known only in the Cascade Mountains of Oregon. The northern limit of its range is precisely defined by the Columbia River, suggesting that the river may be a barrier to northward expansion into the state of Washington. The Clouded Salamander, *Aneides ferreus,* is also seemingly stopped by the Columbia River, although other species such as the Larch Mountain Salamander, *Plethodon larselli,* occur on both sides of the river.

The Oregon Slender Salamander is distinguished from the California Slender Salamander by its large white spots on the dark ground color of the belly and lower sides. It also has fewer costal

84

grooves (16 or 17), longer limbs (4.5 to 7.5 intercostal folds between adpressed limbs), and a shorter tail (about equal to or only slightly longer than head and body length).

This species has a dorsal stripe, usually reddish brown, from the head to the tip of the tail. The stripe is often interrupted with black pigment along the midline. The stripe fades to a duller color in older (larger) individuals. The dorsolateral part of the body is black or dark brown, and the ventrolateral ground color is slate black and covered with large white spots. Like all *Batrachoseps,* the Oregon Slender Salamander has short limbs with only four toes on the hind feet and a slender worm-like body. However, hatchlings and small juveniles have stouter bodies, relatively longer limbs, and shorter tails with little suggestion of the worm-like appearance of adults.

Sexual dimorphism is not marked, but adult females are plumper than males, and adult females are longer (average = 42.5 mm SVL) than adult males (37.9 mm SVL). Eggs of gravid females can be seen through the translucent abdominal wall.

The largest recorded specimen is from the Columbia River Gorge. It measures 60.1 mm from snout to posterior edge of vent (standard length, SL) and 118.2 mm TL. This specimen is a "giant," however, measuring 21 mm TL longer than the next largest specimen.

HABITAT. Oregon Slender Salamanders are most common in the mature Douglas fir forests on the western slopes of the Cascade Mountains. They also occur in the recent lava flows near the crest of the Cascades and in second growth forest. They are largely absent from recently clear-cut areas. The elevational range is 15 to 1,340 m. During the early spring months when the ground is still damp from snow melt, they can be collected in large numbers under bark and logs lying on the forest floor. They are also found inside rotten logs. Substrate temperatures where animals were found in May varied from 10.8° to 13.8° C. Later in the spring and summer they are difficult to find as they retreat to a subterranean existence.

VARIATION. These salamanders are nearly uniform in color throughout their range. Although there is some intrapopulation variation in stripe color, it is slight compared to California Slender Salamanders. Individuals with gold or greenish-gold dorsal stripes frequently are found in the Columbia River Gorge. A remarkable instance of variation in the number of maxillary teeth occurs in the Oregon Slender Salamander. In the northern part of the range, they may have as many as 66 maxillary teeth, the number decreasing southward so that some individuals at the extreme southern end of the

85

range have no maxillary teeth. The significance of this variation is unknown. It is possible that the number of teeth varies seasonally, and the cycle may not be synchronous from north to south. No subspecies have been named.

LIFE HISTORY. Females collected in April, May, and early June are usually gravid and often have caps of spermatophores in their cloacas indicating recent courtship. Females have been found with their clutches during April, May, and June in hidden nests under bark and in rotten logs. Not enough information is available to determine if maternal care consistently occurs in this species. Eggs are large (4.0 mm in diameter), cream colored, and joined together by jelly strands, as described for *Batrachoseps attenuatus*. At 12° C in the laboratory, eggs hatch after 133 days. Hatchlings are about 14 mm SL and 19 mm TL. Clutch size ranges from 3 to 11 (mean = 6.3) eggs, as estimated from ovarian egg counts of 38 gravid females. Larger females usually contain more eggs. Clutch frequency is unknown. Females mature at about 35 mm SVL, and males at 33 mm SVL.

Stomachs of Oregon Slender Salamanders from near Hidden Lake, Lane Co., Oregon contained collembolans, pseudoscorpions, mites, dipteran larvae and adults, spiders, snails, beetle larvae and adults, centipedes, and earthworms. Collembolans were the most common food, and mites were the next most common food.

Batrachoseps wrighti are often found clumped, with two or more individuals found close together under the same object. They usually coil the body, but not the tail, when disturbed. Further disturbance elicits flipping by coiling and uncoiling the body, followed by sudden immobility. This escape behavior also occurs in *Batrachoseps attenuatus* and *Plethodon larselli*. When seized by the tail, Oregon Slender Salamanders shed their tails at any segment. Near Hidden Lake, Lane Co., Oregon, about 13% of the adult population had recently autotomized or regenerating tails.

REMARKS. The life history of this interesting salamander is known imperfectly and should be studied. Especially needed is information on its habitat requirements in view of the progressive deforestation of the western Cascade Mountains.

REFERENCES. Brame and Murray (1968), Hendrickson (1954), Stebbins (1949a), Stebbins and Lowe (1949), Tanner (1953).

ENSATINAS
GENUS *ENSATINA*

This monotypic genus is related to *Aneides* and *Plethodon*. It differs from these two genera in having a basally constricted tail and in lacking spurs on the tibia. The tail constriction coincides with the site of cleavage when the tail is lost to predators. Ensatinas are restricted to western North America.

ENSATINA
ENSATINA ESCHSCHOLTZI GRAY

12. Ensatina *(Ensatina eschscholtzi)*, Coos Co., Oregon; defensive posture.

Ensatinas are recognized easily in that they are the only Northwestern salamanders with a distinct constriction at the base of the tail. The tail is rounded dorsally and is notably thicker in the middle than near the vent and tip. They have short bodies (12 costal grooves) and relatively long, slender legs with extensive overlap when adpressed. There are two subspecies, largely defined by color differences, and intergrades in the Pacific Northwest (see Variation). Males have longer and more slender tails and longer and blunter snouts than females. Adult females average about eight mm SVL longer than adult males. The largest individual from the Pacific Northwest (Oregon) measured by us was a female 115.4 mm TL (64.3 mm SVL).

HABITAT. Ensatinas are mainly forest animals, but they are occasionally found in clearings. They are surface active during the spring and autumn when the ground is damp from rain or snow melt. At these times they are found under leaf litter, bark, rocks, and logs. During the summer dry spells they retreat underground. Ensatinas occur

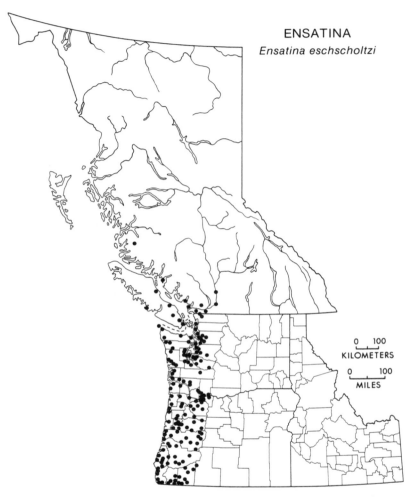

ENSATINA
Ensatina eschscholtzi

0   100
KILOMETERS

0   100
MILES

from sea level to about 3,350 m in California, but in the Northwest they are known only up to 1,700 m.

VARIATION. Of the seven named subspecies, only two occur in our area. The most widespread form is the Oregon Ensatina, *Ensatina eschscholtzi oregonensis*. It has a nearly uniform light to dark orange-brown dorsal surface with a cream to pale yellow venter. Often there is fine black speckling over the dorsum and venter. The sides are sometimes mottled with dark pigment. The bases of the limbs are yellow dorsally. Young of this subspecies also have yellow limb bases, but the body is gray to brown with large black blotches on the dorsolateral surfaces. *E. e. oregonensis* is the subspecies that occurs in British Columbia and Washington. It also occurs throughout most of western Oregon except for the extreme southwestern Klamath-Siskiyou region. The other subspecies in our area is the Painted Ensatina, *E.e. picta.* It has a restricted distribution in southwestern (Curry Co.) Oregon. This form has a blotched dorsal pattern of black, yellow, and orange spots. The limbs are yellow proximally as in the Oregon Ensatina. The venter is light yellow orange to pinkish. The young also have a variegated dorsal pattern. A broad zone of intergradation between these two subspecies occurs in southwestern Oregon. Intergrades between the Oregon Ensatina and a Californian subspecies (Sierra Nevada Ensatina, *E.e. platensis)* occur in Jackson Co., Oregon. Stebbins' (1949) monograph should be referred to for details.

LIFE HISTORY. Courtship takes place on the surface at night and involves nosing and rubbing of the female by the male, culminating in the typical plethodontid "tail walk" in which the female straddles the male's tail with her fore limbs and follows closely behind him. The male then deposits a spermatophore in front of the female, which she may pick up. Courting and egg-laying usually occur in the spring from February to April, but courtship also occurs in the autumn (October) near Corvallis, Oregon. Eggs are deposited below the surface, sometimes as deep as 0.8 m in a cavity and are brooded by the female. The clutch size in the Northwest ranges from 5 to 16 (mean = 10.5) ovarian eggs. Clutch frequency is unknown. The incubation period, during the dry summer months, may last 150 to 180 days. The white eggs are 4 to 7 mm in diameter and surrounded by two jelly layers. The egg capsules are not pedicellate, and the eggs are deposited in grape-like clusters. Hatchlings are about 20 mm SVL. Near San Francisco, Ensatinas reach adult size, usually in their third year, at about 53 mm SVL (males) or 61 mm SVL (females).

Ensatinas often remain immobile when discovered. When harassed they stand up on their legs, arch their back and tail, and slap the tail, dripping with a milky secretion, toward the disturbance. The secretion is sometimes propelled toward the enemy by the whipping action of the tail. Pinched or bitten tails are lost readily at the constriction. The lost tail flips and twitches for several minutes, presumably distracting a would-be predator. As many as 16% of the individuals in a population may be regenerating tails presumably lost to predators. Adults completely regenerate new tails in about two years. Ensatinas also may produce a hissing sound when disturbed.

Ensatinas feed on the usual variety of terrestrial invertebrates. Spiders, beetles, collembolans, millipedes, and camel crickets are among the more common food items. Garter snakes and Steller's Jays are reported to prey on Ensatinas.

Adult males have larger home ranges than adult females. The former moved up to 42 m, whereas the latter moved a maximum of 23 m, over a two-year period. Densities of up to 283 Ensatinas per hectare have been reported.

REFERENCES. Altig and Brodie (1971), Hubbard (1903), Stebbins (1949b, 1949c, 1954- Literature Cited).

WOODLAND SALAMANDERS
GENUS *PLETHODON*

This is the largest genus of the North American herpetofauna, containing about 28 species, and it is also the largest genus in the Pacific Northwest where it is represented by six species. The greatest diversity of *Plethodon* is in the deciduous forests of the eastern United States. A single species is found in New Mexico, isolated high in the coniferous forests of the Jemez Mountains. The genus is restricted to North America north of Mexico.

Plethodon is closely related to *Aneides* and *Ensatina*. It differs from the former in lacking the climbing adaptations of the feet, in having two premaxillae, and in having maxillae that are toothed almost to the posterior tip. *Plethodon* does not have the basal tail constriction of *Ensatina*.

Woodland Salamanders are small to medium in size, usually with slender bodies and short limbs, and they often have a dorsal stripe. They are found mainly in loose rock talus mixed with damp soil and in the litter of the forest floor. They deposit small clutches of large white eggs in hidden terrestrial nests, and, in all reported cases, the female exhibits brooding behavior.

There are three well-defined groups of western *Plethodon:* (1) the Vandykei Group, containing *P. vandykei* and *P. larselli;* (2) the Vehiculum Group, containing *P. vehiculum* and *P. dunni*; and (3) the Elongatus Group containing *P. elongatus* and *P. stormi.*

DUNN'S SALAMANDER
PLETHODON DUNNI BISHOP

13. Dunn's Salamander *(Plethodon dunni)*, Multnomah Co., Oregon.

Dunn's Salamander is one of our larger Woodland Salamanders (to 150 mm TL), distinguished by the presence of a greenish dorsal stripe with uneven edges and small patches of stripe color isolated in the black ground color just below the stripe. The stripe does not extend to the tip of the tail in larger juveniles and adults. The dorsal limb bases are colored like the stripe, and the venter is slate-gray with scattered yellowish flecks. This species usually has 15 costal grooves and 2.5 to 4.0 intercostal folds between adpressed limbs. There are two phalanges in the fifth (outermost) hind toe. Males have a mental gland with posterolateral processes. Sexual dimorphism is not marked, but mature females are usually plumper and have a pleated or folded vent lining compared to the papillose vent lining of males. Adult males have fewer maxillary-premaxillary teeth, longer tails, and wider heads than females. Females are slightly larger (max SVL = 75 mm; max TL = 154 mm) than males (max SVL = 67 mm; max TL = 139 mm).

HABITAT. This species usually is associated with rocks, either alongside streams and waterfalls or in talus. It is usually found on wetter substrate and nearer to water than other species of *Plethodon;* often it is found associated with *Rhyacotriton olympicus*. Although this species, like all salamanders, can swim if it accidentally falls in the water, it is not an aquatic salamander. Substrate temperatures at sites where these salamanders were collected averaged 10.4° C (range = 4.0° to 17.0° C).

VARIATION. Some geographic variation in numbers of teeth and costal grooves, limb length, and head width and length is known, but the variation is slight and does not conform to clear geographic pat-

91

terns. Accordingly, no subspecies are recognized. Specimens from Benton Co., Oregon have more costal grooves (mode = 16) than those from elsewhere. All *Plethodon dunni* have some black pigment in their stripes, but populations in the Coast Range from Benton and Lincoln Cos., Oregon northward have the darkest stripes. Some individuals in Benton and Lincoln Cos. are nearly stripeless, with only scattered spots of stripe color. The stripe of hatchlings and small juveniles is always brighter, faintly metallic, green and more even-edged than in adults.

LIFE HISTORY. Like all Northwestern amphibians, the activity pattern of Dunn's Salamander is influenced greatly by local climatic conditions. At lowland coastal sites, they may be active during any month, contingent upon warm damp weather. At inland sites, or at higher elevations, long periods of winter inactivity occur. *Plethodon dunni* ranges from sea level up to about 1,000 m, and the duration of the growing season at sites where *P. dunni* have been collected varies from 140 to 270 days. This variance causes corresponding variance in the life history of *P. dunni* from place to place.

The reproductive biology of this species is poorly known. Courtship has not been observed, but spermatophores, or remnants of spermatophores, have been found in the cloacas of mature females in April and October, indicating that courtship may occur both in the spring and autumn. Females with enlarged oocytes can be found almost any month, so there is potentially a prolonged period of oviposition. Two observations suggest that the spring may be the major time of egg-laying. Robert C. Stebbins induced a female to oviposit 13 eggs during May in the laboratory, and Philip C. Dumas found a female brooding a clutch of nine eggs in early July. The "grape-like" cluster of eggs discovered by Dumas was about 38 cm deep in a crevice in the shale rock, attached to the substrate by a common gelatinous pedicel. The temperature at the nest was 13° C and the relative humidity was 93 percent. Dumas estimated that the incubation period is about 70 days and that hatchlings measure 16.0 mm SVL. The smallest known specimen is 17 mm SVL, corresponding closely to Dumas' estimate.

Mature ova are 4.5 to 5.5 mm in diameter. Clutch size ranges from 4 to 15 (average = 9.4), and larger females usually contain more eggs than smaller females. Sexual maturity is attained in both sexes at about 50 mm SVL.

Plethodon dunni and sympatric *Plethodon vehiculum* have similar diets, but *P. dunni* eats a wider variety of food, perhaps as a result of the larger size of *P. dunni*. The most frequently eaten prey of Dunn's Salamander are collembolans, but isopods, mites, beetles, and gastropods also are frequent in the diet. In the Columbia River Gorge, *P. dunni* is occasionally cannibalistic. Dunn's Salamanders can live for at least 158 days without food at normal active temperatures in the laboratory.

Dippers and Steller's Jays are reported to eat Dunn's Salamanders. On 28 May 1972, one of us found a partially eaten Northwestern Garter Snake under a Spotted Owl perch. The stomach of the dead snake contained an adult Dunn's Salamander.

During midwinter and midsummer, individuals are restricted largely to talus banks where they go to depths usually greater than eight cm to escape frost and drought. They come closer to the surface and wander away from talus slopes during the warm wet weather of spring and autumn. Maximum movement and surface activity occurs in April.

REMARKS. In Benton, Lincoln, and Lane Cos., Oregon there is an unstriped *Plethodon* which has been considered alternatively a color morph of *Plethodon dunni* or a distinct species, *Plethodon gordoni* (Mary's Peak Salamander). The dorsal coloration is dark gray or brown with scattered white or brassy flecks. The venter is purplish gray with flecks or yellow in life. Juveniles have faint, pinkish, dorsal stripes, but adults are stripeless. Neither adults nor juveniles have any green pigmentation. They have a modal number of 15 costal grooves and 2.0 to 2.5 intercostal folds between adpressed limbs.

14. Dunn's Salamander *(Plethodon dunni)*, Benton Co., Oregon; unstriped morph.

There is a strong possibility that "*Plethodon gordoni*" is only an unstriped morph of *P. dunni*. The facts that the two forms occur in microsympatry, that they share similar size and shape, and that they are similar biochemically argues that the two are conspecific. On the

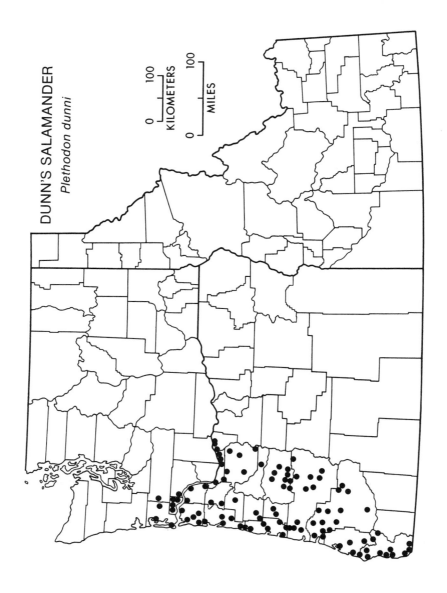

DUNN'S SALAMANDER
Plethodon dunni

other hand, "*P. gordoni*" differs from *P. dunni* in features other than color. "*P. gordoni*" is smaller, more slender, has an average of one less costal groove, a narrower head, and longer legs than sympatric *P. dunni*. Therefore, the differences between the two forms cannot be explained easily by assuming a simple genetic polymorphism. The critical evidence, whether individual females can produce both striped and unstriped offspring, is lacking.

REFERENCES. Altig and Brodie (1971), Brodie (1968a, 1970), Dumas (1955, 1956), Feder et al. (1978).

DEL NORTE SALAMANDER
PLETHODON ELONGATUS
VAN DENBURGH

15. Del Norte Salamander *(Plethodon elongatus)*, Curry Co., Oregon.

The elegant Del Norte Salamander is the most slender western *Plethodon*, with 17 to 20 (mode = 18) costal grooves, and with 6.5 to 7.5 intercostal folds between adpressed limbs. The maximum length is 73 mm SVL. The dorsal ground color is dark brown to black, and there is a reddish, even-edged, dorsal stripe that usually extends to the tip of the tail. The dorsal stripe is often obscured by invading melanophores, especially in larger (older) individuals. Some flecks of stripe color may occur on the sides. The venter is dark gray, but the throat is lighter gray and usually mottled. This species is sympatric with only one other *Plethodon*, Dunn's Salamander, which has fewer costal grooves, longer legs, and an uneven-edged greenish stripe that does not reach the tip of the tail. Females are slightly larger than males. Adult males have mental glands and often slightly swollen vent lobes.

HABITAT. The habitat of the Del Norte Salamander is largely rock talus in coniferous forests, although in coastal areas they also are found on the forest floor under litter and in rotten logs. Their niche is

95

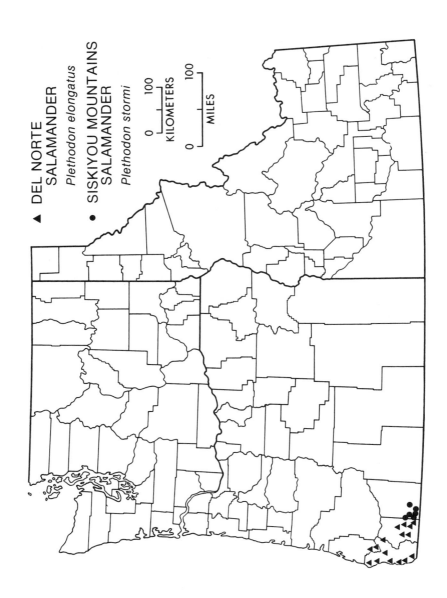

DEL NORTE
SALAMANDER
Plethodon elongatus

SISKIYOU MOUNTAINS
SALAMANDER
Plethodon stormi

100

KILOMETERS

100

MILES

16. Del Norte Salamander *(Plethodon elongatus)*, Humboldt Co., California; juvenile.

very similar to that of the Western Redback Salamander, *Plethodon vehiculm,* and it has been suggested that similar niches, including similar body size, is the reason why these two species have adjacent non-overlapping ranges. It is hypothesized that competition prevents the two from living in the same places. Interestingly, Dunn's Salamander, which is larger and prefers wetter substrate than the Del Norte and Western Redback Salamanders, overlaps the ranges of both of these latter species. The elevational range of *P. elongatus* is sea level to about 1,200 m.

VARIATION. Although there is some variation in color, body proportions, and counts, subspecies are not recognized. Coastal animals in California are smaller and darker with the dorsal stripe nearly obscured in adults; whereas inland animals are larger and have a lighter brown ground color with a persistent stripe. Coastal specimens are immaculate, but inland animals have scattered white spots, especially along the sides. Over its limited range in Oregon, there is very little variation in color. Both coastal and inland Del Norte Salamanders in Oregon resemble those from coastal California. Hatchlings and small juveniles from all populations have a brighter reddish stripe than older individuals.

LIFE HISTORY. As with all of our amphibians, the active season of the Del Norte Salamander depends on local climatic features. There is no information available on courtship, but most mature males captured during April and May have mature spermatozoa in their vasa deferentia, suggesting readiness to court. Limited data suggest that

97

most females oviposit in the spring and brood their eggs in a hidden terrestrial nest during the summer, with hatching occurring in the autumn. A brooding female was discovered with ten eggs "in a grape-like cluster" with a central pedicel on 27 July 1958. The nest was a small cavity under a redwood post. The embryos were estimated to be 3 to 4 weeks old.

Eighteen mature, gravid females from Siskiyou Co., California contained 3 to 11 (average = 7.9) large (average diameter 5.1 mm), white eggs. There seems to be little correlation between female size and clutch size in this population. Hatchlings are about 18 mm SVL. A sample of 80 mature males ranged in size from 45.8 to 68.1 mm SVL, and a sample of 49 mature females ranged from 56.6 to 71.3 mm SVL.

The usual variety of small terrestrial invertebrates occurs in the diet of the Del Norte Salamander. Collembolans are the most frequent food in their stomachs, with larval and adult beetles nearly as frequent.

REMARKS. The Del Norte Salamander is related to the Siskiyou Mountains Salamander, *Plethodon stormi,* and the latter has been suggested to be only a subspecies of the former. See the *P. stormi* account for more details.

REFERENCES. Brodie (1968a, 1970), Bury (1973), Livesey (1959).

LARCH MOUNTAIN SALAMANDER
PLETHODON LARSELLI BURNS

17. Larch Mountain Salamander *(Plethodon larselli)*, Skamania Co., Washington.

The Larch Mountain Salamander is restricted to the vicinity of the Columbia River Gorge in Oregon and Washington, occurring from about 12 to 300 m in elevation. It is a small (max SVL = 52 mm) salamander with a chestnut or reddish dorsal stripe, a pinkish venter (fades to white with black flecks in preservative), and a single phalanx in the short fifth toe of the hind foot. It is also our only *Plethodon* in which adult males lack mental glands. *P. larselli* is sympatric only with *P. dunni* in Oregon and with *P. vehiculm* in Washington. There seems to be very little sexual difference in size, but the few largest individuals are females. Adult males have fewer maxillary-premaxillary teeth than females, and they have poorly developed vent lobes that are lacking in females.

HABITAT . *Plethodon larselli* is restricted to the lava talus slopes of the Columbia River Gorge. It can be found near the surface under rocks during wet weather, but it retreats to considerable depths in the talus during cold and dry weather. Individuals occur far from streams and seepages, and, in fact, they seem to be less common in perpetually wet talus (the preferred habitat of Dunn's Salamander) than in talus that varies from wet to dry with seasonal rainfall. In the early spring

99

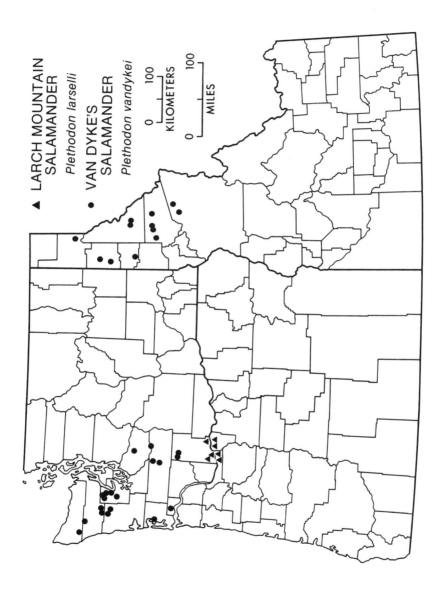

▲ LARCH MOUNTAIN
SALAMANDER

Plethodon larselli

● VAN DYKE'S
SALAMANDER

Plethodon vandykei

0   100
KILOMETERS

0   100
MILES

(March), soil temperatures at collection sites vary from 4.0° to 7.0° C. Later (April), soil temperatures may be as high as 10.0° C.

VARIATION. Individuals from Washington have more black pigment in the dorsal stripe and on the venter than those from Oregon. There is also some variation in tooth counts and body size between populations. In Oregon, *Plethodon larselli* matures at a slightly larger size and grows to a slightly larger size than in Washington. The slight variation is discordant and subspecies are not recognized.

LIFE HISTORY. As a result of the relatively mild climate of the Columbia River Gorge, it is possible to collect *Plethodon larselli* during any month of the year. However, they are less likely to be surface active during midwinter (December to January) and midsummer (late June to early September) than at other times. Surface activity varies somewhat between Oregon and Washington populations. Many populations in Washington are on south-facing slopes that dry out faster than the north-facing slopes of the Oregon side. This slope effect also influences distribution patterns. Populations tend to be patchier in Washington where moist talus banks are scattered. On the Oregon side, moist habitat is more evenly distributed and populations appear to be more-or-less continuous.

Courtship has not been observed, but males have sperm in their posterior vasa deferentia in spring and autumn, and females with fresh spermatophore caps in their cloacas have been collected in both seasons, indicating that courtship occurs at both of these times. Nests have not been found. One hundred and five mature females (40.5 to 52.0 mm SVL, mean = 44.9 mm SLV) from Hood River Co., Oregon had 3 to 11 (mean = 6.9) mature ovarian eggs, ranging in size from 4.0 to 4.3 mm in diameter. There is very little tendency for larger females to have larger ovarian clutches.

Mature males (a sample of 135) in Hood River Co. range in size from 39.5 to 49.4 mm SVL (mean = 44.8 mm SVL). The smallest individual collected, presumably a hatchling, was 17.3 mm SVL.

Larch Mountain Salamanders eat mainly mites and collembolans. Larger individuals eat a wider variety of prey including snails and earthworms that are lacking in the diet of juveniles. When disturbed *Plethodon larselli* coil up and lie still. In this pose they resemble coiled millipedes that are numerous in the range of *P. larselli,* and which have noxious and toxic secretions. It has been suggested that the coiled posture of *P. larselli* affords protection from predators (which are unknown) as they resemble or mimic the distasteful millipedes. If vigorously disturbed, *P. larselli* coil and uncoil rapidly, resulting in fast and erratic propulsion away from the disturbance. After a few such flips the salamanders suddenly come to rest making them difficult to find.

REFERENCES. Altig and Brodie (1971), Brodie (1968a, 1970), Burns (1962).

SISKIYOU MOUNTAINS SALAMANDER
PLETHODON STORMI
HIGHTON AND BRAME

This close relative of the Del Norte Salamander was discovered in 1963 and described in 1965. In the short interval since its discovery, very little information concerning its life history and ecology has been published. It has a very restricted range (about 377 km²) in the Siskiyou Mountains of southern Oregon and northern California. So far, no other species of *Plethodon* has been found within its range. These are slender salamanders with short limbs, similar in size (max SVL = 69.9 mm) and shape to the Del Norte Salamander. *P. stormi* has a modal number of 17 costal grooves and 4.0 to 5.5 intercostal folds between adpressed limbs. Juveniles have an even-edged, olive-tan dorsal stripe that extends half way to the tail tip. The stripe fades to light brown in adults. Juveniles have a black ground color, and adults a light brown to purplish-brown ground color. The venter is almost black in juveniles, purplish in sub-adults, and lavender to purplish-gray in adults. The throat and chin are lighter than the rest of the venter. The body is sprinkled with white to yellowish flecks that are heaviest on the sides of the body and limbs, and nearly absent on the midventral line. Adult females average slightly larger than adult males. Adult males have slightly fewer maxillary-pre-maxillary teeth and larger vent lobes than adult females.

HABITAT. *Plethodon stormi* ranges in elevation from 488 to 1,078 m. Populations of this species are invariably associated with talus deposits and fissured rock outcrops. The related *P. elongatus* is found both in talus and forest litter, but forest litter is utilized only where it is deep and moist, such as in the humid, coastal, redwood forests. Both *P. elongatus* and *P. stormi* are more-or-less restricted to talus in the drier inland areas where forest floor litter is thin or absent. Occasionally, *P. stormi* is found under bark, limbs, or logs on the forest floor, but only during the wettest weather and always near talus. Heavily wooded, north-facing slopes with talus have the densest populations of *P. stormi*. Soil temperatures and corresponding depths

102

where *P. stormi* have been collected during the daytime during the spring range from 3.5° to 11.3° C (average = 5.7° C) and 0 to 45.7 cm (average = 10.3 cm).

VARIATION. So far only variation in the number of costal grooves has been reported. Populations in the Applegate River drainage of Oregon are seemingly isolated from those in the Klamath River drainage of California. Despite the isolation, individuals from the two areas are identical in appearance. No subspecies are recognized.

LIFE HISTORY. Individuals are active near the surface during the spring (March to April) and autumn (September to early November) with only sporadic surface activity during the winter and summer months. However, even during dry summer weather, individuals emerge from the depths at night to feed on insects at the surface. Usually they lie still with their heads at the entrance to the opening until a prey is spotted, at which time they dart forward to snap up the animal, usually a moth or beetle. During wetter times they may emerge completely at night to crawl over the surface of the talus slope.

Males have mature spermatozoa in spring and autumn and seem capable of mating during both of these seasons, although this has not been verified by observations of courtship or spermatophores in the cloacas of females. Limited data suggest that females lay eggs every other year in the spring. Although nests have not been found, females are likely to brood their embryos through the summer in nest cavities deep in talus. Mature females (sample of 37) had 2 to 18 (average = 9.2) enlarged, white, ovarian eggs. There was no correlation between female size and ovarian clutch size. Mature ova range in diameter from 4.2 to 5.2 mm.

Eggs apparently hatch in the autumn, and the hatchlings are 17 to 18 mm SVL. They do not become surface active until the following spring. Mature males range in SVL from 47.2 to 69.8 mm (mean of 62 males = 58.9 mm), and mature females from 56.0 to 69.9 mm (mean of 41 females = 61.9 mm). Juvenile males are estimated to grow at a rate of 6.5 mm SVL/year and females at 8.0 mm SVL/year. Both sexes are thought to mature at 5 to 6 years of age.

Spiders, pseudoscorpions, mites, ants, collembolans, and beetles are the major prey of the Siskiyou Mountains Salamander. Ants were the most important food in the spring, but were not eaten in the autumn. Millipedes were not eaten in the spring, but were eaten by larger adults in the autumn.

REMARKS. Populations thought by some biologists to be intergrades between *Plethodon stormi* and *Plethodon elongatus* occur in the Klamath River drainage of California. However, in Oregon the two species occur within one km of each other with absolutely no indication of intergradation. Therefore, until further data are available, it is best to consider the two forms as distinct species.

REFERENCES. Brodie (1968a, 1970), Bury (1973).

VAN DYKE'S SALAMANDER
PLETHODON VANDYKEI
VAN DENBURGH

18. Van Dyke's Salamander *(Plethodon vandykei)*, Jefferson Co., Washington.

This species has the fewest costal grooves (mode = 14) of all western *Plethodon*. It also is distinguished by the presence of distinct parotoid glands and an uneven-edged dorsal stripe. It differs from its closest relative, *Plethodon larselli*, by having two phalanges instead of one in the fifth toe of the hind foot, fewer costal grooves, and a mental gland in males, and by lacking pinkish ventral color.

Plethodon vandykei is a relatively short (max SVL = 58 mm) long-legged species, with only 0.5 to 3.0 intercostal folds between adpressed limbs. Like *P. larselli,* it has more vomerine and maxillary-premaxillary teeth and a relatively shorter tail than other western *Plethodon* and relatively short slightly webbed toes. *P. vandykei* has the widest head relative to its size of all western *Plethodon*. There are three distinct color phases of *P. vandykei*. The dark phase has a black ground color with a vivid yellow, green, or reddish stripe; the yellow

104

phase is basically tan or yellowish with an indistinct stripe; and the rose phase is similar to the yellow phase except it has a pinkish or salmon cast (see Variation).

Females are slightly larger than males (max female SVL = 57.9 mm, max male SVL = 55.0 mm). Males have fewer maxillary-premaxillary teeth than females, elongate nasolabial cirri that are lacking in females, and vent lobes that are slightly more evident than in females.

HABITAT. *Plethodon vandykei* is often associated with seepages and streamside talus, but it also occurs in talus slopes far from free water. In the latter case, the talus is usually deep, mixed with moist soil, and positioned on well-shaded, north-facing slopes. During wet weather, individuals may be found in leaf litter and under bark and logs in coniferous forests. This species occurs in harsher, colder environments than other western *Plethodon*. Soil temperatures during April at collection sites in Idaho ranged from 5.0° to 7.5° C. In southwestern Washington it is sympatric with two other *Plethodon* (*dunni* and *vehiculum*); in Northwestern Washington and in the Cascade Mountains it occurs only with *P. vehiculum;* and in Idaho and Montana it is the only *Plethodon*. The elevational range of this species is from sea level to 1,550 m.

VARIATION. *Plethodon vandykei* exhibits considerable geographic variation in color and less dramatic variation in morphometric and meristic characters. Color variation has resulted in the naming of two subspecies that we believe cannot be justifiably recognized. These are *P. vandykei vandykei* (Van Dyke's Salamander) and *P.v. idahoensis* (Coeur d'Alene Salamander), the former restricted to western Washington the latter to northern Idaho and western Montana. Individuals from Washington have more even-edged, wider, yel-

19. Van Dyke's Salamander *(Plethodon vandykei),* Kootenai Co., Idaho.

105

low or reddish stripes that extend to the tip of the tail; no or few melanophores within the stripe; and light-colored limb bases with dark flecks. All three color phases described above, occur in western Washington. The rose phase is common in the Willapa Hills of southwestern Washington and rare in the Olympic and Cascade Mountains. The yellow phase dominates in the Willapa Hills and in the Olympic Mountains. In the Cascade Mountains, most individuals have the dark phase color pattern. Individuals from Idaho and Montana have green, orange, yellow, or reddish stripes that are usually invaded with melanophores and that usually do not reach the tip of the tail, and dark limb bases with light flecks. Only the dark phase is present in these interior populations. Hatchlings everywhere have the dark phase color pattern.

Subspecies of *Plethodon vandykei* based on geographic variation in color are arbitrary because other characteristics (*e.g.,* number of vomerine teeth and number of costal grooves) do not vary concordantly with color.

LIFE HISTORY. The time and duration of activity of *Plethodon vandykei* varies from a relatively long active period in the mild climates of southwestern Washington to a relatively brief active period in the harsh environments of the high Cascades and Rocky Mountains. In northern Idaho, this species emerges from winter hibernation in late March, is active near the surface through April and May, retreats to subterranean life (except near seepages and waterfalls) from June to mid-September, and emerges for a brief period during the autumn rains (mid-September to early November) before hibernating from late November to early March.

Partial courtship has been observed during the early spring. Spermatophore caps have been found in female cloacas during both the spring and autumn in Idaho indicating that courtship may occur just before and just after winter hibernation. A single nest (under a moss covered stone) of Van Dyke's Salamander is known. Eggs were in the usual grape-like cluster and attached to the stone by a single gelatinous thread, as in other *Plethodon*. It is not known whether a female was in attendance. The highest percentage of hatchlings among large samples from northern Idaho occurs in the autumn, suggesting that the majority of females oviposit in the spring and brood through the summer, and that hatching usually occurs during late summer and autumn. Females with either small or large ovarian ova are present at any given time in most populations indicating that females do not oviposit every year and that they probably oviposit every other year. Mature ovarian ova range in diameter from 4.3 to 5.0 mm. Females from northern

Idaho have 4 to 12 (mean = 6.71) ovarian eggs, with larger females containing, on the average, only a few more eggs than smaller females. Mature females range in SVL from 47.2 to 57.9 mm, and mature males from 44.5 to 54.0 mm. Hatchlings range from 15 to 18 mm. Growth rate and age at maturity are unknown, but based on size-frequency histograms of populations from northern Idaho, both sexes probably mature during their fourth year (including the embryonic period) to breed for the first time in their fifth year.

There is no available information on the food of this species, and its predators are also unknown. Disturbed individuals will occasionally coil up as described for *Plethodon larselli* and, rarely, they will use the coiling and uncoiling behavior to flip away from the source of disturbance.

REMARKS. Recently it was suggested that the Idaho and Montana populations of *Plethodon vandykei* be afforded species status (= *Plethodon idahoensis*). This was based on very limited and unconvincing biochemical evidence.

REFERENCES. Brodie (1968a, 1970), Highton and Larson (1979), Noble (1925).

WESTERN REDBACK SALAMANDER
PLETHODON VEHICULUM
(COOPER)

20. Western Redback Salamander *(Plethodon vehiculum)*, Skamania Co., Washington.

The Western Redback Salamander is one of the most commonly encountered terrestrial salamanders throughout its range. This

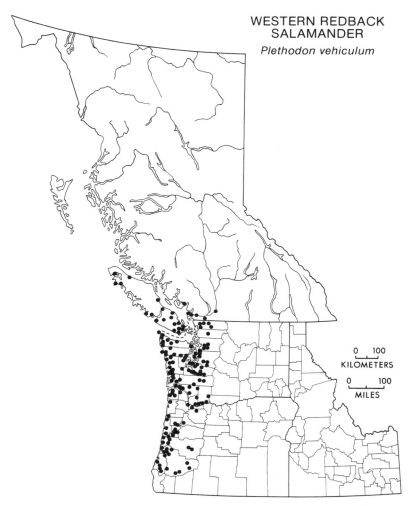

WESTERN REDBACK
SALAMANDER
Plethodon vehiculum

relatively small (max SVL = 60 mm) species can be identified by having a modal number of 16 costal grooves and an even-edged dorsal stripe
that extends to the tip of the tail. There are no isolated patches of
stripe color below the stripe in the dark, lateral, ground color, as in
Plethodon dunni, the only other *Plethodon* through much of the range
of *P. vehiculum*. *P. vehiculum* has the most intrapopulation variation in
color of any western *Plethodon*. Most individuals have a dorsal stripe
that is red, orange, yellow, olive, or tan; but stripeless melanistic individuals are relatively common, and individuals with reduced
melanism occasionally are found. These latter individuals are the

color of their dorsal stripe all over the body. Striped specimens have various densities of melanophores middorsally in the stripe on the body but the stripe on the tail is without melanophores. Patches of stripe color flecked with melanophores and iridophores occur on the dorsal surfaces of the limb bases, and smaller flecks of stripe color occur on the distal limb segments, sides of the head, and venter. Scattered white iridophores are present on all ventral surfaces, resulting in a salt-and-pepper effect. The species has 14 to 18 costal grooves and 2.5 to 5.5 intercostal folds between adpressed limbs. Females are the larger sex, averaging about 3.5 mm SVL longer than males. Mature males have small vent lobes and squarish snouts, whereas mature females lack the vent lobes and have more rounded snouts.

HABITAT. The Western Redback Salamander occurs from sea level up to 1,250 m elevation, mainly in dense coniferous forests. It is common in talus slopes, but it also occurs in leaf litter, under bark, and under other surface debris of the forest floor. Although it is found occasionally in saturated streamside substrate, the preferred habitat of *Plethodon dunni,* it is more common in slightly drier environments. Soil temperatures at collection sites for this species ranged from 5.0° to 19.0° C, with an average of 10.4° C.

VARIATION. Some populations (those in Lane and Douglas Cos., Oregon) have a modal number of 15 costal grooves instead of the usual 16. Populations inhabiting islands, including Vancouver Island, tend to have larger bodies; and the Vancouver Island population has relatively longer legs than other populations. Individuals from coastal populations tend to have the most black middorsally in the stripe, and the highest percentages of melanistic individuals occur in coastal populations. As high as 10.8% of the animals from the western Olympic Mountains are melanistic. The frequency of each stripe color varies geographically. On Destruction and Vancouver Islands, almost all individuals are red-striped, but in most mainland populations red-striped morphs account for only about 50 to 60% of the population. Some local populations, such as those in the Corvallis Watershed, Benton Co., Oregon, have numerous individuals with reduced melanism. These individuals are reddish or light yellowish-tan, occasionally with some black spotting or streaking. Piebald specimens occur in some populations. No subspecies are recognized.

LIFE HISTORY. In Benton and Lincoln Cos., Oregon courtship occurs from November through early March when the temperatures are well above freezing. Females oviposit in the spring (brooding females have been found in hidden nests during May), and development occurs in the summer. Hatchlings emerge from the eggs in the autumn at 13 to 15 mm SVL. Both sexes grow at a rate of about 10 mm SVL/year for the first three years. Mature males range from 42 to 53 mm SVL (mean = 45.7) and females from 44 to 58 mm SVL (mean = 49.1). Males produce sperm every year, but females oviposit every other year. Mature ova range in diameter from 4.0 to 5.0 mm. Near Corvallis, Oregon, females lay 6 to 19 (mean = 10.4) eggs, with larger females laying significantly more eggs than smaller females. Near Auburn, Washington, females lay 4 to 18 (mean = 9.8) eggs, but here, small females lay as many eggs as large females. Five gravid females from Destruction Island, Washington had 11 to 18 (mean = 14.2) mature ovarian eggs.

Plethodon vehiculum eats a wide array of terrestrial invertebrates. Mites and collembolans are staples and spiders and isopods are commonly eaten. Predators of *P. vehiculum* are thought to include garter snakes, Steller's Jays, shrews, and shrew-moles.

REFERENCES. Brodie (1968a, 1970), Dumas (1956), Hanlin et al. (1979), Peacock and Nussbaum (1973), Stebbins (1951).

NEWTS
FAMILY SALAMANDRIDAE

The Salamandridae is primarily an Old World family with 16 genera and 45 species found across Europe, extreme northern Africa, and temporate and subtropical Asia. Only two genera and six species occur in North America, and only one species occurs in the Pacific Northwest.

Most salamandrids have a two-stage life cycle with aquatic larvae and terrestrial adults. Some species have populations with paedogenetic larvae, but there are no obligatory paedogenetic species. One species in Japan lays eggs on land, but has aquatic larvae. A few species in Europe are viviparous (bearing live young) with an unusual form of cannibalism, in which embryos eat each other within the oviducts of their mother. No species has parental care.

There is a tendency in this family for terrestrial adults to remain in breeding ponds and lakes (some few are stream breeders) for prolonged periods and to develop some secondary aquatic adaptations such as thin skin, high tail fins, and fleshy lip folds. This "aquatic phase" may last for several months until they return to land and regain their terrestrial morphology with darker thicker skin. Some species, like the Red-spotted Newt, *Notophthalmus viridescens,* of eastern North America, undergo a virtual "second metamorphosis" when the juvenile terrestrial "eft" returns to the water to breed for the first time. The adults may then remain aquatic for the rest of their lives.

All amphibians have granular (poison) glands in their skin as a defense against predators, but salamandrids have evolved the most potent skin toxins of all salamanders, and most have some kind of bright red, orange, or yellow warning (aposematic) color to further protect them from predators. Often these bright colors are hidden, as on the belly, and are displayed by stereotyped behavior only when the newt is disturbed. Some newts have bizarre defensive mechanisms such as sharp ribs that pierce through the skin along the side of the newt and jab the mouths of would-be predators, and sharp hook-like bones on the skull for deterring predators.

Other characteristics of the Salamandridae include (1) internal fertilization via a spermatophore, (2) vomerine teeth in two longitudinal rows, diverging posteriorly, (3) no parasphenoid teeth, (4) no nasolabial grooves, and (5) absence of maxillary teeth in larvae.

PACIFIC NEWTS
GENUS *TARICHA*

This genus is confined to western North America, where it occurs from Alaska southward to northern Baja California. It is the only newt genus in western North America. There are three species of *Taricha,* one in the Pacific Northwest and two additional species in California. Pacific newts are uniformly dark above and bright yellow or reddish-orange below. When disturbed by a predator or poked with a stick, they expose their bright, ventral, warning colors by curving their head, neck, and tail up over their body in an "unken reflex." Newts of this genus have a potent skin toxin called "tetrodotoxin" that is chemically identical to that found in some marine puffer fishes, in a frog, and in the saliva of an octopus. Unlike most salamanders, they are often active on the surface during the daytime.

ROUGHSKIN NEWT
TARICHA GRANULOSA (SKILTON)

21. Roughskin Newt *(Taricha granulosa),* Benton Co., Oregon.

Roughskin Newts are the most commonly encountered salamanders in the Pacific Northwest. This is partly because they occur in very dense populations and partly because their diurnal habits make them readily visible. The eggs and the skin of both larvae and terrestrial individuals contain a potent toxin, and, as a result, all life stages of the newt are well protected from predators. This may account for the commoness and diurnality of this species.

Terrestrial newts are recognized easily by their dark brown dorsolateral coloration and bright, yellowish-orange, ventral coloration. Larvae are of the pond type, which in life have greenish-yellow dorsolateral surfaces with light spots along the sides and pink or salmon ventral surfaces. They are the only Northwestern larval salamanders without maxillary teeth, and the only pond-type larvae in the Northwest with fewer than eight gill rakers along the anterior row of the third gill arch.

Males have relatively longer tails and limbs than females. The cloacal lips of the male are prominent and enclose a relatively long cloacal opening. Females have a cone-shaped cloacal region with less prominent lips and a shorter opening. Larvae seldom exceed 75 mm TL. Adult males average about 169 mm TL (184 mm max) and 73 mm SVL (79 mm max). The smaller adult females average 142 mm TL (154 mm max) and 67 mm SVL (73 mm max).

HABITAT. Roughskin Newts occur in a variety of habitats in mountainous or hilly country. They are found most commonly in mesophytic forests of conifers and/or hardwoods, although they also occur in open valleys and farmland. They range from sea level up to 2,800 m. Adults can be found in lakes, ponds, and sluggish streams or on land, walking about fully exposed or under surface litter.

VARIATION. Two subspecies are recognized, the Northern Roughskin Newt, *Taricha granulosa granulosa* and the Crater Lake Newt, *T.g. mazamae*. The latter differs from the former in having encroachment of the dark dorsolateral pigment onto the ventral surfaces (see Remarks.). All Northwestern newts belong to the northern subspecies, except those found in the immediate vicinity of Crater Lake. Spotted or blotched (dorsally) individuals occur in some populations. Transformed individuals with gill stubs or remnants occur in some lakes, especially in areas of cold harsh climate. "Terrestrial phase" adults are darker and have thicker rougher skin, reduced tail fins, and a slimmer appearance. "Aquatic phase" adults are lighter colored and have thinner smoother skin; higher tail fins (especially males); and a fatter, almost bloated appearance.

LIFE HISTORY. Adults migrate to the breeding sites from December until July depending on local climate. The breeding migration is earlier where winters are shorter and milder. Males arrive at the breeding sites earlier and stay longer than females. The mating and egg-laying season may last several months in regions like the Willamette Valley where the growing season is long. Eggs have been found from April through mid-July near Corvallis, Oregon.

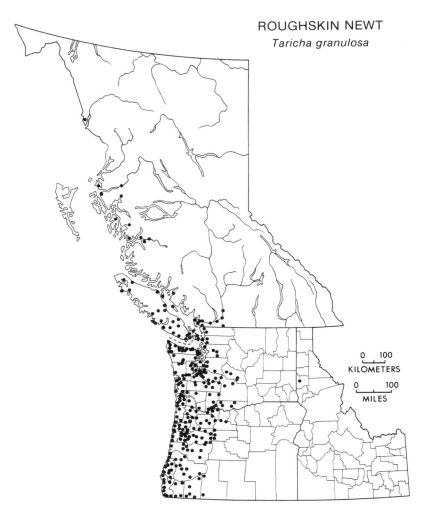

ROUGHSKIN NEWT
Taricha granulosa

0   100
KILOMETERS

0   100
MILES

On southern Vancouver Island, there is evidence that adult males are permanently aquatic, and only the females return to land after breeding; whereas on nearby mainland British Columbia (Marion Lake), both the males and females are thought to leave the water after breeding to overwinter on land.

Courtship involves the male amplecting the female from above just behind her fore limbs with his fore limbs, as in Long-toed Salamanders. The male also strokes the female with his hind limbs and rubs his chin across her snout, often with his mouth open. After dismounting, the male deposits a single spermatophore in front of the

22. Roughskin Newt *(Taricha granulosa)*, Humboldt Co., California; defensive posture.

female, which she may pick up with her cloacal lips.

Eggs (1.8 mm diameter) are tan dorsally and cream ventrally. They are laid singly, usually attached to the stems or leaves of submerged plants. Eggs are scattered about the pond in this manner, perhaps as a strategy to avoid the loss of an entire clutch to predators or accident. The clutch size is unreported and may be difficult to determine because of continuous laying. Because females may stay and feed in the breeding ponds for several months, it is possible that they yolk up and deposit eggs without leaving the ponds, as has been reported for some European newts. Females are thought to breed annually.

Eggs hatch in 20 to 26 days, and the hatchlings are about 18 mm TL after the yolk is gone. Hatchlings have balancers. Larvae typically metamorphose late in their first summer at 23 to 75 mm TL, but they may overwinter where growing seasons are short, metamorphosing in their second summer. Paedogenesis is unknown. Terrestrial newts mature at about 105 to 110 mm TL. The age at first breeding is unknown.

The food of larvae seems not to have been reported, but is likely to consist of zooplankton and small aquatic invertebrates. Terrestrial adults eat both aquatic and terrestrial prey, mainly small invertebrates. They are known to eat eggs of their own kind in addition to eggs of *Ambystoma* spp. and *Rana* spp. In a temporary pond near Corvallis, Oregon, the stomachs of 50 aquatic adults contained 479 amphibian eggs. Aquatic adults are significant predators of *Rana aurora* tadpoles in some coastal lakes. Garter snakes occasionally eat larval Roughskin Newts, and one subspecies of the Common Garter Snake, *Thamnophis sirtalis concinnus,* eats adult newts with no ill effects from the poison. Dead birds (ducks), fish, and frogs (Bullfrogs) have been found with adult newts in their stomachs; presumably they were poisoned. Human illness and death have resulted from ingesting live newts.

Newts are slow animals, seldom attempting to escape. They have a defensive unken reflex (see generic account) and have been reported to vocalize. It has been shown that males find females in water by olfaction, and olfaction and orientation to the position of the sun have been implicated in the remarkable homing ability of terrestrial newts.

Large aggregations, or "newt rafts," have been seen in some Oregon lakes. One such raft observed in September, measured 2.0 by 9.2 m and contained over 5,000 adults. These rafts may retain their integrity for over a month. The meaning of these aggregations is unclear. They apparently are not directly related to reproduction as they occur after the breeding season and sometimes contain larvae and subadults as well as adults.

REMARKS. The Rocky Mountain populations of the Roughskin Newt are probably the result of introductions. In Idaho they have been found in only a few ponds near Moscow, and they are rare in these ponds. Only one specimen has been recorded from Idaho in the past 10 years. The presence of this species in Montana is based on a single specimen from Thompson Falls, Saunders Co. Recent attempts to collect additional material from Montana have failed. The validity of the subspecies *Taricha granulosa mazamae* should be questioned, because many individuals in Crater Lake do not have the dark ventral color, and some individuals from scattered localities away from Crater Lake do have dark ventral color. Slater (1964) reported a specimen of *T. granulosa* from Benton Co., Washington, far to the east of other Washington localities in atypical habitat. We do not include this locality on our range map because of the possibility of error.

116

REFERENCES. Brodie (1968b, 1982), Brodie et al. (1974a), Chandler (1918), Coates et al. (1970), Davis and Twitty (1964), Efford and Mathias (1969), Efford and Tsumura (1973), Johnson and Brodie (1975), Landreth and Ferguson (1967), Neish (1971), Nussbaum and Brodie (1971), Oliver and McCurdy (1974), Pimentel (1959b, 1960), Riemer (1958), Tihen (1974), Twitty (1942, 1966), van Frank (1955), White (1977).

FROGS AND TOADS
ORDER ANURA

Frogs and toads are the only living amphibians that lack tails and have fully developed fore and hind limbs in the metamorphosed stage. They thereby differ from salamanders, which have tails, and from caecilians, which lack limbs.

Anurans typically have an aquatic herbivorous tadpole stage, but some species have evolved direct development with the eggs laid on land and the tadpole stage lost. Some few species are viviparous. There are no paedogenetic species.

Temperate species of anurans mate in the early spring during which time many species can be heard calling near marshes, ponds, and lakes. The calls are complex signaling devices used for establishing social dominance and territorial rights, attracting mates, indicating unwillingness to mate, and startling predators. Normally, it is only the males that call, but both sexes may have release calls and defensive calls. Release calls signal another frog to "let go," usually because a mistake has been made. This may occur when a male clasps another male; the clasped male will signal the mistake by emitting a quiet, low-pitched, chuckling sound. Or, a female may protest similarly if she is unwilling or unable to mate with a clasping male. Defensive calls are high-pitched shrieks, vocalized with the mouth open, apparently used to startle an attacking predator and perhaps facilitate escape.

During courtship, males clasp females from above with their fore limbs. There are two kinds of embrace, or amplexus, found among northwestern frogs. The most primitive type is "inguinal amplexus," in which the male grips the female in front of her hind limbs in the groin or inguinal region. Only the Tailed Frog and the Great Basin Spadefoot, among northwestern species, have this kind of amplexus. All other Northwestern species have "axillary amplexus," in which males clasp the females just behind their fore limbs in the axillary region.

In the Northwest, all species mate and spawn in the water, and all species, except the Tailed Frog, have external fertilization. Many tropical anurans have various complex forms of egg guarding or parental care, but none of our Northwestern species has parental care. In the Northwest, tadpoles of most species metamorphose after their first summer, but a few species, such as the Tailed Frog and Bullfrog, have prolonged tadpole periods of one to three years, and tadpoles of some other species may overwinter at high elevations where the growing season is short.

Metamorphosed frogs are carnivorous, mainly eating small invertebrates, although the Bullfrog and the two toad species occasionally eat small vertebrates as well. Prey are located mainly by vision, and the sticky tongue is used to capture and draw prey into the mouth. Anurans are heavily preyed upon by snakes, birds, and mammals. River Otters are especially fond of frogs.

Anurans are most diverse in the tropics, with the diversity dropping toward the poles. World-wide, there are about 23 families, 295 genera, and 2,800 species of anurans; only five families, six genera, and 14 species occur in the Pacific Northwest.

23. Western Toad *(Bufo boreas)*, Klamath Co., Oregon; tadpole aggregation.

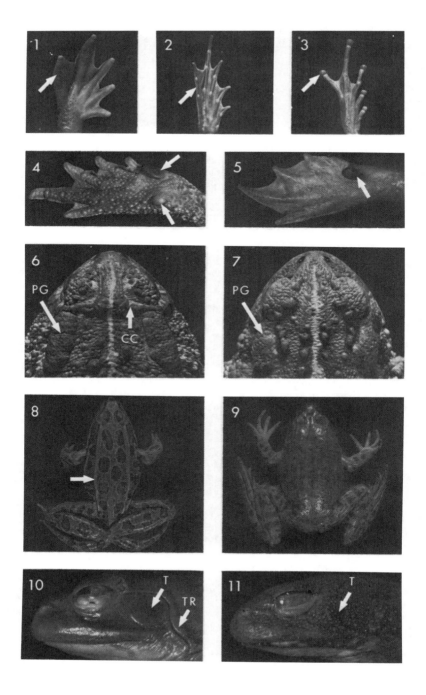

KEY TO THE FROGS OF
THE PACIFIC NORTHWEST

(metamorphosed forms only)

1A. Outer digit on hind foot broader than other digits (1); no tympanum; males with tail-like extension of the cloaca ... Tailed Frog, *Ascaphus truei*

1B. Outer digit on the hind foot not broader than other digits (2); tympanum present; males without cloacal extension 2

2A. Intercalary cartilages (extra step-like joint) present before the terminal phalanx of each digit; toe pads present (3) but may be very small (Hylidae) 3

2B. No intercalary cartilages; no toe pads (2, 4, 5) 4

3A. Toe pads well-developed (3); hind toes webbed for about half their length (3) ... Pacific Treefrog, *Hyla regilla*

3B. Toe pads barely expressed or missing; very slight webbing between toes of hind feet ... Striped Chorus Frog, *Pseudacris triseriata*

4A. One or more cornified cutting tubercles on soles of hind feet (4, 5) 5

4B. No enlarged cutting tubercles on soles of hind feet (2) (Ranidae) .. 7

5A. Parotoid glands present (6, 7); two cornified cutting tubercles on the soles of hind feet (4); pupil horizontal; no teeth in upper jaw (Bufonidae) 6

5B. No parotoid glands behind eyes; a single, black cutting tubercle on the soles of the hind feet (5); pupil vertically elliptical; teeth present in upper jaw ... Great Basin Spadefoot, *Spea intermontana*

6A. Prominent L-shaped cranial crest around each eye on top of head (6) ... Woodhouse's Toad, *Bufo woodhousei*

6B. No prominent cranial crests (7) ... Western Toad, *Bufo boreas*

7A. Dorsolateral folds present (8) 8

7B. Dorsolateral folds absent (9) 13

II. Key Illustrations - Frogs

Figs.: (1) Right hind foot of *Ascaphus truei;* (2) Right hind foot of *Rana* sp., ventral view; (3) Left hind foot of *Hyla regilla*, dorsal view; (4) Right hind foot of *Bufo boreas*, ventral view; (5) Right hind foot of *Spea intermontana*, ventral view; (6) *Bufo woodhousei* showing elongate parotoid glands (PG) and cranial crests (CC); (7) *Bufo boreas* showing short parotoid glands (PG) and lack of cranial crests; (8) *Rana pipiens*, arrow indicates dorsolateral fold; (9) *Rana catesbeiana*, lacking dorsolateral folds; (10) *Rana catesbeiana*, large distinct tympanum (T) and tympanic ridge (TR) shown; (11) *Rana boylei* with small inconspicuous tympanum shown.

8A. Large conspicuous dark spots on the back, outlined with color lighter than ground color ... Northern Leopard Frog, *Rana pipiens*

8B. Dorsal spots if present not large and not set off with light halos .. 9

9A. Dorsolateral fold does not extend posteriorly past sacral hump; no eye mask ... Green Frog, *Rana clamitans*

9B. Dorsolateral folds extend to groin region; eye mask present 10

10A. Eye mask extends forward past nostril almost to upper lip, bordered below by a white jaw stripe; light vertebral stripe present or absent; no dark spots between dorsolateral folds; no red, orange, or yellow on ventral surface in life ... Wood Frog, *Rana sylvatica*

10B. Eye mask less extensive; no light vertebral stripe; usually with spots between dorsolateral folds; red, orange, or yellow ventral surfaces in life 11

11A. Heel does not reach nostril when the hind leg is extended along the body; webbing between hind toes nearly to tips of toes; dorsal spots with fuzzy or indistinct edges; eyes dorsally oriented; bright color on ventral surfaces of body and hind legs appears to be "painted" on ... Spotted Frog, *Rana pretiosa*

11B. Heel reaches to nostril or beyond; last 1-2 joints of the hind toes usually are free of webbing; dorsal spots with sharp edges; eyes laterally oriented; bright colors appear to lie deep in skin 12

12A. Ventral surfaces of posterior body and hind legs rosy red in life; groin area heavily mottled with black and creamy white; central abdominal region with dark mottling ... Red-legged Frog, *Rana aurora*

12B. Ventral surfaces of posterior body and hind legs tannish-yellow in life; groin area lightly mottled; central abdominal region without mottling ... Cascade Frog, *Rana cascadae*

13A. Large tympanum (10), as large as eye in females and larger than eye in males, of a different color than the rest of the head; conspicuous ridges run from eye across the top of the tympanum and down behind the tympanum (10); greenish brown dorsally, few spots except in juveniles; up to 200 mm snout-vent length ... Bullfrog, *Rana catesbeiana*

13B. Small inconspicuous tympanum (11); no ridge over tympanum (11); dorsum color variable from greenish, brownish, or reddish with variable spotting; whitish ventrally grading to yellow posteriorly and on the ventral surface of the legs; small, less than 90 mm snout-vent length ... Foothills Yellow-legged Frog, *Rana boylei*

KEY TO THE TADPOLES OF THE PACIFIC NORTHWEST*

1A. Spiracle ventromedial (2), nearer to mouth than cloacal opening; oral disc large and ventrally oriented, sucker-like (2, 3); labial tooth row formula 2-3 anterior/10-12 posterior to mouth, some tooth rows in double series (3); tail fin low, with a light spot on the tip; mainly found in mountain streams ... Tailed Frog, *Ascaphus truei*
1B. Spiracle on left side (sinistral) (4); mouth not sucker-like; labial tooth row formula 2-7/3-6, all tooth rows in single series 2

2A. Cloacal opening medial (7) (Bufonidae and Pelobatidae) 3
2B. Cloacal opening to the right (dextral) (4) (Hylidae and Ranidae) . . 5

3A. Marginal papillae either completely around oral disc or with a narrow, anterior gap; spiracle low, ventral to lateral midline of body; eyes close together, dorsally oriented; labial tooth rows more than 2/3 ... Great Basin Spadefoot, *Spea intermontana*
3B. Papillae only on sides of mouth, posterior labium without papillae (7); spiracle higher on body, near midline; eyes more lateral, usually closer to lateral outline of head than to midline; labial tooth rows 2/3 (Bufonidae) 4

4A. Fins moderately pigmented, dorsal fin darker than ventral fin; tail musculature unicolored or with narrow ventral area unpigmented; dorsum uniformly dark ... Western Toad, *Bufo boreas*
4B. Fins unpigmented or with a few scattered, stellate melanophores, more numerous in dorsal fin; tail musculature bicolored; but light areas may occur anywhere on tail musculature; dorsum may be mottled in life ... Woodhouse's Toad, *Bufo woodhousei*

5A. Eyes lateral, outline of eyes included in dorsal silhouette (8); oral disc not laterally notched (Hylidae) 6
5B. Eyes dorsal, outline of eyes not included in dorsal silhouette (9); oral disc notched laterally (6) (Ranidae) 7

6A. Anteriormost tooth row (1st row) on posterior labium with a medial gap; one row of marginal papillae posteriorly ... Pacific Treefrog, *Hyla regilla*
6B. Anteriormost tooth row (1st row) on posterior labium without a medial gap; two rows of marginal papillae posteriorly ... Striped Chorus Frog, *Pseudacris triseriata*

7A. Four or more rows of teeth on anterior labium 8
7B. One to three rows of teeth on anterior labium 9

* In part after Altig, R. 1970. Herpetologica 26 (2):180-207.

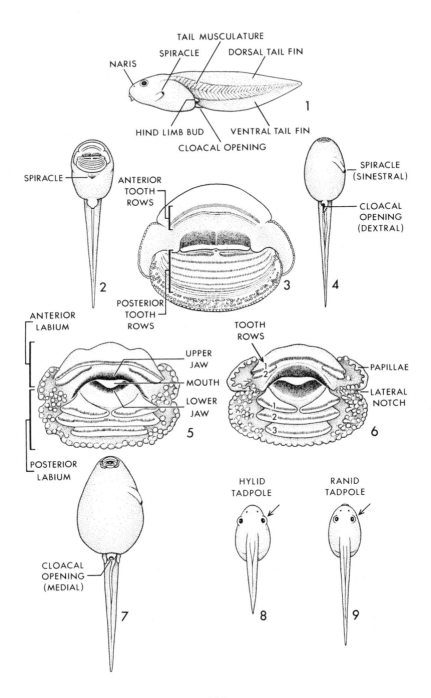

TAIL MUSCULATURE
SPIRACLE
NARIS
DORSAL TAIL FIN

1

HIND LIMB BUD
CLOACAL OPENING
VENTRAL TAIL FIN

SPIRACLE

2

ANTERIOR TOOTH ROWS

SPIRACLE (SINESTRAL)

CLOACAL OPENING (DEXTRAL)

4

3

POSTERIOR TOOTH ROWS

ANTERIOR LABIUM

UPPER JAW

MOUTH

LOWER JAW

5

POSTERIOR LABIUM

TOOTH ROWS

1
2

PAPILLAE

LATERAL NOTCH

1
2
3

6

CLOACAL OPENING (MEDIAL)

7

HYLID TADPOLE

8

RANID TADPOLE

9

8A. Tail mottled or spotted; found in streams ... Foothills Yellow-legged Frog, *Rana boylei*
8B. Tail not mottled or spotted; found in still water ... Wood Frog, *Rana sylvatica* (part)

9A. Four rows of teeth on posterior labium 10
9B. Two or three rows of teeth on posterior labium 11

10A. Submarginal papillae well-developed on anterior labium; dorsal fin terminates at or anterior to spiracle; tail length/tail height 4.4 or less; fins usually unicolored; venter pink in life (part) ... Red-legged Frog, *Rana aurora*
10B. Submarginal papillae poorly developed or absent on upper labium; dorsal fin terminates posterior to spiracle; tail length/tail height 4.4 or more; tail often with small blotches; venter not pink in life ... Cascade Frog, *Rana cascadae*

11A. Nares small and difficult to discern; tail and body greenish; unicolored or often with distinct black dots; tail fin clear with black dots or with dark mottling and streaks; often large........................ 12
11B. Nares large and easily seen; tail and body not greenish with black dots; tail fins may be speckled 13

12A. Third row of teeth on posterior labium long, 3/4 to nearly as long as first row of teeth on posterior labium (5); dorsum of body, tail musculature, and dorsal fin with distinct, punctate spots; large size, up to 140 mm total length ... Bullfrog, *Rana catesbeiana*
12B. Third row of teeth on posterior labium short, about half as long as first row of teeth on posterior labium; dorsum of body, tail musculature, and dorsal fin without distinct, punctate spots, or if present, with indistinct borders; smaller maximum size, up to 90 mm total length ... Green Frog, *Rana clamitans*

13A. Lower jaw massive in all dimensions, much wider (longitudinal measurement) than upper jaw (6); white line from nostril to snout ... Northern Leopard Frog, *Rana pipiens*
13B. Lower jaw not so large, not larger than upper jaw (as in 5); no white line from nostril to snout.. 14

III. Key Illustrations - Tadpoles
Figs.: (1) Tadpole general morphology; (2) *Ascaphus truei,* ventral view; (3) Oral sucker of *Ascaphus truei;* (4) Ventral view of tadpole; (5) Mouth region of *Rana catesbeiana* tadpole; (6) Mouth region of *Rana pipiens* tadpole; (7) Ventral view showing cloacal orientation of bufonid and pelobatid tadpoles; (8) Dorsal view of hylid tadpole showing eyes in outline of silhouette; (9) Dorsal view of ranid tadpole showing eyes not included in outline of silhouette.

14A. Long tail, total length/body length 2.6 or more; dorsal fin terminates posterior to spiracle; tail with small flecks and blotches ... Spotted Frog, *Rana pretiosa*

14B. Short tail, total length/body length 2.6 or less; dorsal fin terminates at or anterior to spiracle; tail darkly pigmented without numerous flecks and blotches 15

15A. West of Cascade Mountains ... Red-legged Frog, *Rana aurora* (part)

15B. Northern Idaho, northeastern Washington, or British Columbia ... Wood Frog, *Rana sylvatica* (part)

Plate 1. (a) Pacific Giant Salamander (*Dicamptodon ensatus*), Cowlitz Co., Washington. (b) Pacific Giant Salamander, Valley Co., Idaho; defensive posture. (c) Pacific Giant Salamander, Benton Co., Oregon; albino larva. (d) Pacific Giant Salamander, Benton Co., Oregon; adult female guarding eggs.

Plate 2. (a) Northwestern Salamander (*Ambystoma gracile gracile*), Benton Co., Oregon. (b) Northwestern Salamander, Benton Co., Oregon: larva. (c) Siskiyou Mountains Salamander (*Plethodon stormi*), Jackson Co., Oregon. (d) Ensatina (*Ensatina eschscholtzi picta*), Curry Co., Oregon.

Plate 3. (a) Clouded Salamander (*Ameides ferreus*), Benton Co., Oregon; piebald color pattern. (b) Roughskin Newt (*Taricha granulosa granulosa*), Benton Co., Oregon; piebald color pattern. (c) Tailed Frog (*Ascaphus truei*), Linn Co., Oregon; adult male; photo by R. W. Van Devender. (d) Bullfrog (*Rana catesbeiana*), Coos Co., Oregon; albino.

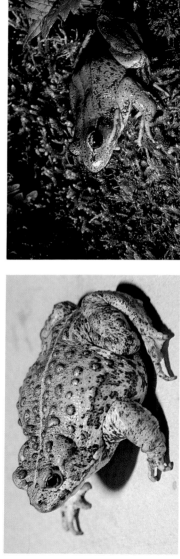

Plate 4. (a) Western Toad (*Bufo boreas*), Linn Co., Oregon. (b) Red-legged Frog (*Rana aurora*), Tillamook Co., Oregon; photo by Alex Walker. (c) Cascade Frog (*Rana cascadae*), Douglas Co., Oregon; photo by K. M. Walker. (d) Spotted Frog (*Rana pretiosa*), Lane Co., Oregon.

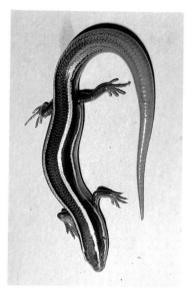

Plate 5. (a) Short-horned Lizard (*Phrynosoma douglassi*), Lake Co., Oregon. (b) Western Skink (*Eumeces skiltonianus*), Humboldt Co., California. (c) Side-blotched Lizard (*Uta stansburiana*), Deschutes Co., Oregon; adult male. (d) Longnose Leopard Lizard (*Gambelia wislizenii*), Harney Co., Oregon; female with postnuptial coloration.

Plate 6. (a) Sharptail Snake (*Contia tenuis*), Curry Co., Oregon. (b) Southern Alligator Lizard (*Elgaria multicarinata*), Benton Co., Oregon. (c) Ringneck Snake (*Diadophis punctatus amabilis*), Benton Co., Oregon. (d) Northern Alligator Lizard (*Elgaria coerulea principis*), Lincoln Co., Oregon.

Plate 7. (a) Racer (*Coluber constrictor*), Benton Co., Oregon; adult. (b) Racer, Benton Co., Oregon; juvenile. (c) Striped Whipsnake (*Masticophis taeniatus*), Harney Co., Oregon. (d) Smooth Green Snake (*Opheodrys vernalis*), Crawford Co., Michigan; photo by R. W. Van Devender.

Plate 8. (a) California Mountain Kingsnake (*Lampropeltis zonata*), Jackson Co., Oregon. (b) Western Ground Snake (*Sonora semiannulata*), Ada Co., Idaho. (c) Northwestern Garter Snake (*Thamnophis ordinoides*), Lane Co., Oregon; (d) Common Garter Snake (*Thamnophis sirtalis concinnus*), Benton Co., Oregon.

TRUE TOADS
FAMILY BUFONIDAE

The toad family Bufonidae is distributed throughout the world except for the eastern Indo-Australian Archipelago, Polynesia, Madagascar, and Australia. Africa seems to be the center of diversity. All bufonids lack teeth in the upper jaw, and the males of all species have a peculiar structure called a Bidder's organ near each testis. If the testes are removed surgically, the Bidder's organs become functional ovaries in about two years. In addition, bufonids usually have rough or warty skin and a squat body with short legs. Toads are notorious for their distasteful and poisonous skin secretions used to deter predators. The warts are concentrations of poison glands. There are 20 genera and about 280 species of bufonids in the world, but only a single genus, *Bufo,* occurs in North America.

TOADS
GENUS *BUFO*

The genus *Bufo* is widespread, having nearly the same distribution as the family Bufonidae (see above). There are about 121 species in this genus, 18 of which occur in the U.S. and Canada, but only two are found in the Pacific Northwest. Toads are the only anurans in the Northwest that lack teeth in the upper jaw.

WESTERN TOAD
BUFO BOREAS BAIRD AND GIRARD

Western Toads are the only true toads throughout much of our area. They can become rather large, and adults range in SVL from about 55 to 125 mm. The ground color of these toads is quite variable, normally being various shades of green or brown. A light stripe runs down the center of the back from about even with the nostrils to the posterior end of the body. This stripe is usually white to light yellow or pale green. The skin of the back, sides, and upper legs is covered with small (to about 5 mm), rounded or elongated warts, which are often reddish-brown in younger toads, In toads with lighter ground color, a darker halo may border each wart. Behind each eye is an oblong swelling (8 to 9 mm long in larger toads) somewhat larger than the eye; these are the parotoid glands. Ventrally, Western Toads

127

are light colored with many irregular dark marks on the abdomen and smaller rounded black marks on the throat. The undersurface is covered with tiny black-tipped tubercles. Unlike frogs, toad skin appears dry. The pupil of the eye is a horizontal oval.

Bufo boreas tadpoles are very dark in color, appearing to be black in the water. They are somewhat lighter ventrally. The tail fins are low, the dorsal fin being about as high as the greatest height of the tail musculature. The fins are slightly pigmented, the dorsal fin being darker than the ventral. Labial teeth are arranged in two rows anterior and three rows posterior to the mouth (tooth row formula = 2/3). The first anterior row is complete and wide. The second row has a medial gap, which is narrower than the tooth row segments. The three posterior rows are complete, and all are about as long as the first anterior row. There are no papillae on the posterior margin of the labial area.

HABITAT. Metamorphosed toads are largely terrestrial, and occur from sea level to high mountainous areas, as well as in northern desert regions. We have seen a multitude of their tracks made overnight in the sand dunes of the Oregon coast, have seen them emerging from rodent burrows just before dark in ponderosa pine forests, and have found them in an old root cellar of an abandoned ranch in the southeastern Oregon desert. At Santiam Pass, Linn Co., Oregon, we observed adult Western Toads burying themselves in loose soil (volcanic ash) by shuffling their hind limbs and digging with the tubercles on the bottoms of their hind feet, much in the manner of spadefoot toads. The burying process took about 30 minutes. They are nocturnal during dry weather, but forage during daylight on rainy or overcast days. Optimal areas are probably those with moderate to dense undergrowth in more humid regions. These toads are entirely absent from the Willamette Valley of western Oregon, for reasons not clear to us.

At least some toads hibernate in terrestrial situations. In late April, we found a few toads beginning breeding activity in an inlet of Fish Lake in the Oregon Cascades (950 m elevation). We removed at least one dozen *Bufo boreas* from beneath bark and from within the decayed wood of a Douglas fir log, about 1.0 m in diameter, that extended some 2.5 to 3.0 m over the water; only the bottom 15 to 30 cm were submerged.

Sexually mature toads move to water for breeding. In montane areas, they utilize spring pools, ponds, lake shallows, and slow-moving portions of streams. In the Oregon Cascades, they may prefer mud-

128

bottomed shallows of lakes and ponds. On the Oregon coast, freshwater ponds in dunes are favored, and in desert regions, stock ponds and reservoirs are used.

VARIATION. *Bufo boreas,* currently is divided into three subspecies, of which *Bufo b. boreas,* the Boreal Toad, is the only one to occur in our region. The most obvious variation in Western Toads involves their dorsal ground color. Individuals from a single population may range from various shades of green through grays and browns to almost black. Occasional yellowish or reddish individuals have been seen. Individuals can lighten or darken their ground color considerably, being darker at cooler temperatures. Recently-metamorphosed toadlets appear almost uniformly dark brown to black. The tubercles on the undersides of their feet are yellow, but these darken as the toads mature. Spotting on the throat is usually present, but may be absent in some individuals. The vertebral, or middorsal, stripe is absent in some individuals.

LIFE HISTORY. Reproductive activities of *Bufo boreas* occur from late January or February in coastal areas to early July in higher montane situations. Interestingly, these toads breed during early July in the hot Snake River Canyon (about 225 m elevation), apparently as an adaptation to high levels of runoff water during May and June. The males, which are usually 60 to 90 mm SVL (females 80 to 120 mm SVL), congregate in the water of the breeding sites in numbers up to several hundred or more. In one study, it was estimated that between 2,000 and 5,000 adults utilized a lake of approximately 100 hectares in the Oregon Cascades (1,200 m elevation) for breeding. During two years, it was estimated that there were about four times as many males as females in the lake. On 30 June, we observed mating activities of Western Toads in a shallow inlet of a lake in the Strawberry Mountains of Oregon (2,280 m elevation). The males (about two dozen) either rested quietly at the water's surface or swam vigorously toward other moving males. The males gave frequent bird-like twittering calls, which seemed to be in response to nearness or actual touching by another male. Male Western Toads do not have a mating call. Whereas the male activity was 1 to 10 m from shore, three amplectic pairs were within a few cm of shore, and one pair was producing eggs. The bottom within 75 cm of shore was covered with egg strings.

Females produce an average of 12,000 eggs per clutch. The eggs are laid in two gelatinous strands (one from each oviduct), the individual eggs being closely spaced along each strand. Each egg measures 1.5 to 1.7 mm diameter. Because the pair moves about somewhat during laying, the strands become tangled about one another and the pond

129

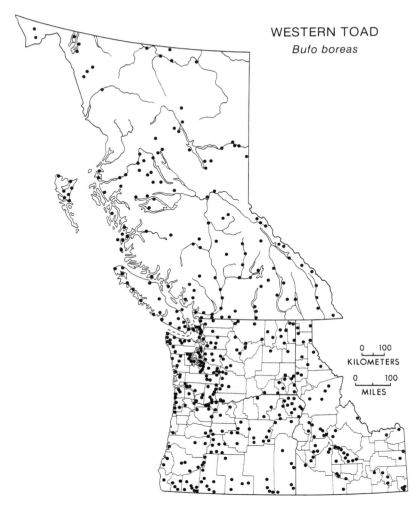

WESTERN TOAD
Bufo boreas

0   100
KILOMETERS

0   100
MILES

vegetation. Egg-laying in one location is completed in a very short time, usually a week or less. Time of hatching is dependent on water temperature and is fairly short; however, we have no precise data on this.

Tadpoles are only about 10 mm TL at hatching, but grow rapidly once they begin feeding. The larvae are usually restricted to areas over muddy bottoms where they feed by filtering suspended plant material or feed on detritus on the bottom. *Bufo boreas* larvae characteristically form dense aggregations during the day, consisting of hundreds or thousands of individuals. These swarms move from place to place around a lake shore, and there is a constant seething movement of individuals within the mass. The masses stir up food material from the bottom, and it has been shown that temperatures within an aggregation are 2° to 3° C higher than the surrounding water. The tadpoles may also move in smaller schools, following one another in a wandering course through the water. We once measured such a school at about 0.3 km in length as it wound its way through the shallows of a high Cascades lake. Nowhere was this serpentine line wider than about one meter.

The tadpoles seek out areas of warmer temperatures within a lake, and this behavior undoubtedly speeds up metamorphosis. When given a choice in a temperature gradient in the laboratory, the larvae selected a temperature of around 30° C, but temperatures in mountain lakes are seldom if ever this high. Metamorphic aggregations form along gradually sloping open shores of mountain lakes in August and early september in Oregon. The adjacent shores become littered with hundreds of emerging toadlets, which tend to disperse along the more moist avenues leading away from the lake. The little toads measure 12 to 13 mm SVL (Oregon Cascades).

Mortality in larvae and young toads must be enormously high. They are fed upon by some birds, garter snakes, and predaceous insect larvae, even though the larvae and probably the toadlets are somewhat unpalatable to many predators. In the Oregon Cascades lake where at least 2,000 adults were breeding, one can estimate 400 females laying at least 4,500,000 eggs. It is quite evident that mortality between egg-laying and the return of adults two or three years later is well over 99%. Once adulthood is reached, toads may live for several years, as their skin secretions are highly distasteful to would-be predators.

Western Toads eat virtually every kind of flying insect in addition to spiders, crayfish, sowbugs, and earthworms.

REMARKS. We have almost no information on life history features of this toad in western lowland and coastal populations. The species seems to adapt well to agricultural irrigation and even to suburban residential areas, given available breeding water.

REFERENCES. Dorsch (1967), Metter (1961), O'Hara (1981), Samallow (1979, 1980).

WOODHOUSE'S TOAD
BUFO WOODHOUSEI GIRARD

This species can be distinguished from the similar-sized Western Toads by the presence of ridges on top of the head, known as cranial crests. In Woodhouse's Toad, these are like two L's placed back to back. The longitudinal parts of the L's are parallel and somewhat fused together on top of the head; the transverse parts extend laterally behind the eyes. A further difference is seen in the parotoid glands located behind the eyes; in this species they are twice as long as wide, whereas they are less than twice as long as wide and more oval-shaped in *Bufo boreas*.

24. Woodhouse's Toad *(Bufo woodhousei)*, Umatilla Co., Oregon; photo by R. Altig.

These toads attain a maximum SVL of 125 mm, the females being about 20 mm larger than the males. The dorsal ground color varies from gray or yellowish-brown to tan and from dark brown to almost black. There is a pale longitudinal stripe down the center of the back in most individuals. In light individuals, cranial crests and spots on the head and body may be dark. Small warts over the dorsal area may be tipped with a different color than adjacent ground color and are often surrounded by a narrow dark border. Ventrally, these toads are yellowish, with varying intensities of dark markings on the throat and chest areas. Males have dark throats and develop a dark horny patch on the thumb during the breeding season.

Recently-metamorphosed toads lack cranial crests, and the vertebral light stripe is only faintly evident. The small dorsal warts are conspicuously light-colored, and each one or two is contained in a dark brownish spot. These spots tend to form two irregular rows down the back.

The tadpoles attain a TL of about 25 mm. The body is dark brown to black in color, but the musculature of the tail is bicolored, dark above and without dark markings below. The dorsal fin may have a few darker spots, and it does not reach anteriorly to the level of the spiracle on the body. The labial teeth are in two rows anterior and three posterior to the mouth (2/3). The first anterior row is complete and longer than the width of the mouth. The second row has a medial space as long as either lateral segment, the entire row being as long as the first. The first and second lower rows are complete and about as long as the upper rows. The third row is complete and somewhat shorter.

HABITAT. These toads are at least partly terrestrial during the non-breeding season. They normally forage at night in a variety of habitats, but usually near permanent water in more arid regions. They are known to collect under urban streetlights to feed on insects attracted to the lights. Diurnal retreats are under surface debris, in rodent burrows, or in shallow, self-dug burrows. We have seen them at night on a blacktop road during a June rain in the Nyssa area of southeastern Oregon. Younger toads are said to move about diurnally to some extent.

Reproduction occurs in relatively permanent waters: irrigation ditches and canals, pools in streams, ponds, lake margins, reservoirs, and so on. During May, we found Woodhouse's Toads breeding in a weedy pond up to 40 cm deep and approximately 1/4 hectare in size and surrounded by willows. This was located near the Columbia River in northeastern Oregon.

VARIATION. There are presently four subspecies of *Bufo woodhousei;* only *B. w. woodhousei,* Woodhouse's Toad, occurs in the Northwest. The number and distribution of dorsal spots is variable. In 12 preserved specimens from Morrow Co. in northeastern Oregon, four have dark spots over the entire back region, including spots on the parotoid glands in two; two have a few spots at the posterior end of the back; and the remainder appear to have no spots. These toads measure 52.5 to 79.0 mm SVL. The anterior ends of the cranial crests are fused and somewhat enlarged into a hardened boss on the snout. The intensity and extent of ventral dark spotting varies somewhat. Seven individuals have a few very faint spots on the chest and anterior edges of the throat, and five have dark spots varying in intensity over the entire throat, chest, and anterior abdomen.

LIFE HISTORY. Literature records indicate that the breeding season for this species may extend from March into late June. We have scant information on this for the Northwest. We encountered a breeding congress in mid-May in northeastern Oregon (see Habitat)

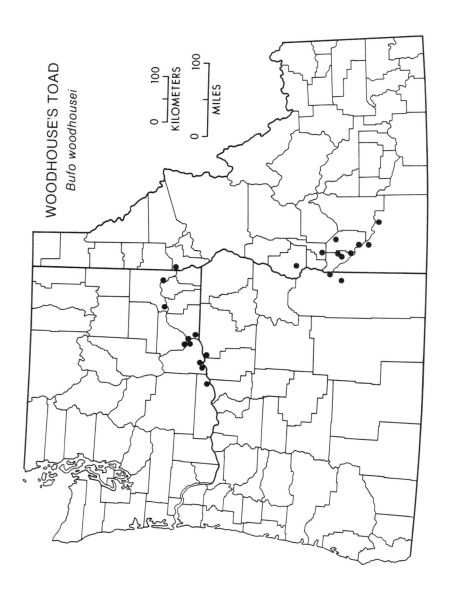

WOODHOUSE'S TOAD
Bufo woodhousei

KILOMETERS
0   100

MILES
0   100

and collected singing males on the evening of 8 June, from a shallow weedy inlet of the Owyhee Reservoir in southeastern Oregon. The song of the male is a high-pitched trill lasting 0.8 to 4.0 seconds, with pauses of up to one minute between trills.

Studies of *Bufo woodhousei (B. w. fowleri)* in North Carolina suggest that larger males are more successful in obtaining mates than are smaller males, and that females choose males based on characteristics of their calls. Because the calls are affected both by male body size and temperature, males have the opportunity to increase their chances of reproductive success by selecting calling sites with (lower) temperatures that result in calls similar to calls of larger males calling from sites with higher temperatures.

In a study in New Mexico, males arrived at the breeding ponds before the females and remained up to eight days in the pond. Females spent only a single night in the pond. The breeding season lasted from 31 March until 9 May, but calling and mating occurred only on nights when temperatures were above freezing. Males that were larger and/or stayed in the pond longer had higher reproductive success. The reproductive success varied from 0 to 3 matings per male.

The female deposits eggs in strings, which become entangled in submerged vegetation as the pair moves about. The egg strings can be distinguished from those of *Bufo boreas* by the fact that those of *B. woodhousei* consist of one layer of gel, those of *B. boreas* of two. A single female can produce as many as 25,000 eggs, each egg being 1.0 to 1.5 mm in diameter. We have no information on time to hatching or larval length at hatching.

The tadpoles reach about 25 mm TL and probably transform about two months after hatching. The SVL of newly-metamorphosed toadlets is 10.0 to 13.5 mm. We have no information on age at maturity. The literature states that both sexes become adults at about 55 to 60 mm SVL.

Virtually every kind of terrestrial invertebrate has been found in the stomachs of these toads. They are capable of eating enormous quantities of food. Up to 16% of their body weight may be stomach contents consisting of a single species of prey.

REMARKS. Very little is known of the details of life history of this species in the Northwest. It appears that this species, like the Northern Leopard Frog *(Rana pipiens),* has invaded the Northwest from the East using the Snake and Columbia Rivers as avenues of dispersal.

REFERENCES. Fairchild (1981), Woodward (1982), Wright and Wright (1949).

TREEFROGS
FAMILY HYLIDAE

Hylids occur throughout the New World, Europe, Asia north of the Himalayas, and Africa north of the Sahara. The "hylids" of New Guinea and Australia are now thought to belong to an independently evolved lineage of treefrogs. The family Hylidae is most diverse in South America, less diverse in Central America, and even less diverse in North America. Only the genus *Hyla* reaches the Old World (Eurasia and northern Africa). Thirty genera and about 400 species comprise the family, of which seven genera and 25 species occur in the United States and Canada (one genus and species introduced). In the Northwest, we have two genera, each with a single species.

All tree frogs have an extra cartilaginous element called an "intercalary cartilage" between the ultimate and penultimate phalanges of the fingers and toes. This element gives the toes and fingers a "stepped" appearance when viewed from the side. The intercalary cartilages are thought to give the fingers and toes greater maneuverability to aid in climbing. For example, they allow the tips of the toes and fingers to rotate so that the adhesive toe pads can lie flush against irregular surfaces. Not all species are arboreal, however, and those that are not have reduced or missing toe pads, but they retain the intercalary cartilages.

Treefrogs generally have long slender limbs and digits commensurate with their climbing ability. Many species are green, and some have bright, hidden, "flash" colors along the sides of the body and behind the hind limbs, which are exposed only when the frogs are moving. These colors are thought to function to confuse predators, or perhaps to warn them that the frogs are distasteful.

TRUE TREEFROGS
GENUS *HYLA*

This is a large genus of 291 species with a range as broad as that of the family. *Hyla* is most diverse in tropical America, there being only 13 species in the United States and Canada. We have a single species in the Northwest.

PACIFIC TREEFROG
HYLA REGILLA BAIRD AND GIRARD

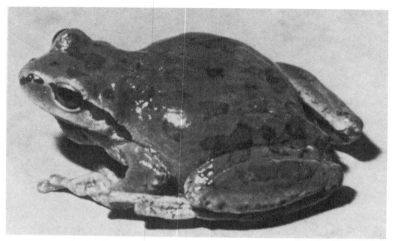

25. Pacific Treefrog *(Hyla regilla),* Lane Co., Oregon.

These are our only small frogs with enlarged terminal discs, or "toe-pads," on the end of each digit. The adults are usually under 50 mm SVL, the males averaging a few millimeters smaller than the females. Pacific Treefrogs vary considerably in ground color, green or shades of brown being the usual color; however, red or gray to almost black also occur. Frequencies of these colors vary with locality (see Variation). These frogs usually have a conspicuous black eye stripe, which extends as a narrow band on each side of the rostrum, or snout, in front of the eyes and as wider bands from the rear of the eyes to the shoulders. Dark spots and longitudinal blotches usually occur on the head, back, and legs, often forming an irregular triangle on the top of the head between the eyes. Ventrally, these frogs are white or pale yellow, the males having a gray to almost black throat, indicating the vocal sac, during the breeding season.

Tadpoles may attain a total length of nearly 50 mm before metamorphosing. They are usually some shade of brown, heavily marked with black dorsally; ventrally they are whitish with metallic iridescence. When viewed from above, their eyes are usually near or interrupt the outline of the head. Labial tooth rows are usually 2/3 and the lateral margins of the oral disc are not notched. They differ from the very similar larvae of the Striped Chorus Frog, *Pseudacris triseriata,* in having a lower less arched dorsal fin.

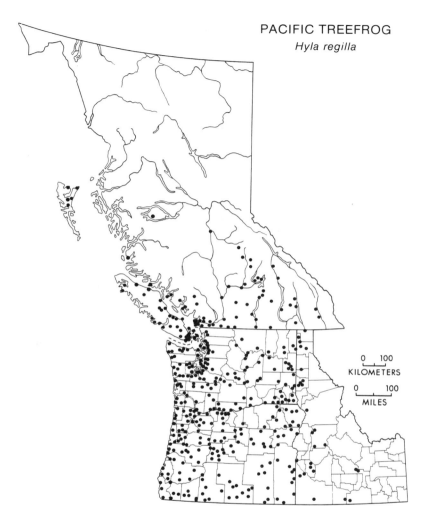

PACIFIC TREEFROG
Hyla regilla

0   100
KILOMETERS

0   100
MILES

HABITAT. This is the most common and widespread frog in most of our area. They occur from sea level to high montane elevations, providing there are suitable breeding waters. During the non-breeding season they are terrestrial, moving about on the ground and in low shrubbery during moist weather. During dry periods or in drier regions, they are frequently nocturnal in activity, taking refuge in dense vegetation, rock or log crevices, rodent burrows, and other protected places during non-active periods.

Pacific Treefrogs are most likely to utilize rather shallow quiet waters for breeding, especially waters with submerged and/or emergent vegetation. They will lay eggs in almost any small body of temporary water and, as a result, may lose a year's reproductive effort in ponds or puddles that dry up too quickly.

VARIATION. There has been one major attempt to divide Pacific Treefrogs into subspecies. This division generally has not been accepted, but it is instructive regarding variation in *Hyla regilla* to look at some aspects of these potential subspecies. According to the above study, four subspecies occur in the Northwest: an Oregon and Washington coastal form; a form found in the major valleys of western Oregon and in the Puget Trough of western Washington and southern British Columbia; a form in the Cascade Mountains of Oregon, Washington, and southern British Columbia; and a form occurring east of the Cascades in Washington and Oregon, and in southern Idaho. These populations differ in such characteristics as head and body length, smoothness of dorsal and ventral skin, proportional head width, amount of hind foot webbing, relative hind leg length, and others.

The basic background colors of *Hyla regilla* are green, brown, gray, and red, and a single frog may have one or more of these colors. Individual frogs can vary from very pale to quite dark, but the basic colors remain the same. These colors have been shown to be genetically fixed; for example, green depends on two pairs of genes, and the dominant gene of each pair must be present to produce green. The frequencies of these colors vary geographically, from year to year in one locality, and even within a breeding population over the course of the breeding season. Brown and green predominate in our coastal populations, although about one-third of coastal frogs have some red. Willamette Valley-Puget Trough frogs are largely green or brown, or a combination of these, whereas Cascade frogs are more likely to be brown or gray. In a population of Pacific Treefrogs in the central Willamette Valley of Oregon, we found that frogs having at least some green accounted for 81 to 97% of those encountered during the most active breeding months over a two-year period. In a northern Idaho population, breeding Pacific Treefrogs were predominantly non-green (gray or brown) in one year and predominantly green the next. Several bright blue, newly-metamorphosed Pacific Treefrogs from Salem, Oregon developed a reddish-silver coloration by the time they were a year old.

LIFE HISTORY. Depending on locality, Pacific Treefrogs move to aquatic breeding sites from November (coastal populations) to July (mountains). During a two-year study in the Willamette Valley, frogs began moving in numbers to the breeding ponds in the second week of

January the first year and in the first week of February the second year. In northern Idaho, frogs first moved to breeding ponds in the first week of April in one year and the second week of April in the following year. In western Oregon and Washington, such breeding migrations are triggered by warm (near 10° C), winter rains.

Once in the water, males begin "singing." These choruses are usually nocturnal but may continue, at least sporadically, during daylight hours. The usual call is two-parted (diphasic) and is roughly imitated by saying "ribbet" rapidly at a pitch near that of the frogs'. Groups of two or three males tend to call in sequence during their calling bouts, and the sequence is consistently started by one frog known as the bout leader. Females are attracted by these calls and usually select the bout leader to mate with. Male frogs also have a single note call (monophasic) and a trill. These apparently function to space the males within the pond. It has been shown that there is considerable geographic variation in call characteristics, and that relatively isolated populations have especially distinctive calls. During humid or rainy periods outside of the breeding season, males frequently give a short grating call, which may be of territorial significance.

Amplexus is axillary, and the pair may remain in this position for several hours before egg laying begins. The eggs are laid in packets averaging about 25 eggs (9 to 70), which are attached to underwater stems or laid on the bottoms of shallow pools. Each egg is about 1.3 mm in diameter, brown above and yellow below, and surrounded by two gelatinous envelopes. Females remain in the ponds a much shorter time than males. During one breeding season in a Willamette Valley pond, female *Hyla regilla* remained an average of 9.6 days (1 to 27) and males an average of 33 days (1 to 90). The eggs hatch in 3 to 5 weeks in western Oregon, the tadpoles measuring 6 to 8 mm TL at hatching. Their growth is fairly rapid so that they attain a pre-metamorphic total length of 45 to 55 mm in about two months in western Oregon or two and one-half months in northern Idaho. Recently metamorphosed frogs averaged 13.8 mm SVL (12.1 to 15.3) in one western Oregon study. In this same study, the young frogs almost doubled their length within two months after metamorphosis, and some were members of the breeding chorus the following spring, attaining sexual maturity in less than a year.

The food habits of *Hyla regilla* are not well known, but small beetles, flies, spiders, ants, leaf-hoppers, and isopods occur in their stomachs. Pacific Treefrogs and their larvae are preyed upon by Bullfrogs, garter snakes, and various birds and mammals. The larvae are known to be attacked by carnivorous aquatic insects. One observer stated that he never found Pacific Treefrogs breeding in ponds containing Bullfrogs. Because *Hyla regilla* can utilize temporary ponds, and Bullfrogs cannot, this does not appear to be a serious problem.

REFERENCES. Allan (1973), Altig and Brodie (1968), Jameson (1956, 1957), Jameson et al. (1966), Resnick and Jameson (1963), Schaub and Larsen (1978), Snyder and Jameson (1965), Storm and Pimentel (1954), Whitney (1980), Whitney and Krebs (1975a, 1975b).

CHORUS FROGS
GENUS *PSEUDACRIS*

Pseudacris, with seven species, is found only in North America. These are small, secretive, terrestrial frogs that are seldom seen but often heard. During the early spring breeding season, chorus frogs can be heard singing in great numbers, night and day, from the low vegetation emerging from shallow ponds, marshes, and roadside ditches. They have small toe pads and only a slight amount of webbing between the digits. There is a single species in the Pacific Northwest.

STRIPED CHORUS FROG
PSEUDACRIS TRISERIATA (WIED)

26. Striped Chorus Frog *(Pseudacris triseriata).*

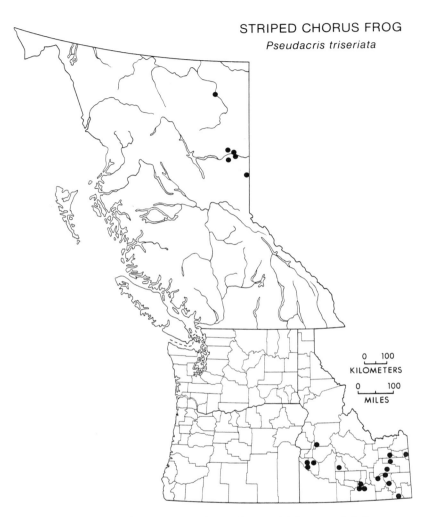

STRIPED CHORUS FROG
Pseudacris triseriata

0   100
KILOMETERS

0   100
MILES

These are small frogs, up to 38 mm SVL, which superficially resemble Pacific Treefrogs. However, they lack the more expanded toe tips of *Hyla regilla,* and a dark stripe runs from the snout through the eye and along the side of the body to the groin. There is a light lip-line below this. The dorsal ground color varies from gray or brown to olive or green. There are usually three longitudinal dark stripes on the back, which may be broken or spotty. The ventral surface is white or cream, sometimes with dark markings anteriorly. These frogs have a rather pointed snout and appear to be long-bodied and short-legged. The webbing on the hind toes is very reduced.

The tadpoles are small, reaching a total length of about 30 mm before metamorphosis. They are dark brown above, with metallic flecking, and lighter below with metallic iridescence. The tail fins are marked with small dark spots, and the dorsal fin reaches anteriorly to about the level of the spiracle on the body. Its greatest height is about equal to that of the tail musculature. The eyes are near the lateral outline of the head. There are two rows of teeth anterior and three posterior to the mouth. The first anterior row is complete and much wider than the mouth. The second row has a wide medial space, but this is shorter than the remaining tooth row segments. All three posterior rows are complete, the first two being longer than the mouth and the third about half the length of the other two.

HABITAT. Striped Chorus Frogs spend the non-breeding season in damp grassy or marshy areas and may also be found in damp wooded areas. They may climb somewhat into low shrubbery. For reproduction they move to a variety of temporary or permanent waters, including ditches, small ponds, marshes, lake shallows, and the quiet backwaters of streams. There is usually some sort of vegetation present to which eggs can be attached.

VARIATION. The species is divided into four subspecies, of which only *Pseudacris triseriata maculata,* the Boreal Chorus Frog, occurs in our area. We have almost no information on variation in this species in the Northwest, and it is difficult to find information in the literature that applies solely to our subspecies. The three longitudinal stripes on the back vary considerably; they are often not continuous, being broken up into a few or many spots. In Wyoming, the dorsal ground color may be pinkish in some individuals, and others may have greenish stripes or spots rather than the usual brown. A dark triangle may or may not be present on the head between the eyes. Males have dark throats compared to the whitish throats of females, and they develop a pad on the first finger during the breeding season.

LIFE HISTORY. The reproductive season is probably from late March into May or early June, depending upon the elevation and latitude. The first indications are congregations of singing males. The song is a loud (for such a small frog) chirping sound and can be roughly imitated by running the thumb over the teeth of a stiff comb. Each call lasts 0.5 to 1.0 second, and the frogs give 30 to 70 calls per minute, the rate probably depending on temperature. A chorus was heard during the evening of 6 April in southwestern Idaho, and they have been heard calling as late as 8 July in Minidoka Co., Idaho.

The female produces a total of 150 to 1,500 eggs, but fastens them to vegetation in packets of 30 to 75 eggs, the packets usually being less than 25 mm in diameter. Individual eggs are about 1.0 mm in diameter and take 10 to 14 days to hatch. Hatchlings vary in size from 4.5 to 7.5 mm TL and metamorphose in about two months at a total tadpole length of about 30 mm (British Columbia) to 43 mm (Utah). The froglets are tiny, 7.5 to 12.0 mm SVL. We assume that, like *Hyla regilla*, these frogs may breed in the year following their metamorphosis.

Adult males range in size from about 21 to 32 mm SVL and adult females from 20 to 38 mm SVL. In Colorado, females in high elevation populations are larger (average SVL = 31.4 mm) than females in low elevation populations (average SVL = 24.1 mm), and the high elevation females produce larger but equal numbers of eggs. The larger eggs are thought to facilitate more rapid development to the metamorphic stage as an adaptation to the shorter growing seasons at higher elevations.

Ants, spiders, flies, beetles, aphids, and other insects are eaten by these frogs.

REMARKS. Very little has been published concerning the Striped Chorus Frog in the Northwest. Additional information on the distribution, ecology, and life history of this species for this region is greatly needed.

REFERENCES. Baxter and Stone (1980), Evendeh (1946), Pack (1920), Pettus and Angleton (1967).

BELL TOADS
FAMILY LEIOPELMATIDAE

This family contains species that are thought to be the most primitive of living frogs. Some primitive characteristics are the high number of vertebrae (9; 8 in most advanced frogs), the shape of the vertebrae, the presence of ribs (lost in advanced frogs), numerous chromosomes, and inguinal amplexus. The family has a broadly disjunct amphitropical (temperate) distribution, with one genus *(Leiopelma)* and three species restricted to New Zealand, and one genus with a single species in the Pacific Northwest. The two genera share primitive traits, which each lineage may have retained independently for millions of years. The two genera differ by several specialized characterisics that reveal their long separate evolutionary histories. Fossil species of this family are known from South America, suggesting the route by which the two groups were linked historically.

The New Zealand forms have direct terrestrial development and external fertilization, whereas the Northwestern species has internal fertilization and aquatic tadpoles. The two genera are sometimes assigned to different families, Ascaphidae for the Northwestern genus and Leiopelmatidae for the New Zealand genus.

TAILED FROGS
GENUS *ASCAPHUS*

Ascaphus, and its single species, is endemic to the Pacific Northwest, including northwestern California and western Montana. This is the only genus of anurans in North America that is highly specialized for life in cold, clear, mountain streams.

TAILED FROG
ASCAPHUS TRUEI STEJNEGER

Tailed Frogs are small (37 to 50 mm SVL), and the males possess a short (to about 10 mm), somewhat bulbous "tail," which is actually an erectile copulatory device for inseminating the female. Both sexes of all sizes have rather dorsoventrally flattened hind toes, and the outer (fifth) toe is wider and less tapered than the others, with webbing to the tip on the inner side. No external ear membrane is present. The skin varies from almost smooth to warty, the warts being small and

27. Tailed Frog *(Ascaphus truei)*, Linn Co., Oregon; adult male; photo by K.M. Walker.

sometimes with sharp black tips. The ground color is usually some shade of gray or brown to almost black, variously marked with dark lines or blotches. A dark eye line frequently is present, and the top of the head anterior to about the middle of the eyelids is usually lighter than the ground color of the body.

The tadpoles are unique among Northwestern frogs in having the oral disc modified into an adhesive or sucker-like device that enables them to adhere to rocks in a swift current. On the inner surface of this disc are 2 or 3 rows of labial teeth anterior and 8 to 13 rows posterior to the mouth, resulting in a tooth row formula of 2-3/8-13. Tadpoles are either black or brown with or without lighter flecks. Most larvae have a whitish spot at the tip of the tail. Larvae are of various age groups within one population (see Variation) and thus differ in total length up to a maximum of about 60 mm.

HABITAT. Tailed Frogs are found from sea level to near timberline, occurring in or near fast-flowing, permanent streams within forested areas. These frogs usually remain hidden under rocks or debris during the day, emerging at night to feed along stream edges or from the surfaces of exposed rocks, downed logs, and so forth. They appear to be active out of water only during periods of high relative humidity. During a study of a Tailed Frog population on the lower west slope of the Oregon Cascades, we regularly measured relative

146

humidity during times of frog activity and consistently got measurements between 74 and 90%, with a mean of 80%. During rainy weather, *Ascaphus* are known to forage up to 25 or more meters away from water, and occasionally have been seen doing this during the day. Cold or cool temperatures seem a necessity for this frog. During the above-mentioned study in the Oregon Cascades, summer temperatures of water in a small stream varied from 11° to 12° C, averaging 11.8° C. Nocturnal temperatures at the exposed sites where frogs were collected ranged from 11.6° to 16.9° C, averaging 14° C.

The larvae are almost invariably seen in stretches of rapidly moving water where there are smooth rock surfaces, with at least some water flowing over them. Larvae are capable of inching their way about on very steep rock slopes with water cascading over them, often barely covering their backs. They avoid moss-covered rocks and deposits of silt.

VARIATION. Although this species exhibits considerable variation between populations, it is now agreed that the differences are neither great enough nor consistent enough to warrant the naming of subspecies. Within a population, males are smaller than females, but there is no consistent pattern of large or small animals correlated with geographic distribution. The average SVL of females from populations throughout much of the frog's range varied from 41.8 to 49.8 mm; males averaged from 36.9 to 42.2 mm. There is a slight trend towards smaller animals in the southeastern portion of the inland parts of the range.

The number of warts on various parts of the body varies greatly, but with no consistent geographic pattern. Frogs from inland populations and from southwestern Oregon are more likely to have cornified black tips on their warts. Concerning morphological variation in general, there are situations where adjacent populations show more differences than do populations from opposite ends of the range. Adult color and pattern likewise show no consistent geographical differences. Color patterns match rather closely the color of rocks in and adjacent to streams. Coastal animals have more dark pigmentation on the venter than do members of inland populations.

As with adults, larvae demonstrate differences that do not correlate well with geographic areas. Tail height may be correlated with the type of stream inhabited by the larvae. Tadpoles from streams with a gentle flow have higher less muscular tail fins than those from swifter streams with falls and rapids. Larval color and pattern tend to match their habitat. The white tail spot may be missing in some tadpoles of

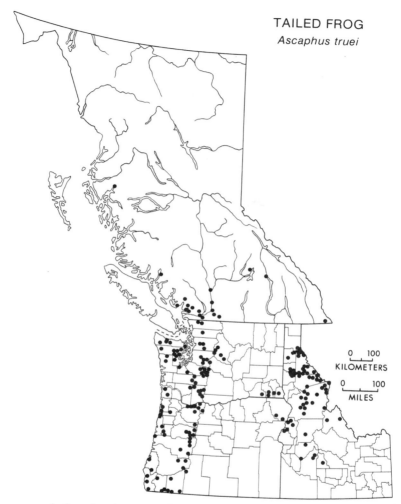

TAILED FROG

Ascaphus truei

0   100
KILOMETERS

0   100
MILES

any population, but is more often absent among larvae in streams with uniformly dark rocks.

LIFE HISTORY. We believe that *Ascaphus truei* adults normally breed in the early fall (late August and September) in all populations, even though males may clasp females at any time of the year. About mid-summer, the large tubercle on the inner side of each forefoot and a round spot on each forearm of males turns gray, and, by mid-August to September, these become black and horny. Small black spines within the cloacal opening increase in number to a maximum in late summer and early fall. During successful mating, the "tail" of the male

28. Tailed Frog *(Ascaphus truei)*, Lane Co., Oregon; pair in amplexus.

becomes engorged with blood and is directed forward. The male locks his arms around the pelvic or inguinal region of the female, interlocking his fingers. The "erected" cloacal extension is inserted into the cloaca of the female, and copulation normally lasts 24 to 30 hours. During the process, the female assumes a normal resting position with her rear legs drawn forward.

Tailed Frogs are unusual in that they appear to be voiceless; at least they do not call out of water. Because they mate under water, it is possible that they vocalize underwater like frogs of the family Pipidae. There is no evidence for this, however.

Sperm remain viable in the lower portions of the oviduct for at least ten months, and the fertilized eggs are deposited during July of the year after mating throughout the range of the species. With the possible exception of some coastal populations, females lay eggs every other year. The eggs are laid in a rosary-like string, which tends to become a more globular mass as it is attached to the underside of stones in the water. Each egg is 4 to 5 mm in diameter and unpigmented. Average clutch size (based on ovarian eggs) in populations throughout the range is 44 to 75, with individual ranges from 33 to 98. Hatching occurs in August and September, the hatchlings measuring 10 to 15 mm TL.

There is a distinct difference in the length of larval life in regional populations. Populations on the western slopes of the Cascades and westward to the Coast have a two-year larval period, whereas inland and certain Cascade populations complete three years as tadpoles before metamorphosing. Whatever the larval period, metamorphosis starts in July and is completed in September. Recently metamorphosed frogs measured during late August and early September from the lower western slopes of the Oregon Cascades averaged 24.6 mm SVL with a range of 23 to 28 mm.

Larval *Ascaphus* feed mainly on diatoms which they scrape off of rock surfaces. Substantial amounts of conifer pollen were found in gut contents of June tadpoles from two interior populations. Fine sand is taken in incidentally to scraping diatom-covered rocks. Minor amounts of filamentous algae and tiny insects may be ingested in the process of getting diatoms. Adults feed on a wide variety of insects and other invertebrates. It is apparent from their stomach contents that they must feed to some extent below the water surface, because such items as caddis and stonefly larvae appear there. They generally feed by sitting in one spot at night, devouring whatever comes their way, including such diverse items as snails, spiders, ticks and mites, colembolans, various dipterans, moths, ants, mayflies, crickets and lacewings. Bits of woody debris are usually included in the stomach contents. It is probable that during wet nights or occasionally even during dark rainy days, they forage actively in the adjacent forest.

Considered a very rare frog for many years, we now know that they may attain very high densities in suitable habitat. An observer in eastern Washington counted over 70 adults in one 60 m stretch of a creek. Another person, who spent many night hours along western Cascade and coastal streams gave estimates as high as one adult *Ascaphus truei* every 1 to 3 m along a variety of streams. It is now evident that Tailed Frogs can maintain their numbers in streams containing trout, a fact doubted by some earlier authors.

REMARKS. Tailed Frogs disappear from streams within logged areas. This probably is because of higher water temperatures and increased siltation. In view of the extensive logging that continues to occur throughout much of their range, the exact effects of logging on populations should be studied. We can find very little data on the growth rate of metamorphosed frogs or on internal details of their reproductive cycle.

REFERENCES. Altig and Brodie (1972), Metter (1964a, 1964b, 1967), Werntz (1969).

ARCHAIC TOADS
FAMILY PELOBATIDAE

Pelobatids are relatively primitive toad-like anurans that are found in both the Old and New Worlds, including North America, Eurasia, and the western Indo-Australian Archipelago. The family includes nine genera and 50 species, of which two genera and six species occur in the United States and Canada. Members of this family have several relatively primitive osteological features and other primitive characteristics such as inguinal amplexus and vertical pupils. North American pelobatids are toad-like in body form with warty skin, but the skin is thinner and smoother than the skin of true toads. Unlike *Bufo* species, pelobatids have teeth in the upper jaws. In America, pelobatids are denizens of prairies and deserts where they lead a terrestrial-burrowing-nocturnal existence. Their surface activity is closely tied to periods of rainfall in their otherwise arid to semi-arid environment.

SPADEFOOT TOADS
GENUS *SPEA*

Spadefoot Toads are sometimes placed in the single genus *Scaphiopus,* but some authorities separate them into two genera, including the former genus and *Spea*. Although we recognize *Spea* here, we do so with no strong conviction. A single species of *Spea* occurs in the Northwest.

GREAT BASIN SPADEFOOT
SPEA INTERMONTANA (COPE)

These are small "toads," attaining a maximum SVL of about 63 mm, the females being slightly larger than the males. Great Basin Spadefoots are relatively smooth-skinned, lacking the conspicuously warty skin of true toads. A black, sharp-edged "spade" occurs on the underside of the inner edge of each hind foot, and is characteristic of all age groups. The snout is short and slightly turned up (pugnosed). Great Basin Spadefoots have a vertical eye pupil, unlike the oval horizontal pupil of true toads.

Dorsally, *Spea intermontana* are predominantly gray and brown or olive. A usual pattern is a middorsal band of lighter brown with darker brown spots, usually having light centers. This blends into irregular

151

29. Great Basin Spadefoot *(Spea intermontana)*, Harney Co., Oregon.

gray longitudinal streaks, and, lateral to these, the color is similar to the middorsal area. A large, dark brown spot usually occurs on each upper eyelid. Ventrally, they are white to light cream with or without light brownish mottling on the chin area.

The tadpoles may reach rather large size, at least 70 mm TL. Tadpoles with hind legs and measuring about 70 mm, appear black in life, with metallic marking on the dorsal body and a golden iridescence on the abdomen. In preserved material, the coloration is tannish-brown. The spiracle is very low on the left side, almost under the body. The dorsal tail fin barely reaches onto the body and is about equal in height to the greatest height of the tail musculature. The tail musculature is light tan in color (darker at the dorsal edge), and the fins are finely reticulated with light brown. The eyes are close together on top of the head.

The mouth area is surrounded by a single row of low papillae and the jaws themselves appear rather wide. The labial teeth are difficult to characterize; apparently there may be two, three, four, or five rows anterior to the mouth, but we found these difficult to see. Our larval material shows three or four rows posterior to the mouth, the first one or two being represented by short widely-separated segments. The third and fourth rows vary in length, and the third sometimes has a medial space.

HABITAT. *Spea intermontana* is an inhabitant of arid open areas in the interior of the Northwest. For breeding, Great Basin Spadefoots utilize a variety of temporary and permanent waters, such as rain pools, pools in temporary streams, roadside ditches, pools caused by irrigation, pond and reservoir edges, and so on. We have even found eggs in a water-filled cow track, but do not know if they hatched and reached metamorphosis.

VARIATION. There are no subspecies. The color of Great Basin Spadefoots generally matches their surroundings. This is indicated by specimens from Diamond Craters in southeastern Oregon. Great Basin Spadefoots from this area of dark lava rocks have extensive black markings dorsally, including the spot on each upper eyelid; even the iris of the eye is heavily flecked with black. Specimens from surrounding sagebrush desert are much lighter in general coloration.

Preserved specimens of mostly immature Great Basin Spadefoots from various parts of southern Harney Co., Oregon are fairly consistent in their pattern. Most conspicuous are the dark upper eyelid spots and the two grayish stripes that run from the edges of the upper eyelids back to near the groin, forming a somewhat hourglass shape. The stripes vary somewhat in width between individuals and are usually widest in the shoulder area. A preserved series of breeding adults from Malheur Co., Oregon includes four females (56 to 62 mm SVL, mean = 60.3 mm) and 19 males (45.0 to 55.5 mm SVL, mean = 51.5 mm). Three females have the typical hourglass-shaped, gray to brownish stripes, but, in the fourth, these are barely evident, and her entire back is covered with rather small light-centered brown spots. The males are fairly uniform in appearance, varying mainly in the conspicuousness and width of the gray stripes. In five of the males, the spots on the upper eyelids are joined in a V-shaped manner across the top of the head. Occasional individuals have black horny skin on the snout and top of the head.

LIFE HISTORY. Great Basin Spadefoots are sporadic in their breeding, entering appropriate waters from early April into June. Amplectic pairs and hundreds of egg packets were found in extreme northern Nevada on 11 April, and the breeding congregation in Malheur Co., Oregon (see Variation) was seen on 10 May. Male spadefoots develop dark keratinized patches on the inner sides of the first three fingers during the breeding season and call from the ponds they enter. The call ("kw-a-a-h" or "w-a-a-h" or "r-a-h") is audible for 100 to 200 m and is rather grating, short (to ¾ of a second), low in pitch, and is repeated over and over.

153

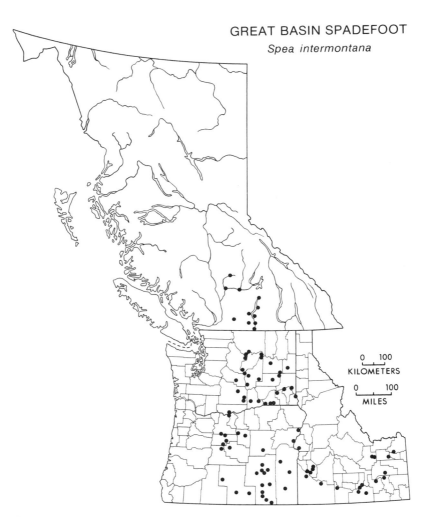

GREAT BASIN SPADEFOOT

Spea intermontana

0   100
KILOMETERS

0   100
MILES

The male seizes the female just ahead of her hind legs (inguinal amplexus), unlike all of our other frogs and toads, except *Ascaphus truei*. The eggs are laid in small packets about 15 to 20 mm in diameter, each packet containing 20 to 40 eggs. The packets are attached to vegetation or bottom pebbles, or may be placed on a muddy bottom. The total egg complement for one female is said to be 300 to 500. Well over one-half of the egg packets originally seen in a northern Nevada pool on 11 April were completely invaded by a fungus when seen on 17 April. Eggs in other packets were close to hatching, even though minimal night air temperatures ranged from -7.2° to 0.6° C. It is possible that nocturnal freezing affected the eggs, even though most were well-submerged. Great Basin Spadefoot eggs probably hatch within two or three days at warmer temperatures.

Hatchlings are 5 to 7 mm TL and grow rapidly, feeding on algae and carrion until they metamorphose in one to two months at a tadpole length of 30 to 70 mm. Tadpoles of some other species of spadefoots occur in both normal and cannibalistic body form. The "cannibal morph" has a larger head, larger jaws, and larger jaw muscles than the "normal morph." Cannibals have a different behavior pattern and are cannibalistic on other tadpoles. Cannibals have not yet been reported among tadpoles of Great Basin Spadefoots but are expected to occur.

Great Basin Spadefoot young are unusual in that they emerge from the water with a considerable segment of their tail remaining. Four "toadlets" collected on 30 June from north central Oregon averaged 19 mm SVL. A fifth, of similar SVL, had a tail 18.5 mm long. Young Great Basin Spadefoots collected on 8 July in southeastern Oregon had tails 4.5 to 15.0 mm long. Males are sexually mature at about 40 mm SVL, females at about 45 mm SVL. It seems possible that they can reach this size by their third summer.

The food of adults has not been studied carefully, but is known to include ants, beetles, grasshoppers, crickets, and flies. Predators of tadpoles include birds and probably fishes. Adults have noxious skin secretions that cause sneezing in some humans and probably repulse predators. Females have been reported to have more toxic skin than males in some species of *Spea*, but this has not been studied in *Spea intermontana*.

Spadefoots survive dry periods by burrowing in the soil or utilizing mammal burrows. We have no information on the length of time the animals are able to stay buried, but presume it may be months in some areas. Great Basin Spadefoots emerge to forage on rainy nights, and it has been shown experimentally in another species of spadefoot toads that vibrations similar to those of rain hitting the ground are sufficient to bring them to the surface. In southeastern Oregon, we have occasionally encountered foraging Great Basin Spadefoots on rainless nights when the humidity was high enough to cause dew.

Spadefoots have numerous adaptations to the xeric environment with its unpredictable rainfall. They can burrow to avoid drought and are largely nocturnal to avoid the heat and low humidity of the daytime. They can tolerate considerable body water loss, up to 48.8% of initial body weight, compared to some aquatic frogs such as the Pig Frog *(Rana grylio)*, which can survive the loss in body water of only up to 31.2% of their body weight. Spadefoots are adapted to the irregularities of desert rainfall by having an irregular facultative breeding season that tracks local conditions, by having rapid development of embryos and tadpoles to escape drying up of temporary pools, and by having omnivorous tadpoles capable of eating both plant and animal foods.

REMARKS. Great Basin Spadefoots have probably benefited from the greatly increased irrigation in the intermontane region, which has provided them with more breeding sites and more prolonged foraging opportunities. More precise details of their life history are needed.

REFERENCES. Bragg (1965), Svihla (1953), Thorson and Svihla (1943).

TRUE FROGS AND THEIR ALLIES
FAMILY RANIDAE

The Ranidae is perhaps the most widespread family of frogs, being found everywhere except south and central Australia, New Zealand, eastern Polynesia, and southern South America. The family has about 45 genera and 590 species, with the greatest diversity in tropical Africa. Ranids are relatively advanced frogs with many different life styles. Some are simple pond frogs, others are adapted for life in streams, and there are also semi-burrowing and semi-arboreal species. They occur in all environments from within the Arctic Circle to tropical rain forests, and from deserts to high mountains. Most have a typical frog life history with aquatic tadpoles and terrestrial adults, but many species have direct terrestrial development, and some have parental care (egg guarding). There is a single genus in the United States and Canada.

TRUE FROGS
GENUS *RANA*

The genus *Rana* has a large range that nearly encompasses that of the family. *Rana* is the only ranid genus that occurs outside of the Old World. It contains 250 species, 21 of which occur in the United States and Canada, and eight of which (including two introduced species) are found in the Northwest. All of our species have a fairly typical life history pattern that involves spring mating, aquatic oviposition sites, aquatic larvae, no parental care, and terrestrial to semi-aquatic adults.

RED-LEGGED FROG
RANA AURORA BAIRD AND GIRARD

Red-legged Frogs are medium-sized inhabitants of moist forests and valley riparian habitats west of the Cascades (below about 850 m elevation). Females may reach a SVL of 100 mm, but males are less than 70 mm SVL. Living frogs are reddish to olive dorsally, usually with a considerable flecking of indistinctly-edged, small, black spots. Concealed parts of the hind legs and at least the posterior abdomen are pinkish-red, the color appearing to be deep within the skin. The groin area is mottled strikingly with black or dark gray and cream to greenish yellow. The chest and abdominal areas are frequently heavily suffused with gray. Red-legged Frogs usually have a light lip-line from eye to shoulder, bordered above by a dark mask. They have longer hind legs than *Rana pretiosa,* the frog they are most likely to be confused with. If the hind leg is held forward against the body, the heel usually extends beyond the external nares. Hind toe webbing is reduced in *Rana aurora;* when the toes are spread, the edges of the webs are quite concave and reach only to the first joint of the longest toe. *R. aurora* has dorsolateral folds consisting of concentrations of granular glands, which are lacking in *R. pretiosa*.

Tadpoles are dark brown dorsally with scattered small clumps of metallic flecks. Ventrally, the abdomen is an iridescent brassy to pinkish color. When viewed from above, the eyes are about their own diameter within the head profile. The dorsal fin terminates at or anterior to the spiracle and is at least as high as the height of the tail musculature. Total length prior to metamorphosis varies depending on the permanency of the breeding water, being about 50 mm in temporary waters and up to 75 mm in more permanent situations.

HABITAT. During the non-breeding season, Red-legged Frogs may occur at considerable distances from water. We have encountered frogs in moist forest situations 200 to 300 m from any standing water. Further evidence for this terrestrialism is the fact that the frogs appear on roads during rainy nights, often some distance from an aquatic habitat. As aridity increases during the summer, at least some Red-legged Frogs move to stream and pond edges. On one occasion in July, we encountered five frogs along some 200 m of a small stream in western Oregon. Each was perched quietly on a dry bank some 0.5 to 1.0 m above the water level, and in each case we only became aware of the frog when it leaped into the water. Upon hitting the water, the frogs swam rapidly to root tangles or crevices beneath the bank

157

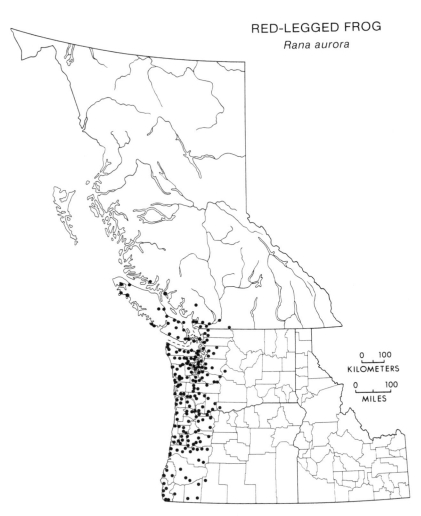

RED-LEGGED FROG
Rana aurora

0   100
KILOMETERS
0   100
MILES

overhang, where they were impossible to locate.

Breeding waters utilized by Red-legged Frogs vary considerably. In the central Willamette Valley, they frequently use temporary waters, usually ponds or overflows that will be dry by late May or early June. A study in northwestern Washington involved frogs breeding in a 0.4 hectare permanent pond. In southwestern British Columbia, researchers studied *Rana aurora* in a temporary pond (dried up in July) where they bred sympatrically with *Rana pretiosa*, in the slow part of a river, in a small overflow pond of a large lake, and in Marion Lake, a 13 hectare permanent lake.

In general, breeding sites seem to have a few certain requirements. They must have little or no flow, must last long enough for metamorphosis to occur, and must contain sturdy underwater stems of some sort for egg attachment.

VARIATION. *Rana aurora* occurs as two subspecies, only one of which, *R.a. aurora,* the Northern Red-legged Frog, occurs in our area. Most Northern Red-legged Frogs have dorsal spotting consisting of more or less distinct irregular black spots, usually two or three mm in diameter, with many tiny black flecks between them. A few frogs have instead a network of black lines over the entire dorsum, and an occasional individual may have no black markings.

There is some variation in tadpole mouthparts, as indicated by one key, which gives the number of tooth rows as three on the anterior and three or four on the posterior lip. The more usual condition seems to be three anterior and four posterior rows. The first anterior row is complete; the second and third are small and have a medial gap. The first posterior row has a small medial gap, but the other three rows are complete. The second posterior row is slightly shorter than the first row, and the third row is slightly shorter than the second; the fourth row is the shortest, being about half the length of the first posterior row. Based on a study in Washington, the mouthparts are not completely developed until stage 33.

LIFE HISTORY. Frogs in the western valleys and along the coastal regions of Oregon and Washington have an early reproductive season. In the central Willamette Valley, eggs are usually deposited in February, but sometimes as early as late January. Males are the first to reach the breeding ponds, and in warm winters they may begin to congregate in mid-December. Males may begin calling soon after entering the water or may wait silently for a few days. Calling may not begin until most males have arrived, indicating that calling is not the cue that attracts males to breeding sites. Males usually call while submerged below the surface. The call, even when given in the air, has very little carrying power, being inaudible to humans more than 15 m away. The call can be approximated by attempting to say "uh-uh-uh-uh-UH" rather rapidly with the lips compressed, with more emphasis on the last syllable or two. The calls consist of 4 or 5 "uh's." In southwestern British Columbia, when no calls could be heard on the surface of a lake, literally hundreds could be heard beneath the surface with the aid of a hydrophone. Males normally call only at night.

Calling males are spaced at least 0.5 m apart, but it is not known whether they defend territories. It is known that some mature males are excluded from breeding in some years, and that some males have multiple matings (are polygynous) within a single season.

Amplexus is axillary, and while clasping, the male emits a single note at a rate of about one per second with his mouth directly behind the female's ear. The note is barely audible to the human ear at 0.5 m. Male Red-legged Frogs are ready to clasp almost anything when they enter the breeding water and are known to have clasped male Bullfrogs, female Spotted Frogs, Northwestern Salamanders, and even an apple! An unreceptive female frog gets rid of an unwanted clasping male by giving a release call (usually unsuccessful) then extending her legs and rolling on her side in a sort of cataleptic trance, a unique behavior among ranid frogs.

The time of egg deposition is closely dependent on water temperatures. Studies in the central Willamette Valley indicated that 7.5° C was the minimum temperature for egg laying. In northwestern Washinton, where eggs were laid in February and early March, egg laying began at about 6° C. In a southwestern British Columbia study, egg laying occurred during the first half of March in one year and the last half of March the next, starting at a water temperature of about 7° C. Eggs are usually deposited at night. In all areas, intensive spawning of eggs lasts about two weeks.

The eggs are invariably deposited in a rounded mass attached to some kind of stiff submerged stem. When freshly deposited, the egg clumps have a clear slightly bluish appearance, but they soon become coated with silt in muddy waters. The mass is usually between 15 and 25 cm in diameter, and contains between 500 and 1,100 eggs. Individual eggs are the largest known for North American ranids, averaging about 3.0 mm in diameter. The gel of the egg mass is thin and streams through one's fingers as the mass is lifted from the water.

Early embryos are tolerant of temperatures only between 4° and 21° C (shown for both British Columbia and Oregon frogs), and both the lower and upper lethals are the lowest known for any North American ranid frog. Hatching time is closely dependent on temperature. Under controlled laboratory conditions, embryos at an average temperature of 4.2° C took 83 days to reach gill circulation (stage 20); eggs at 7.7° C, 35 days; eggs at 9.8° C, 24 days; eggs at 12° C, 14.6 days; eggs at 16.4° C, 7.8 days; and eggs at 19.7° C, 6.6 days. Hatching times in the field are likely to be lengthy. In western Oregon, we recorded hatching times of 35 to 49 days, during which time water temperatures varied from near 0° to 19° C. In northwestern Washington, eggs reached stage 20 (gill circulation) in about 35 days.

For one or two days after hatching, the tadpoles remain crowded near the parental egg mass, resting on the bottom or more frequently hanging onto underwater stems or debris. Average total length at hatching is 11 to 12 mm, and the tadpoles appear quite black at this time. During one year, tadpoles in a temporary pond in western Oregon grew at a rate of about 1 mm/day for a period of five weeks. Tadpoles in a permanent lake in British Columbia increased their body length (tail not included) by 9.0 to 12.5 mm between early May and late July. These metamorphosed at 11 to 14 weeks of age, at which time it was estimated that only 5% of the original egg number attained metamorphosis. Enemies of tadpoles are predaceous water insects, salamanders, and garter snakes.

Recently metamorphosed frogs measure between 20 and 25 mm SVL in western Oregon and averaged 28.7 mm SVL in a northwestern Washington study. Limited evidence from western Oregon studies indicates that Red-legged Frogs become sexually mature in their second year after metamorphosis when males are about 50 and females about 60 mm SVL. Males and females are believed to breed every year. Red-legged Frogs eat beetles, caterpillars, isopods, and other small invertebrates. Their food habits are poorly known.

REMARKS. In the Willamette Valley of western Oregon, *Rana aurora* seems to be less common than it once was. This is our subjective opinion, based on night-driving of roads in rainy fall weather and checking of known breeding sites. We attribute much of this decrease to displacement by the introduced Bullfrog, but think that other agents such as run-off of herbicides and pesticides and the possibility of acid rain should be investigated.

REFERENCES. H.A. Brown (1975), Calef (1973a, 1973b), Dickman (1968), Dumas (1966), Gregory (1979), L.E. Licht (1969b, 1969c, 1971, 1974), Storm (1960), Wiens (1970).

FOOTHILL YELLOW-LEGGED FROG
RANA BOYLEI BAIRD

30. Foothill Yellow-legged Frog *(Rana boylei)*, Lane Co., Oregon.

This is mainly a frog of rocky or gravelly streams in southwestern Oregon and is seldom seen far from water. Foothill Yellow-legged Frogs are small - to medium - sized (up to 75 mm SVL), with skin that appears rough because of the presence of many tiny tubercles over its surface. Hind toe webbing is full, the edges between the toes being only slightly concave, and the webbing extends to the tip of the longest toe. The tips of the toes are slightly expanded. Dorsal color is usually olive, dark to light gray, or brownish; but occasional individuals are brick red in the area between the poorly developed dorsolateral folds. The heel of the hind leg reaches to the nostrils or beyond when the leg is stretched forward along the body. In life, the concealed surfaces of the hind legs and the posterior abdomen are a light yellow. The remainder of the abdomen is white, with variable amounts of dark mottling on the chest and throat. Foothill Yellow-legged Frogs have a somewhat toad-like appearance, which is enhanced by their finely roughened skin. The ear or tympanum is about half the size of the eye and is colored and roughened like the skin around it, often making it difficult to see.

162

Tadpoles reach a maximum total length of 50 to 55 mm. They can be immediately separated from all other ranid tadpoles in our area by their high number of labial tooth rows, 6 or 7 anterior and 5 or 6 posterior to the mouth.This appoaches the number seen in *Ascaphus truei* tadpoles, but the present species possesses the usual ranid papillae on the sides and posterior edges of the lips, and the labial area is not modified into a sucker. The first anterior row of labial teeth is complete and at least twice as long as the jaw width. The remaining anterior rows are all incomplete and each is shorter than the one anterior to it. The first posterior row is interrupted medially, but the remaining rows are not, and, except for a shorter fifth (and possible sixth) row, are as long as the first.

Tadpoles are usually an olive color dorsally and have scattered dark spots on the tail fin and musculature. In lighter tadpoles, the dorsal surface of the body has dark flecking. In life, the ventral surface is silvery. The tail fin is lower than in most ranid tadpoles, possibly an adaptation to living in streams.

HABITAT. The Foothill Yellow-legged Frog is confined to the immediate vicinity of permanent streams, including those that may be reduced to waterholes connected by trickles during the dry season. The frogs are most common along streams having rocky, gravelly, or sandy bottoms, but they may occur in those having muddy bottoms. During low stages of rivers in western Oregon, the frogs sit at the edges of rocky pools, often in open view. When approached, they quickly jump into the water, swim rapidly to the bottom, and take refuge under rocks or debris. Or, they may sit quietly in plain view. A study in California indicated that *Rana boylei* is active in water at temperatures of 7° to 21° C. Little is known of hibernation sites, there being few records. These involved two frogs under rocks about 4 and 5 m from a stream and another under a rock in a stream. Considering the severe winter floods that may occur in many of these streams, determining hibernation sites is a matter of interest.

These frogs usually breed in the pools of streams they normally inhabit. On about 1 June, we found egg masses and adults of this species in a large pool that had resulted from dredging operations near the Applegate River in southern Oregon. The bottom of the pool consisted of gravel and rocks up to about 15 cm in diameter, and the egg masses lay among these rocks in shallow water near shore. During April trips to the upper South Fork of the Coquille River in southwestern Oregon, we occasionally have unearthed small *Rana boylei* (to 30 mm SVL) from moist, rocky outcrops at least 50 m from the river.

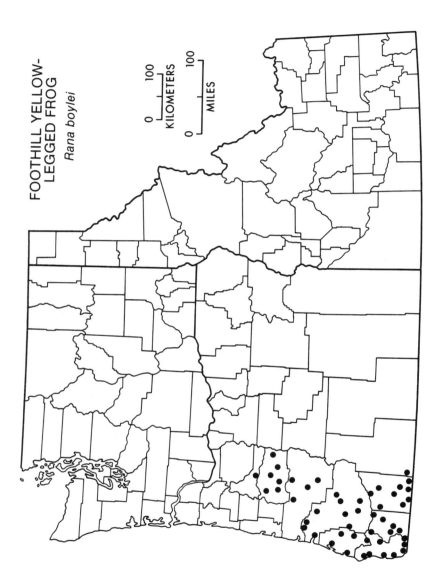

FOOTHILL YELLOW-
LEGGED FROG

Rana boylei

VARIATION. Dorsal coloration is quite variable as indicated earlier, and individual frogs are capable of lightening and darkening considerably. Male frogs average smaller than the females (56 vs 73 mm SVL in a California study). We have almost no information concerning variation in Oregon frogs; the dorsal brick red color seems to be more common in the extreme southwestern part of the state than in northern parts of their range. There are no subspecies.

LIFE HISTORY. Throughout much of its northern range, the reproductive season of *Rana boylei* is attuned to the water conditions of the streams in which they live. Winter and early spring flooding may preclude early egg laying, and the season seems to be relatively late in most areas. In northern California a few records indicate egg laying during May, and two records for the Rogue River Basin of southern Oregon are for early April. Our record from the Applegate River indicates late May or early June. At any single locality, spawning extends over about two weeks.

Male frogs are said to call, but there is little field information on this. The call is described as a gutteral grating sound, lasting for less than a second. Several of these calls may be given at about 1/2 second intervals. The eggs are deposited in rounded clusters attached to gravel or rocks in the margins of streams or pools. Eggs and their jelly coats protrude like grapes on the outer surface of the mass. The number of eggs per mass is about 1,000, and each egg measures nearly 2.2 mm in diameter.

Earlier literature states that *Rana boylei* eggs can develop between 6° to 26° C, but we see little supporting evidence for the lower figure. At 20° C, the eggs hatch in about five days, the larvae measuring 7.3 to 7.7 mm TL. In California, tadpoles metamorphose in three to four months. In Oregon, we estimate that metamorphosis occurs from late July into early September, depending on location. The young frogs measure 22 to 27 mm SVL, reach sexual maturity at about 40 mm SVL, and probably first breed in their second spring or summer.

Rana boylei eat both aquatic and terrestrial invertebrates, including snails, moths, flies, water striders, beetles, grasshoppers, hornets, and ants. Garter snakes *(Thamnophis sirtalis* and *T. couchi)* prey heavily on tadpoles and adults.

REMARKS. Very little is known of the natural history of this frog in the northern (Oregon) part of its range. At one time it was considered one of the most common amphibians in southwestern Oregon, but its present status is unknown.

REFERENCES. Dumas (1966), Storer (1925), Zweifel (1955).

165

CASCADE FROG
RANA CASCADAE SLATER

This medium-sized frog (to 75 mm SVL) is restricted to the Olympic Mountains and to the Cascades of Washington, Oregon, and northern California, occurring above about 800 m in Oregon. Cascade Frogs are brown to olive brown dorsally with a variable number of sharp-edged, irregular, black spots, some of which may have small light centers. Dorsolateral folds are distinct, and there is a dark brown mask evident behind each eye, below which runs a light lip-line ventrally. The frogs have no dark markings on the abdomen, and the posterior abdomen and concealed hind leg surfaces are yellowish tan (honey colored). Hind foot webbing is restricted, and one or two phalanges of the longest toe are free of the web.

In life, the tadpoles usually appear to be dark brown, but we have seen a lighter somewhat greenish phase in laboratory-raised larvae and in some field populations. In these, the dorsal body area has a mottling of small dark spots, and the tail fins have a faint metallic mottling. The ventral surface of the body is silvery to brassy, but not pinkish as in tadpoles of *Rana aurora*. The dorsal fin terminates posterior to the spiracle and is relatively low. Labial teeth are three rows anterior and three or four rows posterior to the mouth.

HABITAT. Cascade Frogs may be extremely abundant in appropriate habitats. In mountain meadows of the Oregon Cascades, we have estimated their numbers in the hundreds within less than one hectare. Such meadows are often old sphagnum bogs that remain damp throughout the summer. Many contain ponds or potholes of various sizes which usually contain little vegetation. The larger frogs tend to occur at the edges of these, but smaller frogs are scattered throughout. *Rana cascadae* also occur along the marshy edges of ponds and small lakes. At times we have encountered them along forest trails at some distance from bodies of water.

Mature frogs utilize quiet ponds for breeding and favor the shallow sunny edges for egg-laying. Temporary waters that dry up by late July or August are sometimes used. One such pond in the Oregon Cascades is about 1/3 hectare in area, with a maximum depth when full of nearly one meter. The bottom is of fine silt with rocks and boulders up to at least one meter in diameter. There is little or no aquatic vegetation, and the pond usually dries up during late July; many advanced larvae die at that time. Of interest is the fact that this pond usually contains a number of albino tadpoles of this species. Isolated populations of

Rana cascadae occur to the east of the Cascades in Central Oregon. One such population occupies a pond formed by a dammed-up spring measuring 19 to 29 m. It is isolated from other waters by many kilometers of dry forest. During a two-year study we estimated that there were 2,500 Cascade Frogs in this pond one year and 1,400 the next. We have no information on the hibernation sites of this species.

VARIATION. Subspecies have not been named Living Cascade Frogs have a bright yellow or yellow-green color in the groin region. The groin in most Oregon frogs is moderately mottled with a darker shade. Washington *Rana cascadae* have a higher proportion of frogs with very dark groin mottling. Dorsal spotting always consists of black spots of various shapes, invariably with distinct margins; the number of spots varies from a few to many large and from a few to many small. Hind leg length varies, but in 3/4 of the *R. cascadae* checked in one study, the heel did not reach the nostril when the leg was stretched forward along the body. In this same study, over half of the frogs had a medium-brown ground color; fewer were either tan or gray.

Tadpole labial teeth are usually three rows anterior and four rows posterior to the mouth. The first anterior row is complete and longer than the width of the mouth. The second row is incomplete, the medial space being as long or longer than the remaining tooth row segments. The third row is represented by very short segments near the upper corners of the mouth. The first lower row may or may not be complete; the second row is complete with its medial portion looping toward the mouth. The third and fourth rows are complete, the third being about the length of the mouth and the fourth shorter. Tadpoles do not have fully developed labial teeth until they have hind limb buds that are longer than wide. By the time front legs are apparent through the opercular skin, the labial teeth are disappearing. Tooth formulae of 2/4 and 3/3 are recorded in the literature, but are unusual.

LIFE HISTORY. Breeding begins as soon as ice and snow are off the waters. After mild winters this may be as early as March in some areas. On the other hand, after more normal winters, frogs at higher elevations may not spawn until June. The males are the first to appear and at first disperse in the shallow waters near sunlit shores. Within a day or two, they form groups in which the non-territorial males are only a few centimeters apart, the groups being in shallow water near shore. The males call during the day. The call is a series of low slow croaks or chuckles. Calling is especially frequent on sunny afternoons.

Females lay their eggs during daylight hours, and they spawn at the

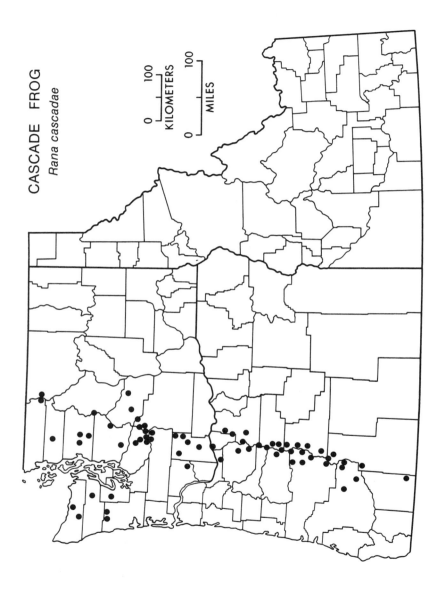

CASCADE FROG
Rana cascadae

sites where males call. At one Oregon pond, egg laying occurred only after the water temperature had reached 8° C. The females tend to lay their eggs on or near other masses, and this can result in large collections of eggs in a small area. A large group of 60 to 70 egg masses in a pond in the high Cascades of Oregon (1,950 m elevation) was contained in about 0.5 m². Eggs usually are placed in shallow open water, and some of the masses may be exposed partially to air. Each female's mass contains 300 to 500 eggs, the individual eggs measuring about 2.2 mm in diameter. In a pond on the east side of the Oregon Cascades, all egg-laying was completed in three days, and "explosive" breeding can be considered typical of this species.

Eggs can develop in the laboratory to hatching at water temperatures between 6° and 27° C, but 8° to 25° C is probably the optimal range. Time to hatching varies with temperature as follows: at 10° C, 590 hours; at 15° C, 200 hours; at 18° C, 145 hours; at 20° C, 114 hours; and at 25° C, 78 hours. In the field, temperatures fluctuate widely between night and day, especially for eggs at or near the surface. Freezing nights are not uncommon, and exposed eggs are often frozen and destroyed. Daily maximum temperatures within an egg mass in a pond in Central Oregon averaged 10.3° C, and daily minimum temperatures averaged 1.7° C, during eight days in March. Temperatures within egg masses in a high Cascades pond in Oregon averaged 12.2° C maximum and 2.5° C minimum during late April and early May.

As hatching time nears, the egg masses become "frothy" with entrapped air, and they acquire a greenish cast from algae within the gel. On 22 June, a group comprising at least nine individual egg masses was hatching in the shallows of a pothole in the western Cascades of Oregon (about 1,340 m). We estimated that at least 700 tadpoles were clinging to the jelly and nearby vegetation. The tadpoles are about 13 mm TL at hatching.

Tadpoles in the laboratory go from hatching through metamorphosis in about 900 hours (37.5 days) at 23° C. At metamorphosis the young frogs measure 20 to 21 mm SVL. On 26 August, at the same meadow where the tadpoles were seen hatching on 22 June, we caught many small frogs measuring 21 to 23 mm SVL, indicating a larval life of about two months. On 20 July we measured 116 *Rana cascadae* caught at random in a meadow in the High Cascades (about 1,500 m). One size-group ranged from 17 to 22 mm SVL and were thought to be recently metamorphosed. A second group ranged from 27 to about 35 mm SVL and were probably from the previous year. Above this size, frogs ranged up to 53 mm SVL, but could not be

169

separated into groups. Frogs (175) at the lower meadow (1,340 m), mentioned above, were measured on 5 and 11 July of the previous year. Small frogs measured 18 to 31 mm SVL, but could not be separated into two distinct groups.

Frogs can be sexed at 35 mm SVL and larger by the presence of thumb pads on males. Males become sexually mature at 45 to 50 mm SVL, whereas females reach maturity at about 60 to 65 mm SVL. Both sexes probably first breed after their third hibernation. Maximum sizes are 60 mm SVL for males and 75 mm SVL for females. Neither sex lives for more than about five years.

Recent studies indicate that *Rana cascadae* larvae are primarily bottom feeders and prefer muddy or silty substrate in shallow water (less than 45 cm depth). The tadpoles tend to remain in the vicinity of egg deposition sites and often form dense aggregations of several hundred tadpoles. Recent laboratory experiments have revealed the rather startling fact that tadpoles from one egg mass are able to recognize one another (sibling recognition) by some means as yet unknown.

REMARKS. Recent field studies have noted a decline in the number of *Rana cascadae*. This may be true only locally or it may be temporary, but it is cause for concern. Nothing is known about the food habits of this species.

REFERENCES. Altig and Brodie (1968), Briggs (1978), Briggs and Storm (1970), H.A. Brown (1975), Dumas (1966), Dunlap (1955), Dunlap and Storm (1951), Haertel (1970), O'Hara and Blaustein (1981), Slater (1939), Sype (1975), Wiens (1972).

BULLFROG
RANA CATESBEIANA SHAW

31. Bullfrog *(Rana catesbeiana)*, Benton Co., Oregon.

The Bullfrog is the largest frog occurring in our area, and individuals may reach SVLs of about 150 mm. Bullfrogs have no dorsolateral ridges on the back, but do have a conspicuous ridge, which runs from the eye posteriorly and then down to the shoulder behind the conspicuous tympanum. The tympanum is at least twice as large as the eye in males, but the same size as the eye in females. Dorsally, the frogs are green or greenish brown, and a frequent pattern is a brownish body with green on the sides of the head. The back may be more-or-less marked with darker spots, and the hind limbs are usually barred with dark brown. Ventrally, Bullfrogs are white to cream colored with varied amounts of dark mottling. Recently-metamorphosed frogs have a green to brown dorsum with scattered, small, black flecks.

The tadpoles may attain a total length of 110 mm or more and in life are olive green on the dorsal body with many, small, black spots. They are white to cream ventrally with or without various amounts of dark mottling. The fins are also marked with small black spots, and the dorsal fin does not extend onto the body. There are two or rarely three rows of labial teeth anterior and three rows posterior to the mouth. The first anterior row is complete, the second has a wide medial space and the third, if present, is represented by very short seg-

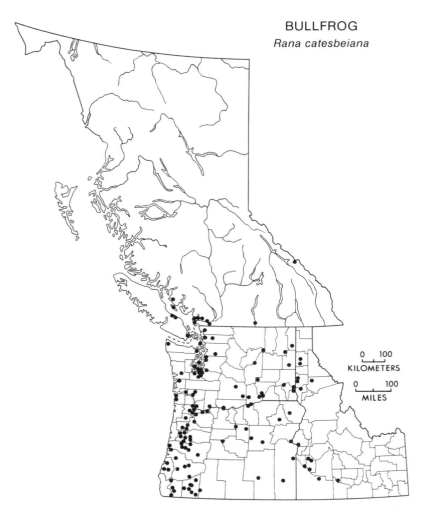

BULLFROG
Rana catesbeiana

0   100
KILOMETERS

0   100
MILES

ments near the mouth corners. The first lower row has a short medial space, the second and third are complete, and the third is shorter than the other two. Tadpoles less than 25 mm TL appear black with transverse gold bands on the head and body.

HABITAT. Bullfrogs were apparently introduced into western Oregon in the late 1920s or early 1930s. We have information that 18 adults were released in the Grant's Pass area of southwestern Oregon in 1931. Within five years they were established in much of the upper Rogue River Valley between Medford and Galice. The species is highly aquatic and will inhabit almost any permanent water, including ponds, lakes, mill ponds, reservoirs, sluggish irrigation ditches, and slow-moving streams and rivers. In the Northwest, they have so far been unable to invade cold high-altitude waters and are uncommon in the cool coastal belt. In the Willamette Valley of Oregon, they are perhaps most abundant in oxbow sloughs along the river and in deserted water-filled gravel pits.

VARIATION. No subspecies are recognized, and we have little information on variation in Northwestern *Rana catesbeiana*. The color varies considerably, and individual frogs are able to lighten or darken. In warm conditions, a frog that is normally a dull olive green may become a light yellow green. Cold frogs may be nearly black. Females tend to be more brown and spotted than males, which are usually greener. In addition, males have a yellow throat versus the white throat of females. Ventrally, Bullfrogs may be plain white or cream, but frequently have variegated dark markings of light gray to black.

LIFE HISTORY. Male Bullfrogs are highly territorial and advertise their position with a deep bass call, sounding somewhat like the roar of a distant bull. Males may actually fight in attempting to oust one another from a territory. During the breeding season, territorial males float high in the water, and their yellow throats are very conspicuous, presumably functioning as signaling devices. Some smaller (younger), adult males keep low in the water, apparently to avoid conflict with larger males. These "satellite" males may attempt to "sneak" matings with females as opportunities arise. The breeding season in western Oregon is prolonged, extending from late May to early August, with most egg-laying occurring in late June and early July. Females move through male territories and approach the male of their choice, the choice probably depending on the quality of the site the male is defending. Generally, larger (older) males have higher quality territories (better egg-laying sites) and are more successful in obtaining mates.

Female Bullfrogs lay 6,000 to 20,000 eggs at one spawning, with larger females laying more eggs. The eggs are spread out as a surface film measuring as much as 90 by 150 cm. We counted 16,491 eggs in one mass from near Corvallis, Oregon. Individual eggs average 1.3 mm in diameter. Before hatching, the film of eggs sinks onto the submerged vegetation below and hatching usually occurs in four to five days, but may take longer in cooler water. Near Ann Arbor, Michigan, older females may deposit a second clutch late in the breeding season which consists of fewer and smaller eggs. We do not know whether "double-clutching" occurs among female Bullfrogs in the Northwest.

In western Oregon, the tadpoles are mainly nonselective feeders on algae, except that they do not eat *Chara*. They are also known to eat some vascular plants when algae are scarce. Elsewhere, there are records of their scavenging on dead animals, including dead Bullfrog tadpoles. The tadpoles, in turn, are eaten by aquatic insects, fish, adult Bullfrogs, garter snakes, various wading birds, and a few edge-prowling mammals.

In western Oregon, growth in tadpoles occurs from May to November, with no growth from December to April, even though the larvae continue to feed. The tadpoles normally overwinter once then transform the following August and September at 115 to 140 mm TL. Length differences at metamorphosis are apparently due to the quantity and quality of food available to the tadpoles. The transformed frogs measure about 50 mm SVL. The frogs may become sexually mature in the year following metamorphosis, at 85 to 105 mm SVL, but do not breed until a year later (New York). Males and females grow to about the same size, and both sexes may live five to eight years.

Young and adult frogs frequently sit at the edge of the water and jump in when disturbed. The young give a characteristic little cry as they jump, which sounds like a high-pitched "eep". Frogs of all ages may bask among vegetation near the surface, with only bulging eyes and a bit of head showing.

Bullfrogs in areas of colder winters probably hibernate in bottom mud, but a record from western Oregon (Albany area) indicates less torpor in areas of warmer winters. During February, the observer noted a mass of frogs about one meter in diameter in the water of a log pond, beneath overhanging willows and cattails. The frogs were moving slowly, but were easy to capture, and he counted 186 by removing them one at a time.

Bullfrogs are highly opportunistic carnivores. Their food includes a variety of invertebrates from insects to earthworms and crayfish, but also includes fish, tadpoles and frogs (including Bullfrogs), salamanders, snakes, small turtles, birds (including ducklings and small land birds), and small mammals. A recent study of the stomach contents of 71 Bullfrogs averaging 105 mm SVL from the Willamette Valley, Oregon indicated that about half of their food, by volume, was vertebrates.

We have observed adult Bullfrogs on blacktop roads at night in the Willamette Valley, during the first heavy rains of late October and November. Stomach analyses of some of these show that they feed on Long-toed Salamanders, which are abundant on some roads at that time. Whether the frogs deliberately move overland for food or are dispersing to other ponds is not known.

REMARKS. A matter for concern is the possibility that the frogs can gradually adapt to colder waters and thus may invade coastal or montane lakes to compete with native frogs. They are well-established in Lake-of-the-Woods in the southern Oregon Cascades at an elevation of 1,520 m.

REFERENCES. R.E. Brown (1972), Emlen (1968), Howard (1978a, 1978b), Ryan (1980), Wiewandt (1969).

GREEN FROG
RANA CLAMITANS LATREILLE

32. Green Frog *(Rana clamitans)*, Plymouth Co., Massachusetts.

This introduced frog is moderate in size, ranging up to about 100 mm SVL. Their most notable feature is a conspicuous tympanum (external ear), which is twice as large as the eye in males and eye-sized in females. There is a light yellow area in the center of each tympanum. Green Frogs have obvious dorsolateral folds (unlike Bullfrogs), which stop before reaching the groin area. A branch of the fold curves down behind the tympanum to the shoulder area. Dorsally the frogs are green to brown, but always have green on the sides of the head. There is usually little or no spotting on the back, but the legs have dark bars. Ventrally, females are whitish with slight, dark chest mottling in some. Males have yellow to yellow-orange throats.

GREEN FROG
Rana clamitans

0   100
KILOMETERS

0   100
MILES

The tadpoles become fairly large, ranging up to 90 mm TL. The larger tadpoles are olive green dorsally, with many small dark spots. Smaller larvae are darker in color. The ventral side of the body is cream colored, and the throat is mottled with dark green. The tail is greenish with brown mottling; the dorsal fin ends posterior to the spiracle, and its maximum height is less than the height of the tail musculature. The labial teeth are two rows anterior and three posterior to the mouth. The first anterior row is complete and longer than the mouth. The second row is represented by very short segments below the ends of the first. The first posterior row may or may not

176

have a small medial gap and is longer than the mouth. The second row is complete and about as long as the first; the third row is also complete but is about one-half as long as the second.

HABITAT. Green Frogs have been introduced at a few localities in western and northeastern Washington and southwestern British Columbia, as well as at Victoria on Vancouver Island. We have little information on its habitat preferences in the Northwest, the literature stating that it occurs in ponds and lakes. The frogs are highly aquatic and in their normal range inhabit permanent, quiet or slow-moving waters with abundant aquatic vegetation. The classic idea of a frog sitting on a lily pad may derive from Green Frog habits. The frogs leave the water to bask and perhaps feed, but are never more than a jump or two from the edge. They feed largely in the water, both at the surface and beneath, usually taking insects and their larvae or other aquatic invertebrates, but they are also known to eat small fish and frogs.

VARIATION. Green Frogs occur natively in the eastern United States and southeastern Canada. In the northern three-fourths of this range, Green Frogs are assigned to the subspecies, *Rana clamitans melanota* (Green Frog), and in the remaining range they are the Bronze Frog *(R. c. clamitans)*. We assume that Northwestern populations are from Green Frog introductions. Because the possibility exists that Bronze Frogs may also have been introduced, we include a brief description of this subspecies. Bronze Frogs have plain brown or bronze-colored backs. The green areas on the sides of the head are often absent. The underside is white with a pattern of dark vermiculations.

LIFE HISTORY. Green Frogs are said to be somewhat tolerant of cool weather and may remain active during warmer periods of our coastal winters. When they hibernate, they burrow into the substrate of ponds, marshes, lakes, and sluggish streams. In the northern part of their native range, Green Frogs breed from early May into August. A study in New York indicated that females that laid eggs prior to 22 July produced a second clutch later in that same summer. Male Green Frogs are territorial, at least during the lengthy breeding season. They advertise their position by calling and defend their territories aggressively. The call has been likened to plucking the bass string of a banjo, and each call may be repeated four or five times. The highly territorial, adult males are spaced at least two to three meters apart. Females move through several territories and probably choose males on the basis of some quality of the male's territory, perhaps the submerged vegetation there. Larger males usually have the best territories and the highest reproductive success. As in Bullfrogs, small adult males known as "satellite" males may attempt a sneak strategy to obtain mates. They do so by assuming a low profile and by not challenging the larger territorial males.

From 1,000 to 5,000 eggs are laid in a floating mass consisting of a single layer of eggs, some 15 to 30 cm in diameter. They are usually attached to vegetation in shallow water. Single eggs average 1.5 mm in diameter. Eggs in New York hatch in 3 to 6 days, depending upon water temperatures. Size of tadpoles at hatching is unknown to us, but those hatched early in the breeding season probably metamorphose in the late summer. Tadpoles from later egg masses are known to overwinter as larvae in the northeastern United States.

At metamorphosis, young frogs are 26 to 38 mm SVL, and they may add 10 mm per month to their length during June through August, and another 4 to 7 mm during September. By June or July of the following year, the males average about 60 mm SVL, the females 65 mm SVL, and both sexes are sexually mature. Therefore, these frogs can reproduce one year after metamorphosis. After frogs of either sex reach 80 mm SVL, growth is slow. A Green Frog in captivity lived for 10 years, but nothing is known of their longevity in nature.

Like the Bullfrog, male and female Green Frogs are about the same size. This is unlike all other species of *Rana* in the Northwest, in which males are considerably smaller than females. This may be related to the shorter breeding season and lack of male territoriality in these other *Rana*.

Green Frogs eat a wide range of invertebrates, mainly insects. Large prey such as crayfish, other frogs, tadpoles, and fish are also found in their stomachs. Some of the latter prey items indicate that Green Frogs feed under water as well as above the surface.

REMARKS. Most of this account is based on studies near Ann Arbor, Michigan and Ithaca, New York. There is almost no published information on Green Frogs in the Northwest. We are very much in need of information on their life history and present status in the Northwest.

REFERENCES. Carl (1943), Martof (1953a, 1953b, 1956), Wells (1976, 1977, 1978).

NORTHERN LEOPARD FROG
RANA PIPIENS SCHREBER

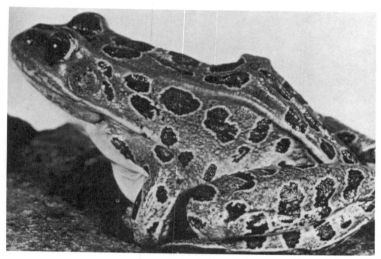

33. Northern Leopard Frog *(Rana pipiens)*, Idaho; photo by E. Skov.

Leopard frogs are recognized easily by the fact that the dark blotches on their back, sides, and legs are surrounded by a narrow light border. They are medium-sized frogs, the males attaining a SVL of 80 mm and the females occasionally reaching about 100 mm. Northern Leopard Frogs are smooth-skinned, and their ground color is usually green or brown dorsally and white ventrally. The dorsolateral folds, which extend from the eye back to the hind legs, are conspicuously lighter than the adjacent ground color. The dorsal blotches between these folds tend to form two irregular rows. The ear is conspicuous and about 3/4 the size of the eye.

The tadpoles are brown to dark brown with metallic flecks over the back, becoming more blotchy on the sides. The ventral area of the body is often almost transparent so that the viscera can be seen through the skin. The fins on the tail are translucent and have fine dark markings. The dorsal fin ends posterior to the spiracle and is not as high as the tail musculature. Labial teeth are usually arranged in two anterior and three posterior rows. The first anterior row is complete and longer than the width of the mouth. The second row has a medial space longer than the tooth row segments on each side. The

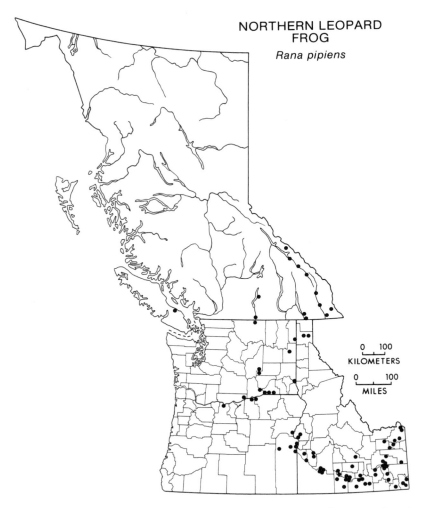

NORTHERN LEOPARD
FROG
Rana pipiens

0   100
KILOMETERS
0   100
MILES

first posterior row has a very small medial space; and the second and third rows are complete, the second as long as the first but the third somewhat shorter. The tadpoles may attain a total length of about 85 mm.

HABITAT. These are usually frogs of marshes and other quiet waters with considerable vegetation. They may range widely into moist meadows and even hay fields and grassy woodlands. Northern Leopard Frogs apparently require a moderately high ground cover for concealment, and when disturbed they leap rapidly and erratically in long low jumps. In southern and eastern Idaho they occur from lowlands to mountain tops, but are more confined to the valleys as one moves westward.

For reproduction, Northern Leopard Frogs avoid any ponds or backwaters that are devoid of vegetation, and they prefer cattail or sedge marshes and weedy ponds or temporary waters with some kind of vegetation in the water. The frogs may move some distance overland to reach suitable breeding sites, and one may see many on roads during warm rainy nights in spring. As temporary ponds dry up in the summer, large numbers of recently- metamorphosed young disperse to moist upland habitats or more permanent waters.

Northern Leopard Frogs probably hibernate in ponds and lakes or other aquatic locations. In Minnesota, hundreds of Leopard Frogs were seen on 1 January crowded together on the clean sandy bottom of an outflow from a dammed lake.

VARIATION. Subspecies are not presently recognized. We have no information on variation of this species within our area. Throughout their entire range, Northern Leopard Frogs are usually some shade of brown or green, with much variation from light and metallic to very dark. Most Leopard Frogs have a dark spot near the tip of the snout in front of the eyes. The literature states that hind foot webbing is quite variable in these frogs, being quite reduced in some to full (only slightly concave between the toes) in others. A specimen (female) from Nampa, Idaho has reduced webbing with the last two segments of the longest toe free of the web except for a narrow keel on each side. Males may have fuller hind foot webbing than females. In addition, males develop an enlarged first finger during the breeding season, and there is a thickened pad on the inner side of the finger throughout the year. We have no information on variation in tadpoles.

LIFE HISTORY. Northern Leopard Frogs breed during the spring, soon after ice and snow have disappeared, usually in March or April. In Wyoming, they are thought to commence reproductive activities when water temperatures reach about 10° C. The males tend to congregate and call in limited areas of the breeding waters, usually in shallows near shore where there is bottom vegetation. A chorus of calling Northern Leopard Frogs has been described as a guttural chuckling. Actually, the chorus is complicated by the fact that each male can produce several different sounds. The call that probably attracts both males and females is a long trill lasting more than one second (usually two but up to five seconds). At 10° C, the pulse rate is ten per second. A second call is a shorter trill with a more rapid pulse, which probably increases the chances that a female will move toward the calling male. The third call consists of three or four pulses in about 1/2 second and seems directed at other males as a spacing mechanism. These varied calls may indicate a dominant male to females, the male being in possession of a superior egg-laying site.

The egg mass is a somewhat flattened sphere 75 to 100 mm in width, containing up to 6,000 eggs, each egg being about 1.7 mm in diameter. The mass is usually attached to underwater vegetation in shallow water, and there may be two or three dozen masses in a limited area. The eggs can apparently develop at water temperatures of about 6° to 27° C (based on laboratory work with Vermont Leopard Frogs), but field temperatures probably seldom range below 10° C, and average higher. In experiments with Vermont *Rana pipiens,* eggs at 11.4° C were hatching at about 400 hours (17 days); at 18.5° C, near hatching at 117 hours (5 days); and at 27° C, about 48 hours (two days). In New York, eggs in nature required 13 to 20 days to hatch.

The larvae are 8 to 10 mm TL at hatching and metamorphose in about two months at lower elevations. In Idaho and northeastern Oregon, tadpoles were found in ponds with water temperatures from 14° to 30 ° C. Sizes of recently-metamorphosed frogs range from 18 to 23 mm TL. Sexual maturity is reached two or three years after the year of hatching.

An amazing variety of prey is eaten by Northern Leopard Frogs. Their food is mainly small insects, but birds, garter snakes, tadpoles, small frogs, fish, snails, leeches, and spiders are also eaten. Cannibalism has also been reported. Northern Leopard Frog larvae and adults are preyed upon heavily by garter snakes *(Thamnophis elegans* and *T. sirtalis).*

REMARKS. Where *Rana pipiens* and *R. pretiosa* should occur in mixed populations in Idaho and Oregon, the latter have gradually disappeared, perhaps as a result of interspecific competition. As a final note, *R. pipiens* seems to have suffered a severe decline in numbers over much of its range, but we have no information on this aspect in the Northwest.

REFERENCES. Baxter and Stone (1980), Breckenridge (1944), Dumas (1964, 1966), Moore (1949), Pace (1974).

SPOTTED FROG
RANA PRETIOSA BAIRD AND GIRARD

This highly aquatic frog is characterized by relatively short legs and full webbing between the toes. If a hind leg is pressed forward against the body, the heel seldom reaches to the nostrils. When the hind toes are stretched apart, the edges of the webbing are almost straight or even slightly convex, and the webbing reaches almost to the tip of the longest toe. Spotted Frogs usually have large, dorsal, black spots with light centers and fuzzy edges. Mottling in the groin area is minimal. In life, concealed hind leg surfaces and the lower abdomen are yellow to yellow orange or red. The color almost appears to be painted on, the pigment being very near the skin surface.

Tadpoles are variable in color, being dark brown to greenish, often with a heavy mottling of brassy flecks on the body and proximal tail region. Ventrally, they are usually silvery. The dorsal fin terminates posterior to the spiracle and is equal or less in height than the height of the tail musculature. Labial teeth are variable, but there are usually two rows anterior and three rows posterior to the mouth (see Variation). Premetamorphic tadpoles may attain a total length of up to 70 mm.

HABITAT. Spotted Frogs are most likely to be found at marshy edges of ponds or lakes, or in algae-grown overflow pools of streams. Although now apparently exterminated in the Willamette Valley of Oregon by introduced Bullfrogs (see Remarks), an early account states that they occurred in a very slow-moving stream in the valley, the edges of which dropped of sharply and were largely devoid of aquatic vegetation. In extreme southwestern British Columbia, *Rana pretiosa* occur together with *Rana aurora* in a wet, flat, lowland area, covered mainly by bulrushes and sedges. A permanent slow-flowing stream moves through the center of the area.

Rana pretiosa occurs in a few high Cascades lakes in Oregon. There, we usually find the frogs sitting at the edge or in the water in areas where there is considerable emergent vegetation plus a layer several centimeters thick, of dead and decaying vegetation on the bottom. The disturbed frogs jump in and take refuge in this layer or, if resting in the water, simply sink into it. In overflow pools or backwaters of creeks in eastern Oregon, the frogs utilize thick algal growth in the same way.

VARIATION. Subspecies are not presently recognized. Throughout much of its range, *Rana pretiosa* is recognizable by a com-

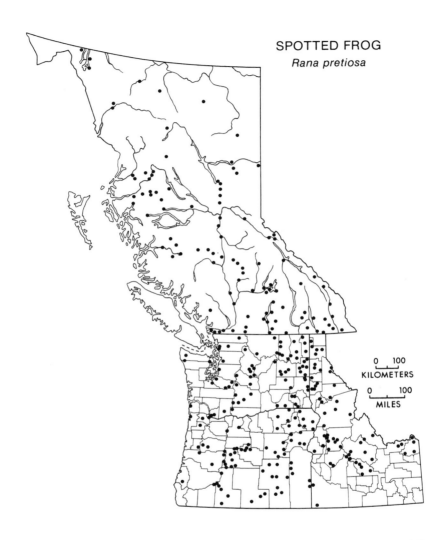

SPOTTED FROG
Rana pretiosa

0   100
KILOMETERS

0   100
MILES

bination of large, light-centered, dorsal spots with "fuzzy" edges; full webbing on the hind toes; and a "painted on" ventral color of yellow, yellow orange or red. We have never encountered the red coloration in frogs east of the Cascades, except at one locality. Spotted Frogs in the Blitzen River system, including Malheur Marsh, in southeastern Oregon all have red ventral coloration. Frogs west of the Cascades, and those occurring in Cascades lakes, are of the red variety. Early descriptions of British Columbia *R. pretiosa* give the ventral color as salmon or red, and we assume that these are based on frogs from the southwestern part of the Province. Frogs from interior British Columbia are said to be orange or reddish-orange, but we have little information on this.

Dorsal ground color varies somewhat geographically. One-third to one-half of the Spotted Frogs in northeastern Oregon and southeastern Washington have an olive-brown ground color, which is rare elsewhere. A grayish dorsal ground color occurs on about 40% of the frogs of northeastern Washington and northern Idaho; it is rare elsewhere. Frogs with gray ground color often have reduced dorsal spotting and a more complete eye mask, which causes them to resemble *Rana sylvatica*. Snout-vent length in adult males ranges up to 68 mm, whereas occasional females reach at least 100 mm.

The tooth row formula of tadpoles is typically two rows anterior and three posterior to the mouth. The anteriormost (first) row is complete and extends the width of the mouth. The second anterior row occurs as very short segments posterior to the ends of the first. The first posterior row is the longest and darkest and may or may not be interrupted in the middle. The second posterior row is shorter and similarly complete or not, as is true of the third row, which is the shortest. The above is based on tadpoles from a lake in the Oregon Cascades. Descriptions in the literature are somewhat at variance with the above, but part of this may be because of differences in the stages of development of the tadpoles described.

LIFE HISTORY. Spotted Frogs become active in late February or early March in southwestern British Columbia, and the same is true in the Pullman area of eastern Washington. Prior to their disappearance from western Oregon, we encountered a very few *Rana pretiosa* on roads during rainy nights, as early as 8 February. Male frogs arrive at breeding locations first and tend to congregate in small areas in shallow water (*e.g.*, in southwestern British Columbia, eight males within a meter square). They begin to call above the surface (rarely below the surface) immediately upon arrival. They do not defend territories.

The males call during the day and do so while floating at the surface or sitting on mats of vegetation. The call has been described as a series of short bass notes, usually six to nine in number. Calls become prolonged (more notes) if a male is approached by other frogs. The calls are low in volume and can be heard only up to about 30 m. Males do not have an "amplexus call" as do *Rana aurora* males.

Amplexus is axillary and most frequently occurs during the day in shallow water. Most egg laying occurs during about a two-week period in early March in southwestern British Columbia, but is undoubtedly much later in mountainous parts of the interior. Eggs in early developmental stages were seen on 30 June in a mountain lake in northeastern Oregon. Spotted Frogs characteristically deposit their egg masses in clusters of several masses, so that as many as 50 masses may occur in an area as small as 75 cm across. Apparently, females are attracted to other egg masses, and the same communal oviposition site may be used in successive years. The eggs are deposited as a rounded mass, which is not attached to vegetation, and which rests on the bottom in shallow water. Often as much as half of each egg mass protrudes above the surface of the water. Each mass is 12 to 20 cm in diameter, and individual eggs measure about 2.0 to 2.3 mm. Egg number per clutch varies greatly, usually being between 700 to 1,500. One Oregon Cascades female, artificially induced to ovulate in our laboratory, produced a total of 2,897 eggs.

The thermal tolerance range of early embryos is 7° to 28° C (British Columbia and eastern Oregon). Time to hatching is dependent on temperature and varies from about 55 hours at 28° C to about 600 hours at 7° C (British Columbia), and from 72 hours at 25° C to about 400 hours at 10° C (eastern Oregon). These figures are based on laboratory experiments; we have no field data for this species. The larvae at hatching are 7 to 8 mm TL and dark brown in color. In eastern Washington, tadpoles reach a total length of 36 mm in about 30 days, at which time hind limb buds have appeared. Tadpoles from a high Cascades lake in Oregon averaged 70.5 mm TL on 1 September. Their hind legs were well developed. Earlier literature indicates that tadpoles metamorphose in their first season in coastal and western valley locations, but overwinter as larvae in mountain and interior sites, metamorphosing the following spring. We have no new data regarding this phenomenon.

Newly-metamorphosed frogs measure about 33 mm SVL and are thought to reach sexual maturity in two years in low elevation (< 100 m), coastal populations. At higher elevations (2,600 m) in Wyoming, newly-metamorphosed *Rana pretiosa* are smaller (16 mm SVL), and they grow to about the same size as those at low elevation sites, but grow more slowly and mature at a later age (males at four and females at six years). Females breed every year at low elevation sites, but every two or three years at the high elevation site in Wyoming.

The food habits of the Spotted Frog were studied carefully in Yellowstone National Park. A very broad range of insects are eaten in addition to a few kinds of mollusks, crustaceans, and arachnids. The study indicated that Spotted Frogs feed opportunistically and that they feed to some extent under water.

REMARKS. *Rana pretiosa* is unable to survive in areas where introduced Bullfrogs establish healthy populations. The last Spotted Frog known by us to have been collected west of the Cascades in Oregon or Washington was taken 14 January 1968 near Brush Prairie, Washington. We are hopeful that a few populations still exist in western areas, particularly in coastal regions, and will welcome recent records from our readers.

REFERENCES. Carl (1943), Dumas (1964, 1966), Graf (1939), Johnson (1965), L. E. Licht (1969b, 1971, 1974, 1975b), Logier (1932), Morris and Tanner (1969), Svihla (1935), Turner (1958, 1959, 1960).

WOOD FROG
RANA SYLVATICA LE CONTE

34. Wood Frog *(Rana sylvatica)*, Albany Co., New York.

These are small- to medium-sized frogs (40 to 50 mm SVL), which always have a narrow dark line from the tip of the snout to the eye and a dark mask from the eye to just behind the tympanum. A contrasting light lip-line runs from the snout tip to the posterior edge of the mask. Dorsal ground color is brown to grayish or blue-greenish with or without dorsal spotting. Many frogs have a middorsal light

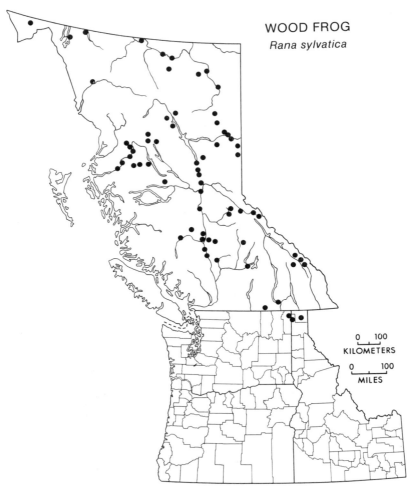

WOOD FROG
Rana sylvatica

0   100
KILOMETERS
0   100
MILES

line. Most Wood Frogs have dark blotches or streaks along the outer edges of the dorsolateral folds and a dark spot on the anterior edge of each upper foreleg where it joins the body. Ventral surfaces are white, with some anterior dark mottling. Northwestern members of this species have short hind legs; when stretched forward the heel reaches about to the eyes.

Tadpoles are uniformly dark olive or brownish dorsally. The ventral surface is cream colored with a pinkish iridescence. Tooth rows are usually two to four anterior and three or four posterior to the mouth.

HABITAT. *Rana sylvatica* is largely terrestrial during the non-breeding season, but is usually not found far from water. They inhabit pond, lake, and stream shores, but also move into shaded portions of adjoining forests or brush where the ground litter remains damp. They are thought to hibernate in terrestrial situations such as burrows, root channels, crevices, and so forth, but we have little information. Recently it has been shown that metamorphosed Wood Frogs can survive freezing temperatures (to about -2.0° C). This ability probably increases their survivorship in terrestrial hibernacula. For breeding, Wood Frogs utilize woodland ponds, the marshy edges of lakes, and quiet stretches or backwaters of streams. They have been known to breed in small pools only a little more than a meter in diameter. During a study in Michigan, breeding aggregations of Wood Frogs were found in ponds as far as 0.45 km from the nearest forest. Wood Frogs are the only North American amphibian found north of the Arctic Circle.

VARIATION. No subspecies are recognized. Wood Frogs in northern Idaho and southeastern British Columbia average 45 to 50 mm SVL, whereas those in the remainder of British Columbia average 40 to 45 mm. Females average a few millimeters longer than males. Northwestern Wood Frogs are short-legged, relative to eastern populations of this species. Hind toe webbing is quite reduced, and the last two phalanges of the longest toe are free of the web. A middorsal white stripe occurs in about half of northwestern Wood Frogs. Our Wood Frogs are more strikingly marked with more and larger lateral markings than those in eastern populations.

We have almost no information on tadpoles of this species in our region. Literature descriptions are based almost entirely on larvae from outside the Northwest. Premetamorphic tadpoles are about 50 mm TL. The tail is almost twice as long as the body, with a narrow attenuated tip. The labial teeth are stated to be two to four rows anterior and three to four rows posterior to the mouth. The first anterior row is as wide as the beak, with the second row represented by short segments at each end of the first. The three lower rows are complete, with the first the longest and the third shortest.

LIFE HISTORY. The most complete data on Wood Frog reproduction in the West are based on studies near Fairbanks, Alaska.

Wood Frogs breed relatively early and are known to move to breeding waters before the ice is off the water. Depending upon climatic conditions in local areas, breeding probably occurs from early

189

March to June. At the appropriate time males move to ponds or even roadside pools and may collect in large numbers in a small area. In central British Columbia, estimated groups of 20 to 60 frogs were seen in as little as one or two square meters. The males usually call while floating at the surface of the water, the call being described as a hoarse clacking sound, suggesting the quacking of a small duck. The calls are given at a rate of two or three per second and are inaudible beyond about 50 m. Males do not defend territories. Instead they search for females and immediately clasp any female that is encountered. Males try to dislodge other males from clasped females, and both males and females may die in the struggle.

Wood Frogs are "explosive" breeders. Egg laying begins from four to six days after the first frogs appear, and most egg laying is completed within 7 to 10 days. Average water temperature in Alaskan ponds at the time the first eggs appeared was 7° to 9° C. The frogs usually lay their globular egg masses near one another, often attached to the same underwater vegetation. There is experimental evidence that the presence of one or more egg masses causes other females to deposit their eggs in the same place, as opposed to independent selection by each female of the same, high quality oviposition site. In the Alaskan study, as many as 61 masses were found close together. Near Ann Arbor, Michigan, 58 egg masses were found within one square meter of a 256 m² pond; only two egg masses were found elsewhere in the pond. In the Alaskan study, the number of eggs per mass averaged about 780, with a range of 42 to 1,570. This is considerably fewer than in Minnesota *Rana sylvatica* (1,000 to 3,000), and frogs in southern British Columbia may be intermediate in this respect. Alaskan eggs averaged 1.6 mm in diameter.

The temperature limits that allow at least 50% of the eggs to survive through hatching are 6° to 24° C (Alaska). In laboratory experiments with Alaskan eggs, the relationship between time to hatching and temperature was approximately as follows: 48 hours at 20.4° C, 150 hours at 15.1° C, 300 hours at 10° C, and about 850 hours at 5.6° C. In ponds in the Fairbanks area, eggs hatched in 4.0 to 7.5 days, depending on the year. Tadpoles are 7 to 10 mm TL at hatching and reach their maximum size of 55 to 60 mm TL in about two months (Alaska). Metamorphosis occurs at this time, but we have no information on body lengths of metamorphosed frogs in the West. Near Ann Arbor, Michigan, mature females average about 44 mm SVL (54 mm max) and mature males average 38 mm SVL (43 mm max). In the same area males mature one year after, and females two years after metamorphosis.

The food habits of this frog in the Northwest are unstudied, but elsewhere they mainly eat insects, snails, millipedes, and other small invertebrates. Some aquatic foods are eaten, especially by recently-transformed individuals.

Adults and metamorphosing larvae have skin secretions that are repulsive to aquatic insect and shrew predators. Most adults (14 of 16 tested) give a defensive call or "mercy scream" when attacked by shrews.

REMARKS. There seems to be very little information on this species as it occurs in the area covered by this book. Its exact distributional status in northern Idaho and northeastern Washington is unknown. Life history data are needed from populations at the southern edge of the range in British Columbia. The locality indicated on our range map for this species in northeastern Washington is based on a sight record that needs to be confirmed.

REFERENCES. Breckenridge (1944), Dumas (1966), Formanowicz and Brodie (1979, 1982), Heatwole (1961), Herreid and Kinney (1966, 1967), Howard (1980), Kessel (1965), Martof and Humphries (1959), Schmid (1982).

CLASS REPTILIA

Snakes, lizards, turtles, crocodiles, and the tuatara of New Zealand constitute the living Reptilia. They have many features in common, including (1) the presence of dry cornified skin containing horny epidermal scales; (2) an ectothermic physiology; (3) an internal mode of fertilization; (4) an amniotic egg; and (5) direct development. Excluding fossil forms, there are about 46 families, 900 genera, and 6,000 species of reptiles.

Reptiles evolved from amphibians during the Pennsylvanian Period of earth history about 300 million years ago. They enjoyed their greatest period of diversity during the Mesozoic Era, which lasted from 225 until about 65 million years ago. This era, called the Age of Reptiles, witnessed the origin, diversification, and extinction of an overwhelming variety of reptiles, including some forms, popularly called dinosaurs that were the largest known terrestrial vertebrates. Some 17 orders of reptiles evolved, but only four orders survive today. These are (1) Testudines (turtles, tortoises), (2) Rhynchocephalia (tuatara), (3) Crocodilia (alligators, crocodiles, gavials), and (4) Squamata (amphisbaenians, lizards, snakes). Only two of these, Testudines and Squamata, are represented in the Pacific Northwest.

The majority of reptiles live in tropical and subtropical environments, with diversity decreasing toward the poles. There are none within the Antarctic Circle, and only two live-bearing species, one snake and one lizard, within the Arctic Circle. Being ectothermic animals, reptiles in temperate zones are forced to hibernate during the winter, and some species aestivate during the hottest driest times of the summer.

Most reptiles are oviparous, but many are ovoviviparous, and some have a mammal-like placenta and are hence truly viviparous. Unlike the other two groups of amniotic vertebrates (birds, mammals), reptiles seldom engage in any form of parental care, although some skinks, pythons, and cobras brood their eggs, and many crocodilians guard their nests against predators.

Reptiles are mainly carnivorous, but omnivores and strict herbivores exist. They are largely terrestrial, but many are amphibious, some (turtles) live primarily in fresh water, and some snakes and turtles are marine. Except for one group of live-bearing sea snakes, all aquatic reptiles must return to land to deposit their eggs.

TURTLES
ORDER TESTUDINES

Turtles and tortoises constitute the reptilian order Testudines (= Chelonia = Testudinata). They are among the most distinctive of vertebrates, and all species will be recognized as turtles at a glance by most people. The protective shell is the most obvious feature of the group. It consists of a dorsal carapace and a ventral plastron joined by a "bridge" on each side. The shell is a two-part structure with an outer layer of horny epidermal scutes and an inner layer of bony plates. The bony plates of the carapace are fused to the ribs and the trunk vertebrae. The size, shape, and texture of the shell vary considerably among turtles. Some species have a small shell and cannot completely retract the extremities (head, tail, limbs) into the shell. Others have hinged shells so that the shell can be closed after the extremities are withdrawn, and yet others have soft shells without dorsal scutes. Unlike most other living reptiles, turtles have a solid skull with no openings in the temporal region (anapsid condition), and the bones of the skull are incapable of movement in relation to one another (akinetic condition). Turtles lack true teeth, but the jaw bones may have tooth-like serrations, and the jaws are covered by horny plates or beaks. Turtles are the only vertebrates that have ribs external to the limb girdles. The males of all turtles have a single median penis, which is everted from the cloaca when used as an intromittent organ.

Turtles have internal fertilization, and all are egglayers. Eggs are buried in loose soil, and even the fully aquatic species must return to land to nest. Turtles do not care for their eggs or young beyond providing a nest. Egg and hatchling mortality is generally very high, but adults have relatively high annual survivorship, and most species are long-lived. Some, like the Seychelles Giant Tortoise, *Geochelone gigantea*, may live 200 years.

Although turtles are relatively uniform in body structure, they are ecologically diverse, occupying terrestrial, amphibious, freshwater, and marine niches. They occur almost everywhere in the world except extreme polar regions. Unlike most other living reptiles, most turtles are herbivorous. Land turtles are largely herbivores, but some aquatic species are omnivores or carnivores.

The largest recorded land turtle was an Aldabran specimen of the Seychelles Giant Tortoise, which had a carapace length of 21.7 cm (55 in) and weighed 254 kg (560 lbs). The largest species is the marine Leatherback *(Dermochelys coriacea)* with a record carapace length of

28.1 cm (71.5 in) and a record weight of nearly 590 kg (1,300 lbs).

Living turtles are placed in two suborders, the Cryptodira (modern turtles) in which the neck is retracted in a vertical plane, and the Pleurodira (side-neck turtles) which retract the neck in a horizontal plane. Side-neck turtles are restricted largely to the Southern Hemisphere. All North American turtles are cryptodires.

There are 11 families, 72 genera, and about 230 species of extant turtles. In North America (excluding Mexico), there are seven families, 18 genera, and 48 species. In the Pacific Northwest, there is a single family with two genera and two species, excluding introduced and marine forms.

KEY TO THE TURTLES OF THE PACIFIC NORTHWEST

1A.

Carapace (dorsal shell) with radiating black flecks and lines; plastron (ventral shell) pale yellow with irregular dark blotches, may be nearly uniform yellow or dark; head without yellow stripes; crushing surface of upper jaw smooth or undulating ... Western Pond Turtle, *Clemmys marmorata*

2A.

Carapace without radiating black flecks and lines; plastron with a large, central dark blotch that branches along the seams of the scutes; head with yellow stripes; crushing surface of upper jaw with ridge or row of tubercles parallel to margin of jaw ...Painted Turtle, *Chrysemys picta*

WATER AND BOX TURTLES
FAMILY EMYDIDAE

Emydids are cryptodiran turtles technically defined by details of the skull, shell, and limbs. They are closely related to land tortoises of the family Testudinidae, but differ from the latter in having hind feet adapted for swimming rather than for walking.

Most emydids are aquatic in freshwater, but some are semiaquatic, and a few, such as the box turtles, are fully terrestrial. The family occurs in the New World from Canada southward to northern Argentina, Europe, northwestern Africa, southern Asia, and Malaysia. This is the largest family of turtles, with 30 genera and about 85 species. Emydid diversity is greatest in the eastern United States and southeastern Asia. There are eight genera and 26 species in North America. Both of our native northwestern species belong to this family.

PAINTED TURTLES
GENUS *CHRYSEMYS*

The genus *Chrysemys,* as presently conceived, contains a single species with four geographic races. Painted Turtles range throughout much of North America from Canada to northern Mexico. They are among the most common and familiar of North American turtles and are often seen basking on logs in ponds, marshes, and sluggish streams.

PAINTED TURTLE
CHRYSEMYS PICTA (SCHNEIDER)

35. Painted Turtle *(Chrysemys picta)*, Spokane Co., Washington; photo by D.R. Paulson.

Chrysemys picta is distinguished by the red color on its ventral shell, or plastron, and on the undersides of the marginal scutes of the carapace. Much of the central part of the plastron displays an irregular dark pattern with outward extensions along the seams between plates. The sides of the head, throat, legs, and tail are marked by contrasting longitudinal lines, which are usually light yellow but may range from yellow to red. The carapace is smooth and olive to almost black in color. These turtles may attain a maximum carapace length of 250 mm, the females averaging larger than the males. The sexes may be distinguished by the facts that the males have elongated front claws and the vent opening is more distally positioned on the tail in males, being outside the margin of the carapace (within the margin in females).

HABITAT. Painted Turtles usually occupy marshy ponds or small lakes, but are also found in slow-moving streams and quiet backwaters of rivers. They prefer muddy bottoms with considerable aquatic vegetation. Painted Turtles inhabit an oxbow lake that is a remnant of the former channel of the Willamette River in western Oregon. The lake is about 300 m long and averages 45 m in width; greatest depths

196

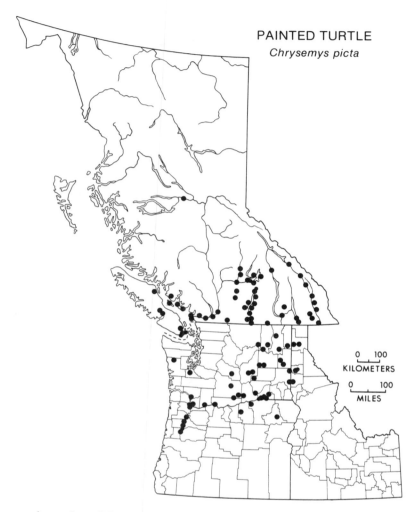

PAINTED TURTLE
Chrysemys picta

0   100
KILOMETERS

0   100
MILES

are about 5 m. Much of the lake is surrounded by thick brush. The pond is rich in aquatic vegetation. About one-tenth of the area is occupied by floating and stationary islands of cattails, and at times the water is almost covered by duckweed. We once estimated that about 60 Painted Turtles occurred in this pond, which is probably at or near their southern limit in the Willamette Valley of Oregon. Of interest is the fact that an estimated 180 Western Pond Turtles also occurred there at the time of our study.

The above lake may be an unusual habitat. Elsewhere, we have usually seen Painted Turtles in shallower and more typical cattail

36. Painted Turtle *(Chrysemys picta),* Oregon; plastron coloration.

marshes, usually with more open banks. The adult turtles spend a considerable amount of time basking during the day, and for this require basking sites such as logs, partially submerged branches, and so on. In the absence of these, they may simply float at the surface. Body temperatures of basking Painted Turtles in Minnesota ranged from 26.3° to 30.2° C.

VARIATION. The species *Chrysemys picta* has been divided into four subspecies. Of these, only one, *C. p. belli,* the Western Painted Turtle, occurs in the Northwest. Its range extends eastward into Wisconsin and upper Michigan. Variation in the size and complexity of the dark markings on the plastron occurs, but we have no information on the nature of this variation within the Northwest. Individuals of certain populations have a reticulated black pattern on a lighter ground color on the carapace. The extent of occurrence of this pattern in our area is unknown. A poorly developed middorsal stripe may occur in some turtles. Hatchling Painted Turtles have a middorsal keel, which disappears as they grow.

LIFE HISTORY. Male Painted Turtles are sexually mature at a carapace length of about 85 mm, whereas females mature at around 125 mm carapace length. Mating occurs in the water and is preceeded by a courtship during which the male swims backwards in front of the female. He extends his arms and, with palms turned outward, vibrates the elongated claws against her chin and cheek area. Actual copulation occurs on the bottom. Courtship and mating may occur in both spring and fall.

Egg laying probably occurs during June and July in the Northwest. There are May records from British Columbia. Nesting usually occurs in late afternoon or early evening. The female turtle leaves the water and may travel as far as 150 m before she nests. Considering the entire range of the subspecies *Chrysemys picta belli,* nests have been found in open beaches, flood plains, shrubby fields, roadsides, gravel or soil roads, and pastures. The site selected is always open to direct sunlight for at least much of the day. The turtle digs the nest by using her hind feet alternately. She usually wets the soil with fluid from her cloaca and continues digging until a flask-shaped hole is constructed, its depth depending upon her size and leg length. Depths of Wisconsin nests were 60 to 90 mm.

The eggs are laid one at a time into this hole, and the female appears to arrange them with a hind leg. The hole is then filled in and the soil pressed down by her feet and plastron. The entire process takes about two hours. The drying of the wet mud creates a hard plug in the hole. Numbers of eggs in single clutches have been given as 4 to 10 (Minnesota), 6 to 20 (British Columbia), and 5 to 11, average 8.8 (Minnesota). Larger females tend to produce more eggs. Each egg is elliptical in shape, with a white, slightly pitted, smooth shell. The shell is flexible at first, but becomes firmer as the egg absorbs water. The average size of each egg is about 34 by 18 mm. Apparently, only one clutch per year is laid in the Northwest, but two clutches per year are common elsewhere, and the possibility of two clutches per year in parts of the Northwest cannot be ruled out.

Incubation time is not well-known. Literature records range from 72 to 104 days for eggs in the field. An artificially incubated egg began hatching on the 69th day, but the hatchling was not completely free of the shell for six more days. This turtle measured 22.2 mm in carapace length. In more northern populations of the Painted Turtle, eggs or hatchlings overwinter in the nest and emerge the following spring. This appears to be the case in British Columbia. The young turtles are round in carapace shape and appear to have a large head. The adult color and pattern are present and appear brighter than in adults.

The young must find their way to the water, and some experiments indicate that they move toward a more luminous sky, indicative of water. Depending mainly on food supply, young turtles attain a plastron length of 85 mm in 3 to 5 years, at which size the males are sexually mature. Ten-year-old males vary in plastron length from about 90 to 110 mm and ten-year-old females from 110 to 155 mm (Michigan). Painted Turtles in the Willamette Valley lake mentioned above varied in carapace length from 95 to 210 mm, with an average length of 150 mm (24 turtles). Males ranged from 105 to 185 and females from 95 to 210 mm carapace length.

In a study of Painted Turtles in southwestern Michigan (the Midland Painted Turtle, *Chrysemys picta marginata*), it was estimated that male turtles live at least six years, females at least 12, and a few turtles were estimated to be close to 40 years old. Of 6,000 eggs produced in that pond each year, only an estimated two percent got into the pond as juveniles. Most of them reached maturity.

Juvenile and adult Painted Turtles are aggressive toward one another when competing for basking sites, which may be limited in number. Aggression takes the form of open-mouthed threats, biting, and pushing.

Painted Turtles are omnivorous feeders, and feed on most kinds of plants and small animals in their waters. The younger turtles tend to be carnivorous, becoming more herbivorous as they grow older. The eggs of Painted Turtles are preyed upon by terrestrial predators such as skunks and raccoons, which may smell out the nests because of the odorous fluids passed by the females as they dig them. Bullfrogs may feed on hatchlings, and raccoons prey upon hatchling and adult Painted Turtles.

REMARKS. Two Washington localities indicated on our range map are based on reliable sight records, and voucher specimens are needed. These localities are Lake Quinalt, Grays Harbor Co. and near Olympia, Thurston Co.

REFERENCES. Brattstrom (1965), Breckenridge (1944), Bury et al. (1979), Carl (1968), Carr (1952), Christiansen and Moll (1973), Ernst and Barbour (1972), Evenden (1948), Gibbons (1968), Mahmoud (1968), Pritchard (1979), Tinkle et al. (1981).

POND TURTLES
GENUS *CLEMMYS*

Clemmys contain four species of small- to medium-sized turtles restricted to the United States and Canada. Among other features, *Clemmys* differs from *Chrysemys* in having smooth or undulate crushing surfaces along the upper jaw, the latter genus having ridged or tuberculate crushing surfaces. One species of *Clemmys,* the Wood Turtle of northeastern United States and adjacent parts of Canada, is largely terrestrial; two eastern species, the Spotted Turtle and the rare Bog Turtle, are semiaquatic; and the single western species, the Western Pond Turtle, is aquatic.

WESTERN POND TURTLE
CLEMMYS MARMORATA
(BAIRD AND GIRARD)

37. Western Pond Turtle *(Clemmys marmorata)*, California; photo by D.R. Paulson.

This is the less brightly colored of the two turtle species in the Northwest. The upper shell is olive or dark brown to blackish, and in many specimens there are fine radiating black and cream lines on the large dorsal plates. The ventral shell (plastron) is yellowish tan in color, sometimes with varied dark markings. The limbs and head are light to dark brown with scattered black markings. The carapace is

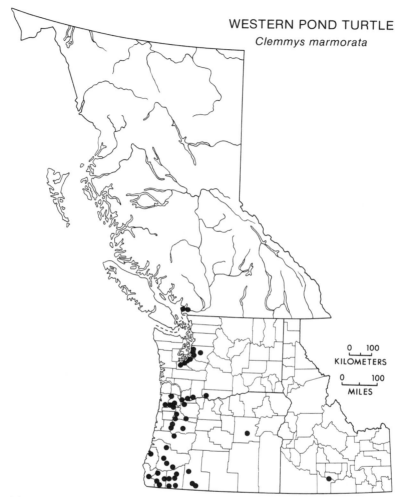

WESTERN POND TURTLE

Clemmys marmorata

0   100
KILOMETERS

0   100
MILES

widest posterior to the middle, and both shells usually have growth ridges on the individual plates. Adults reach 160 to 190 mm in carapace length, and there is apparently no sex-related size difference.

Young recently-hatched turtles are uniformly olive-brown on the carapace, whereas the plastron is dark gray centrally, with cream-colored edges. Cream-colored areas occur on the throat, the legs, and the undersides of the carapace edges. There may be a slight keel down the middle of the carapace.

HABITAT. Western Pond Turtles inhabit marshes, sloughs, moderately deep ponds, and slow-moving portions of creeks and

38. Western Pond Turtle *(Clemmys marmorata),* Oregon; plastron.

rivers. They occur from sea level to about 1,830 m. They require basking sites, such as partially submerged logs, vegetation mats, rocks and
mud banks, and may even climb a short way onto tree branches that
dip into the water from bank vegetation. An oxbow lake in the Corvallis, Oregon area of the Willamette Valley, measuring 1.5 to 2.0 hectares, contained an estimated 75 Western Pond Turtles. An oxbow
lake near Salem, Oregon (Willamette Valley) contained an estimated
180 Western Pond Turtles, a considerably larger population in a lake
of about the same size. About 60 Painted Turtles also occurred in this
lake, which appeared to contain much more aquatic vegetation than
the Corvallis lake. Vegetation in the latter, which was studied over a
period of five springs, consisted of pond lily, pondweed, smartweed,
burreed, and bulrush.

Clemmys marmorata usually hibernate in bottom mud, but occasionally have been seen basking during winter months in the Willamette Valley, Oregon. A turtle taken from water with a temperature
of 8.3° C had a body temperature of 9.0° C.

VARIATION. The Western Pond Turtle is divided into two subspecies, of which *Clemmys marmorata marmorata,* the Northwestern
Pond Turtle, is the only one to occur in the Northwest. Pond Turtles
have some individual variation in number, size, and shape of the
plates on the plastron and carapace. The carapace color pattern
sometimes varies from the usual radiating lines on an olive or dark
brown background; some individuals have no lines while others have a

dark and light reticulated pattern over the shell. Most individuals have a solid yellowish plastron, but in others there may be varying amounts of dark brown pigment over the yellow, even to the extent of nearly completely obscuring the yellow.

LIFE HISTORY. Western Pond Turtles become sexually mature at a carapace length of about 120 mm. At this time, males can be distinguished from females by the fact that the male's plastron is slightly concave in the posterior half; the female's is flat or slightly convex. The carapace of the male is slightly flatter than that of the female. In over half of the males, the anal opening is outside the margin of the carapace; in females, it is at or within the margin.

We have no information on courtship and mating of this turtle; presumably both occur in the water. Female turtles leave the water in late May to July to find nesting sites. They are said to utilize sandy banks near the water or sunny fields or banks hundreds of meters from the water. We have seen females on roads or streets at considerable distances from known water. We have one record from the Willamette Valley, Oregon of a Western Pond Turtle that had just finished her nest in a clover field about 100 m from water. The turtle had dug a hole about 10 cm deep in very hard soil during the first week in June. Scattered information in the literature indicates that females produce 3 to 11 eggs per clutch. The eggs are white, elliptical in shape, and 32 to 42 mm in length by 20 to 23 mm in width.

The incubation period of the eggs in nature is unknown, and we have no information on whether the eggs or young overwinter in the nest. Artificially incubated eggs (30° C) hatched between 73 and 80 days. The hatchlings emerge with a carapace length of about 25 mm. Literature records for growth may be based on the southern subspecies, but are approximately as follows: after two seasons of growth, the turtles are about 60 mm in carapace length, and by ten years of age they have a carapace length of about 140 mm. Sexual maturity is probably attained in about eight years.

In a lake near Corvallis, Oregon, 38 male Western Pond Turtles ranged from 146 to 176 mm in carapace length, with a mean of 163 mm; 26 females ranged from 143 to 175 mm (one exception), with a mean of 161 mm. The exception was 123 mm in length, the smallest turtle seen in a five-year study. Twenty-eight male turtles in a lake near Salem, Oregon averaged 174 mm, excluding two individuals of 105 and 140 mm, and 13 females averaged 169 mm. The smallest turtle in this pond measured 105 mm in carapace length. We believe the larger turtles in the Corvallis pond to be 30 to 40 years old.

Like the Painted Turtle, Western Pond Turtles are reported to be aggressive when competing with one another for basking sites. Juveniles and adults of both sexes are aggressive. Aggression involves biting, pushing, and open-mouthed threats, in which the bright edges of the mouth and reddish tissues inside the mouth are exposed and may serve as warning signals.

There is little information available on the food and predators of Western Pond Turtles. They apparently are omnivorous as pods of water lilies, fish, worms, and other invertebrates have been reported among their food. They also feed on carrion, including in one case a dead mallard duck. They have been attracted to pungent meat bait set for larval Pacific Giant Salamanders in cold clear streams in the vicinity of Mount Shasta in northern California. A Bullfrog was retrieved from the stomach of a Western Pond Turtle in California.

In the 1930s, Western Pond Turtles were trapped for food in California. They were sold to markets in San Francisco for $3.00 to $5.00/dozen.

REMARKS. The two isolated localities shown on our range map, one in Grant Co., Oregon and the other in Jerome Co., Idaho, require comment. The Grant Co. record is based on a reliable sight record, and voucher specimens are needed for confirmation. The Jerome Co. record is based on a specimen collected in 1894 on an island in the Snake River. The specimen is extant in the collections of the California Academy of Science. As no subsequent specimens have been collected in Idaho, it seems likely that an error in record keeping has been made, or, that a once extant Idaho population is now extinct.

REFERENCES. Black and Storm (1970), Bury and Wolfheim (1973), Carr (1952), Ernst and Barbour (1972), Evenden (1948), Feldman (1982), Graf (1939), Moyle (1973), Pope (1939), Pritchard (1979), Seeliger (1945), Slater (1962), Storer (1930).

AMPHISBAENIANS, LIZARDS, SNAKES
ORDER SQUAMATA

The Squamata is the most diverse of the four living orders of reptiles, containing 96% of the known species. On a world-wide basis there are about 135 species of amphisbaenians, 2,300 lizards, and 3,300 snakes. The group is defined by technical details of the skull morphology, the presence of a transverse cloacal opening, and having paired, eversible, male reproductive organs called hemipenes. The hemipenes (only one is used at a time) serve to transfer sperm to the female urogenital tract during copulation and thus to facilitate internal fertilization.

Amphisbaenians (Suborder Amphisbaenia) are peculiar, worm-like, burrowing forms, largely confined to the tropics and subtropics. None occurs in the Northwest. Lizards (Suborder Lacertilia) and snakes (Suborder Ophidia) are differentiated readily at a glance in the Pacific Northwest, because all of our lizards have well-developed limbs and short bodies in contrast to all snakes which are elongate and have, at most, vestigial hind limbs that are not visible except by close examination. In other parts of the world, however, including parts of the United States, limbless elongate lizards occur that are often mistaken for snakes. These snake-like lizards (the glass lizards are examples) usually have movable eyelids, external ear openings, and lower jaws with solidly sutured right and left halves. Snakes, on the other hand, have lidless eyes (can't blink), no external ear openings, and highly mobile lower jaws in which the right and left halves are not sutured at the point of the chin and can move independently. The jaw types of lizards and snakes facilitate their different modes of feeding. Lizards generally feed on smaller prey which are masticated to some extent, and snakes eat much larger prey which are swallowed whole.

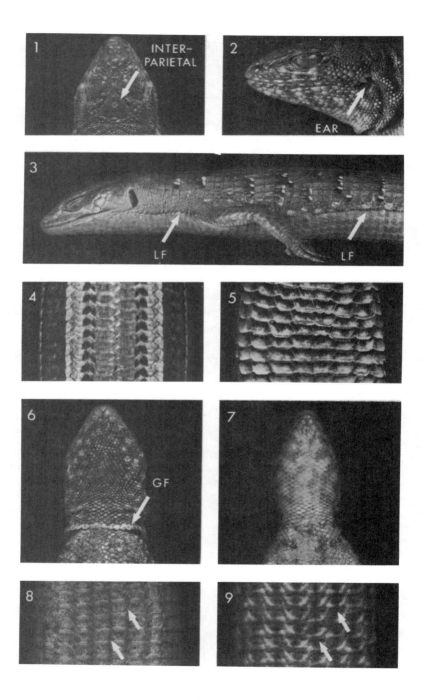

KEY TO THE LIZARDS
OF THE PACIFIC NORTHWEST

1A. All scales smooth, flat, rounded posteriorly (4) .... Western Skink, *Eumeces skiltonianus*

1B. Scales not as above 2

2A. Longitudinal skin fold on each side of body (3) (*Elgaria*)........ 10

2B. No longitudinal skin folds 3

3A. Large, quadrangular belly scales in 8 longitudinal rows (5) .... Western Whiptail, *Cnemidophorus tigris*

3B. Belly scales not as above 4

4A. Spiny ridges or spines at rear of head *(Phrynosoma)* 9

4B. No ridges or spines at rear of head 5

5A. Gular fold with granules (6) 6

5B. No fold with granules (7) *(Sceloporus)* 8

6A. Interparietal (1) larger than ear opening (2), dark spot on body behind front leg .... Side-blotched Lizard, *Uta stansburiana*

6B. Interparietal smaller than ear opening, no dark spot behind front leg 7

7A. 1-2 rows of large scales between orbits, dark collar on neck. Mojave Black-collared Lizard, *Crotaphytus bicinctores*

7B. Several rows of small scales between orbits, no dark collar .... Longnose Leopard Lizard, *Gambelia wislizenii*

8A. Scales on rear of thigh granular, not overlapping, throat with mottled blue patches ... Sagebrush Lizard, *Sceloporus graciosus*

8B. Scales on rear of thigh overlap, throat with solid blue patches ... Western Fence Lizard, *Sceloporus occidentalis*

9A. Spines on head short, about as long as wide ... Short-horned Lizard, *Phrynosoma douglassi*

9B. Spines much longer than wide ... Desert Horned Lizard, *Phrynosoma platyrhinos*

10A. Dark stripes along edges of belly scales (8) ... Northern Alligator Lizard, *Elgaria coerulea*

10B. Dark stripes on center of belly scales (9) ... Southern Alligator Lizard, *Elgaria multicarinata*

IV. Key Illustrations - Lizards

Figs.: (1) Dorsal view of head of *Uta stansburiana;* (2) Lateral view of head of *Uta stansburiana;* (3) Lateral view of *Elgaria multicarinata* showing lateral fold (LF); (4) Dorsal scales and coloration of *Eumeces skiltonianus;* (5) Ventral scales of *Cnemidophorus tigris* in 8 longitudinal rows; (6) Gular fold (GF) of *Uta stansburiana;* (7) Gular region of *Sceloporus graciosus* illustrating lack of gular fold; (8) Ventral scales of *Elgaria coerulea* with longitudinal dark lines running between scale rows; (9) Ventral scales of *Elgaria multicarinata* with longitudinal dark lines along middle of scales.

ANGUIDS
FAMILY ANGUIDAE

This family, consisting of six genera and 74 species, is widespread in North and South America, Europe, North Africa, and Asia. There are two genera and nine species in the U.S. and Canada, but only one genus and two species in the Northwest. Anguids have bony plates (osteoderms) beneath the scales, skin that is fused to the top of the head, and a fleshy tongue that can be protruded. There are members of this family without legs including the genus *Ophisaurus* (glass lizards), which occurs in the eastern U.S. All North American members of this family have lateral skin folds.

ALLIGATOR LIZARDS
GENUS *ELGARIA*

The six members of this genus are restricted to western North America and are placed by some herpetologists in the genus *Gerhonotus*. However, we find the arguments of Tihen (1949) and Waddick and Smith (1974) for recognition of *Elgaria* compelling. *Elgaria* have quadrangular dorsal and ventral scales separated by a series of granular scales in the skin fold. The skin fold allows the body to be expanded after eating a large meal or during egg development. Alligator lizards are secretive, spending most of their active periods in dry leaves or grass. They are aggressive when captured. They may bite and at the same time twist their bodies to increase the effectiveness of the bite. Alligator lizards often live in high population densities, and there is no evidence of dominance hierarchies or territorial defense within these groups. The tail is broken easily when grasped. We have found tails of these lizards in snake stomachs attesting to the survival value of tail autotomy.

NORTHERN ALLIGATOR LIZARD
ELGARIA COERULEA (WIEGMANN)

This species is smaller than the Southern Alligator Lizard (it is seldom more than 100 mm SVL) and has a tail less than twice the body length. The Northern Alligator Lizard can be distinguished easily from the Southern Alligator Lizard by the presence in the former of dark pigment in the eye and dark streaks down the edges of each ventral scale row. The Northern Alligator Lizard is characterized by 12 rows of ventral scales, and 12 of the scale rows above the base of the tail are keeled. The other scale characters and coloration are geographically variable.

HABITAT. The Northern Alligator Lizard occurs in more humid areas and at higher elevations (to 1,800 m in the Oregon Cascades) than the Southern Alligator Lizard. It is the only lizard inhabiting the cool coastal strip of northern Oregon and Washington. It is most common along the margins of coniferous forests, or in cut-over areas under logs and rocks or in talus slopes. It is especially common around old sawmills and other abandoned buildings.

VARIATION. There are four subspecies recognized but only two occur in the Northwest, the Northern Alligator Lizard, *Elgaria coerulea principis,* and the Shasta Alligator Lizard, *E. c. shastensis. E. c. principis* is the smallest subspecies (up to 100 mm SVL) and has 14 rows of dorsal scales and weakly keeled temporal scales. The broad (6 to 8 scales wide) dorsal stripe is olive, brown, or grayish with small dark brown spots down the middle of the back from the head down the tail. Dark flecks on the sides are irregular and not arranged in vertical bars. Scales on the side of the body are not white tipped. The chin is cream colored and the venter is bluish white. *E. c. principis* is the only subspecies found in Idaho, Washington, and British Columbia. It also occupies most of the species range in Oregon, being replaced by *E. c. shastensis* only in the southern parts of Jackson, Klamath, and Lake Cos. Individuals, possibly intergrades, with many of the characteristics of *E. c. shastensis* have been collected in southern Coos Co. and in Curry and Josephine Cos., Oregon. The Shasta Alligator Lizard is confined largely to northern California.

Elgaria coerulea shastensis is larger than the other subspecies, reaching 135 mm SVL. Individuals of this subspecies have 16 rows of dorsal scales and smooth temporal scales. The dorsal stripe (5 to 7 scales wide) is brown, greenish, or yellowish. The dark pigment on the dorsum is irregular and not arranged as a row of dots down the middle

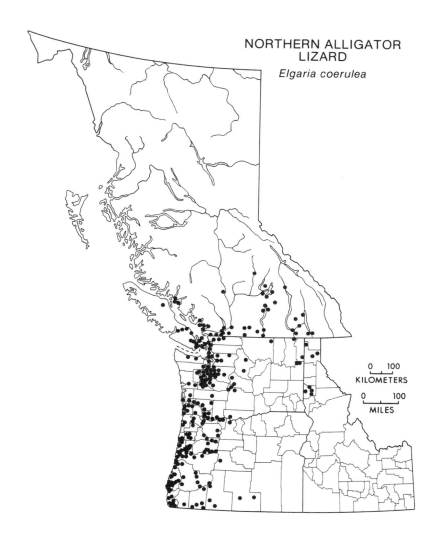

NORTHERN ALLIGATOR
LIZARD
Elgaria coerulea

0   100
KILOMETERS

0   100
MILES

of the back or as crossbands. The black coloration on the sides is arranged in irregular vertical bars; the posterior portion of many of the scales making up the black bars are white. The venter is gray or cream.

LIFE HISTORY. These lizards apparently mate in April and May. Males bite the females on the back of the neck during mating, and pairs may remain in copulation for 24 hours or more. Females give birth to fully formed young some three months later. The newly-born young have wide, bright, brassy stripes and are 25 to 30 mm SVL. The litter size is 3 to 8 in the Seattle area and 2 to 6 along the central

Oregon coast. In both areas the normal litter size is four. There is evidence that larger females of some populations may have more and larger young. Populations at higher elevations mate later in the summer and have shorter active seasons.

This species has food habits similar to the Southern Alligator Lizard but generally takes smaller prey. Alligator lizards often roll their body after grasping prey in their mouths. This action can tear chunks from large prey, which can then be eaten in pieces.

REMARKS. The geographic variation of this species needs to be reexamined. Occasional individuals are found in southwestern Oregon that are difficult to identify even to the species level. Several of these lizards offered caterpillars of the cinnabar moth in the laboratory ate one each and died. The cinnabar moth was introduced into southwestern Oregon to control the poisonous plant Tansy Ragweed. There is a possiblity that the introduction of the cinnabar moth may have adverse effects on populations of the Northern Alligator Lizard.

REFERENCES. Pimentel (1959a), J.R. Stewart (1979), Tihen (1949), Vitt (1973, 1974), Waddick and Smith (1974).

SOUTHERN ALLIGATOR LIZARD
ELGARIA MULTICARINATA (BLAINVILLE)

This is a large (up to 141 mm SVL) lizard with a tail more than twice the length of the body. The Southern Alligator Lizard can be distinguished from the Northern Alligator Lizard by its yellow eyes and dark streaks down the center of each ventral scale row. In the Northwest, the Southern Alligator Lizard has dorsal scales arranged in 14 rows; the eight middorsal rows are keeled. The scales on the side of the tail are smooth. The ventrals are arranged in 12 rows. The dorsal coloration is usually brown, but some individuals are olive gray or dull yellow; the sides tend to be darker than the back. There are irregular dark bands on the back and sides (usually one scale row wide). These bands are black and fairly regular on the sides; they are lighter and irregular across the back. The posterior edges of some scales are white, especially those scales making up the black bands along the sides. Ventral coloration is pale gray or yellowish.

Juvenile coloration is similar to the adult except the back is without dark bands and is tan to reddish. Juveniles often have a row of small, black dots down the middorsal line.

HABITAT. This species ranges widely through California and the Northwest where it occupies oak-grassland areas and the edges of pine

213

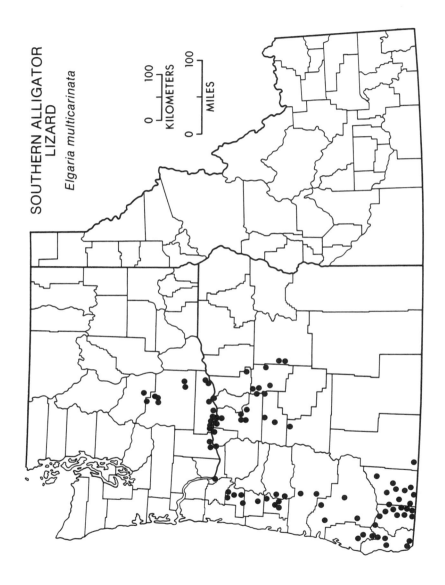

SOUTHERN ALLIGATOR
LIZARD
Elgaria multicarinata

0 100
KILOMETERS

100

0
MILES

forests. They are most often found in thickets, rock piles, or under wood. The long tail is prehensile and is used in climbing. This species is sometimes seen moving through branches of low shrubs using the tail to support its weight. When moving rapidly along the ground the legs are held along the body and the lizard moves with a snake-like series of lateral undulations.

VARIATION. There are five subspecies currently recognized but only one occurs in the Northwest; it is the Oregon Alligator Lizard, *Elgaria multicarinata scincicauda,* and geographic variation within this subspecies has not been studied carefully. Males have larger heads and longer tails than females. California subspecies are larger (up to 175 mm SVL) than the Oregon Alligator Lizard.

LIFE HISTORY. Females deposit eggs in burrows or in stable talus. At the time the eggs are deposited (usually in June) they have begun to develop. In the Corvallis, Oregon area females deposit 8 to 14 eggs that measure 10 to 14 by 15 to 20 mm. Larger females deposit more eggs than smaller females. The hatchlings emerge in September or October and are about 30 mm SVL.

These lizards eat all kinds of arthropods including black widow spiders and scorpions. They also prey on small vertebrates, except amphibians. Alligator lizards (both species in our area) are so sensitive to the skin secretions of amphibians that they sometimes die after biting newts of the genus *Taricha.* When capturing prey, these lizards strike with the head and neck, much like snakes.

REFERENCES. Brodie et al. (1969), Goldberg (1972), Tihen (1949), Waddick and Smith (1974).

IGUANIDS
FAMILY IGUANIDAE

This is a large diverse family of lizards containing about 52 genera and 700 species. It is primarily a New World family, ranging from southern Canada southward through the Americas to Tierra del Fuego. Three genera have relict island distributions in the Old World; two on Madagascar, and one on Fiji and Tonga in the South Pacific.

Iguanids are highly variable in external appearance and life style. Many are arboreal, saxicolous (rock-dwelling), and arenicolous (sand-dwelling), but there are no highly adapted burrowing forms. Most iguanids are carnivorous and primarily insectivorous, but a few of the larger species are herbivorous. Most are oviparous, but ovoviviparity has evolved several times in the family. Iguanids tend to be diurnal lizards with highly developed territorial behavior. Males are usually larger, more territorial, and more brightly colored than females. Males often have a distensible brightly colored throat fan (dewlap) used in lateral threat displays during aggressive encounters. Throat displays often are accompanied with "push-up" and "head-bobbing" behavior, the rhythm of which is species specific.

There are five genera and seven species of iguanids in the Pacific Northwest. For the most part, they are restricted to the arid flatlands and hot rocky canyons of the region.

COLLARED LIZARDS
GENUS *CROTAPHYTUS*

Members of this genus are closely related to the leopard lizards of the genus *Gambelia*. Collared lizards, however, have broader heads than leopard lizards, and the two groups differ in numerous details of the head and body scalation. *Crotaphytus* is strictly a North American genus with four species found in the United States, only one of which ranges into the Pacific Northwest.

MOJAVE BLACK-COLLARED LIZARD
CROTAPHYTUS BICINCTORES
SMITH AND TANNER

39. Mojave Black-collared Lizard *(Crotaphytus bicinctores)*, Harney Co., Oregon.

This is a brightly-patterned diurnally-active lizard with a very large head and a distinct narrow neck. The most distinctive feature of this species is the pair of black collars that is located above and anterior to the front legs. Females attain a maximum size of 98 mm SVL, and the much larger males reach 109 mm SVL and 330 mm TL.

The black collars are present in males, females, and juveniles. The sides of the anterior collar usually join ventrally and may be separated by up to 12 lighter colored scales along the middorsal line. The posterior black collar is usually complete across the dorsum and extends down the sides to or near the base of the front legs. The two black collars are separated by a white collar that may be interrupted by small black flecks. The mouth lining is unpigmented in this species, which distinguishes it from eastern members of the genus.

The dorsal color pattern in females and juveniles is of broad, diffuse, brownish bands separated by narrow, tan, or dirty-white bands. In females the brown coloration extends onto the sides of the belly and is present as distinct spots. The tail is tan with brownish spots along the sides. Males are as colorful as females are drab. Adult males have bodies of chocolate brown with rows of white flecks and faint darker brown bands. The legs are cream colored with brown spots, and the head is tan with brown spots. There are sometimes several narrow yellow orange bands on the body, and the light area between the black collars can be pink, yellow, or orange. The chin of males is white with gray or light blue spots along the sides, and the dewlap is gray blue or

217

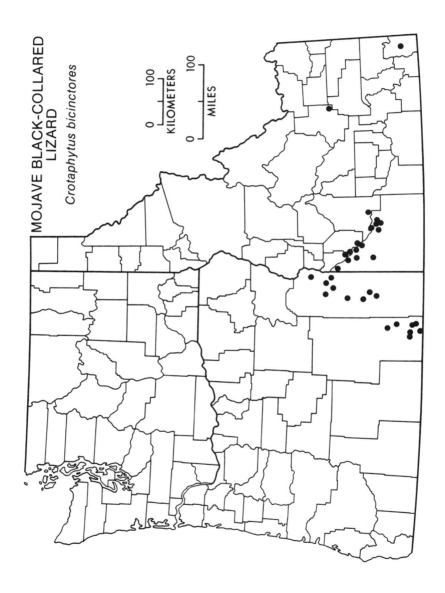

MOJAVE BLACK-COLLARED
LIZARD
Crotaphytus bicinctores

black. The groin region and parts of the lateral surfaces of the belly are also black in adult males.

Scales are small on the body with those on the top of the head between the eyes being somewhat enlarged. The scales on the tail are also distinctly larger than those on the body. The tail is somewhat laterally compressed with a low crest that is not spotted with brown. This crest is more prominent in males. Males also have distinct femoral pores that number fewer than 20 on each leg. Males also have much larger heads than females and broader tail bases. The dewlap can be extended slightly in males.

HABITAT. The Mojave Black-collared Lizard occupies more arid regions than other members of its genus. It is generally most common on dry hillsides with sparse vegetation. It is found only in areas with boulders or piles of rocks. This species does not climb well and is therefore not found on large boulders with vertical sides nor on cliff faces. It does, however, frequent talus slopes at the bases of cliffs.

VARIATION. Nothing is known about geographic variation of this species (see Remarks).

LIFE HISTORY. This is an agile and aggressive lizard. When encountered, it first attempts to escape by running to a rodent burrow, or, if encountered in a very rocky region, it will jump quickly and surely from rock to rock, escaping in a burrow under a large rock. When running at top speed on flat ground these lizards lift their front legs and tail off the ground and run on their hind legs. This has caused a number of scientists to remark that they look like miniature dinosaurs. If cornered, they become aggressive and posture with the mouth open. This posture is not a bluff as they will readily bite captors or predators.

Males spend a great amount of time on top of rocks displaying their ventral and lateral coloration. These displays are thought to attract females and establish territories between males. Males are commonly seen chasing each other during the spring breeding season. We have seen males display to an approaching human being, and in one instance jump onto the leg of a would-be photographer.

These lizards eat any animal smaller than themselves and have also been reported to eat small amounts of flowers and tender leaves of some plants. Their primary food, however, is large insects and other reptiles. The stomachs of 11 *Crotaphytus bicinctores* from southeastern Oregon contained 56.1% by volume crickets and grasshoppers. They have been reported to eat *Sceloporus, Uta, Cnemidophorus,* and *Phrynosoma.* They are aggressive to members of their own species, and cannibalism has been reported in captivity.

Nothing is known in regard to reproduction in Northwestern populations, but the following can be predicted from information on other populations of this species and on other members of the genus. Members of this genus have the potential of depositing two clutches of eggs per year, but it is not known if the northernmost populations (in the Northwest) deposit one or two clutches. Eggs are deposited in sandy soil, in rodent burrows, or under large rocks. Clutch size is 3 to 8 in this species and eggs (deposited in June or July in Arizona populations) measure 11 to 12 by 18 to 20 mm. Eggs hatch in October in Arizona, and hatchlings are 34 to 38 mm SVL.

Some, but not all, females mature after one year in more southern populations. Females develop orange spots and bars on the body after mating. This coloration is also found on hatchlings and might serve to prevent aggressive attacks from males of their own species.

REMARKS. Since 1972 when the name *bicinctores* was first used, the collared lizards of the Northwest have been placed in three different species: *Crotaphytus collaris bicinctores, C. insularis bicinctores,* and *C. bicinctores.* In all of these studies only one Oregon, two Washington, and seven Idaho specimens were examined, and no detailed information was presented on these. In this book we follow the latest taxonomic treatment but the status of this lizard in the Northwest is not understood and detailed taxonomic studies are needed. There is an old record for this lizard from Spokane Co., Washington, which we consider to be erroneous, perhaps the result of faulty bookkeeping. The record from Bear Lake Co., Idaho is based on a specimen in the collections at Idaho State University. The specimen was taken at Montpelier, and there seems to be no reason to doubt the record.

REFERENCES. Axtell (1972), Ingram and Tanner (1971), Montanucci et al. (1975), Sanborn and Loomis (1979), N.M. Smith and Tanner (1972, 1974), Whitaker and Maser (1981).

LEOPARD LIZARDS
GENUS *GAMBELIA*

Leopard lizards are related to collared lizards of the genus *Crotaphytus*, but differ enough morphologically and ecologically to warrant a separate genus. *Gambelia* is restricted to western North America where there are two species, one of which occurs in the Northwest.

LONGNOSE LEOPARD LIZARD
GAMBELIA WISLIZENII
(BAIRD AND GIRARD)

40. Longnose Leopard Lizard *(Gambelia wislizenii)*, Harney Co., Oregon.

This is a large aggressive lizard restricted to the arid portions of the Northwest. It is related to collared lizards and is similar in many ways. Both have large heads, gular folds, and small scales; and both are bipedal when running at full speed. The Longnose Leopard Lizard lacks black neck collars and has a narrower head than the Mojave Black-collared Lizard. Maximum size of females is 127 mm SVL and 384 mm TL, but males are significantly smaller than females. Tails are round and rarely broken in this species and are more than twice the SVL.

The dorsal coloration is light gray or tan with dark brown spots. In the Northwest, these lizards usually have two rows of large squarish spots; one series on each side of the middorsal line. There are normally

221

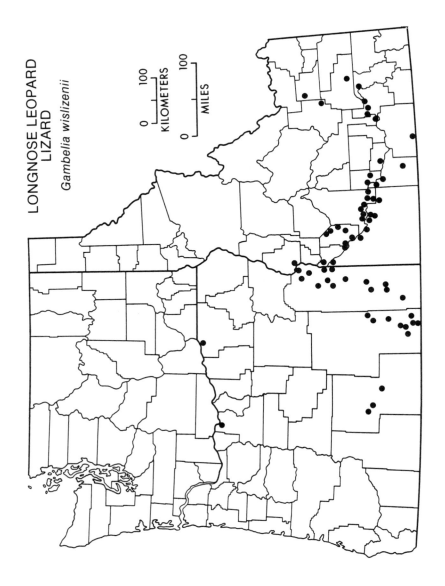

LONGNOSE LEOPARD
LIZARD
Gambelia wislizenii

KILOMETERS
0   100

MILES
0   100

two additional, smaller rows of spots on each side. The dark spots are surrounded by light coloration. Transverse light bars are found between spots on the dorsal surface but do not extend onto the sides. The light bars meet or alternate at the middorsal line and are distinct in young animals but fade in adults. The basal third of the tail has round spots which join into bands posteriorly. The legs are covered with distinct round spots. The head is covered with small brown dots, smaller even than the spots on the legs. The ventral surfaces are white, with longitudinal dark streaks on the throat. The inner lining of the throat is black and is exposed during the aggressive display of these lizards.

The color pattern of hatchlings is brown with about 11, narrow, light, cross bands on the body. The dorsal head pattern is of black and white bars, and orange spots are present on the back.

Males are smaller than females and have enlarged postanal scales and 14 to 16 well-developed femoral pores on each hind leg. Females develop a postnuptial color pattern of orange spots and bars along the back and sides and become orange on the underside of the tail.

HABITAT. The Longnose Leopard Lizard generally inhabits sandy desert shrub areas and is found in hardpan areas only if abundant rodent burrows afford cover. They are especially common in the islands of sand accumulated around scattered greasewood shrubs. These small dunes of sand are normally riddled with the burrows of kangaroo rats and pocket mice, which are used by the lizards. They also construct their own burrows to a depth of about 35 cm.

VARIATION. Until recently four subspecies were recognized, three of these in the U.S., the form in the Northwest being *Gambelia wislizenii wislizenii*. Recently, the populations in the Northwest and northern Nevada were named *G. w. maculosus* on the basis of their having larger and more squarish spots than other populations of the species. More studies of geographic variation of characteristics other than color pattern are needed before *G. w. maculosus* can be accepted as a valid subspecies.

LIFE HISTORY. If encountered in the open, these lizards run to a bush and freeze against the ground allowing one to approach very closely before darting to another bush. If pursued, they sometimes run under a bush and out the other side to a second bush. Another favorite escape is down a rodent burrow. When captured or cornered they gape their mouths wide open exposing the black lining and bite viciously. When captured or threatened, they may "squeal" and then attack their tormentor. Apparently, vocalization in this species is a warning device. The Longnose Leopard Lizard is one of few lizards other than geckos that has a voice. Often, they are seen up in bushes, and it is uncertain whether they are thermoregulating or searching for insects.

Food habit studies of Utah and Colorado populations of this species revealed that the most important foods are grasshoppers, beetles, and other lizards; smaller numbers of other insects and spiders also are eaten. In southeastern Oregon, 46.2% of the food in 21 stomachs was crickets and grasshoppers. Small amounts of flowers and tender green vegetation are eaten when available. Among the lizards eaten are *Cnemidophorus, Uta* and *Sceloporus*. One Longnose Leopard Lizard (102 mm SVL) had eaten a 71 mm SVL *Cnemidophorus tigris,* but another (117 mm SVL) had apparently choked to death on an 80 mm *C. tigris*. One of us observed a large female run about 10 m, leap 60 cm to a greasewood branch and seize a cicada, indicating very good eyesight.

Adults apparently live for 6 to 8 years, and 50% of the adults survive each year. Mating occurs during late May and early June in southeastern Oregon. We observed a copulation attempt from 1830 until 1917 hrs on 31 May in extreme northern Nevada. For much of this time the male held the female's dorsal neck skin in his mouth, and actual hemipenis insertion lasted for only about two minutes. In the northern parts of the range, females deposit only one clutch of eggs each year, but in the south they deposit multiple clutches. The eggs are deposited in sandy soil. In northern Utah, females return to the same site year after year to deposit eggs. They dig L-shaped burrows 20 cm long and 7 to 8 cm deep for their eggs. Some apparently deposit their eggs communally. In Idaho 3 to 4 eggs are deposited in June or July. In more southern populations females deposit more eggs. Eggs from Utah populations weighed 1.75 to 3.50 g and hatched after an incubation period of 41 to 63 days. Hatchlings are 38 to 48 mm SVL. There is a higher rate of reproduction in years with spring rains owing to increased vegetative growth and greater availability of insect prey. The minimum size of maturity in Idaho (at about 22 months of age) is 84 mm SVL for males and 93 mm SVL for females.

REMARKS. The record for the Longnose Leopard Lizard from near the Dalles, Wasco Co., Oregon is thought to be a valid record for a population that is now extinct. The population at Hat Rock, Umatilla Co., Oregon also may no longer exist, but was extant in the 1950s.

REFERENCES. Jorgensen et al. (1963), McCoy (1967), Montanucci et al. (1975), Parker and Pianka (1976), Tanner and Banta (1977), Tanner and Krogh (1974), Turner et al. (1969), Wever et al. (1966), Whitaker and Maser (1981).

HORNED LIZARDS
GENUS *PHRYNOSOMA*

Horned lizards, frequently called "horny toads" or "horned toads," are flat-bodied short-tailed lizards with blunt snouts and prominent lateral fringes of scales. Most species have a crown of enlarged horn-like scales on the head, and all species have enlarged projecting scales scattered among the smaller granular scales of the dorsum. Like most iguanids, males have a swollen tail base where the hemipenes are housed and a pair of enlarged post-cloacal scales.

They are strictly ground-dwelling lizards, and all burrow into loose soil or sand to avoid heat and predators. Ants constitute the main diet of horned lizards. They have the remarkable ability to squirt blood from their eyes, presumably as an antipredator mechanism. Horned lizards lack tail autotomy. When they emerge from the soil in the morning their dorsal surfaces are darkly colored. They often tilt or orient their flat backs to catch the morning sun for rapid warming. As they warm up, their color lightens considerably. These lizards rely largely on camouflage to avoid predators. Once detected they may run, but they are slow and easily caught. There are 14 species of horned lizards, ranging from Guatemala northward through Mexico, the western United States, and into extreme southwestern Canada. Two species occur in our area.

SHORT-HORNED LIZARD
PHRYNOSOMA DOUGLASSI (BELL)

The very short horns on the back of the head of this species distinguish it from the only other horned lizard in the Pacific Northwest. The horns are about as long as they are wide at the base in the Short-horned Lizard, whereas they are much longer than the width at the base in the Desert Horned Lizard. In our region, the maximum size is about 65 mm SVL. The color generally matches the substrate. The dorsum is usually light to dark gray, but brownish and even cinnamon-red individuals occur. There are about 12 large dark blotches on the back, usually arranged in transverse rows or 2 to 4 blotches. Each blotch is light-edged posteriorly. The tail has dark dorsal bands. The venter is white to yellowish white, sometimes with a faint gray suffusion. Mature females average about seven mm SVL longer than mature males.

HABITAT. The Short-horned Lizard is more cold tolerant than

225

41. Short-Horned Lizard *(Phrynosoma douglassi),* Lane Co., Oregon; female with newborn young; photo by R.W. Van Devender.

other species of horned lizards. It ranges up to 3,200 m elevation, and it ranges farther north than any of its congeners (it is the only horned lizard in Canada). *Phrynosoma douglassi* occurs at relatively low elevations in the northern part of its range, but it is more-or-less restricted to high mountains in the southern part of its range. *P. douglassi* lives in a variety of habitats including sagebrush plains, short-grass prairies, open pinion-juniper forests, and open pine forests. The soil where it lives varies from hardpan to sandy to rocky, but always there are patches of loose soil or sand for burrowing, and the substrate is always well-drained.

VARIATION. Six subspecies of *Phrynosoma douglassi* are recognized. Only two, the Pigmy Short-horned Lizard (*P. d. douglassi*) and the Salt Lake Short-horned Lizard *(P.d. ornatum),* occur in the Pacific Northwest. The former is smaller and has shorter horns and more distinct blotches than the latter. *P. d. douglassi* is the most widespread subspecies in the Northwest, being replaced by *P. d. ornatum* only in extreme southeastern Idaho, including Bear Lake, Franklin, and Oneida Cos., and southern parts of Caribou, Bannock, and Cassia Cos. Some populations of *P. d. douglassi* are dichromatic. One morph has a grayish dorsal ground color and the other has a reddish cast. These dichromatic populations usually occur where reddish volcanic soil and pebbles are found. Light gray (almost white) in-

226

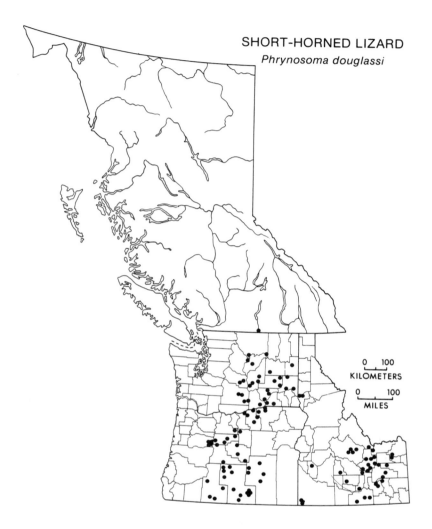

SHORT-HORNED LIZARD
Phrynosoma douglassi

0   100
KILOMETERS

0   100
MILES

dividuals of *P. d. douglassi* have been observed on white powdery soil from eroded, ancient lake beds, such as Fossil Lake, Oregon.

LIFE HISTORY. Like all northwestern lizards, *Phrynosoma douglassi* hibernates during the winter months. It emerges in the spring shortly after the snow melts, usually from late March to early June depending on local conditions. Males emerge from hibernation a few days before females. When the females emerge, courtship and mating immediately ensue. Embryos are retained in the oviducts and the young are born alive about two months after fertilization, in the late summer or early autumn (early August to mid-September). In the Pacific Northwest, females bear 3 to 15 young per year. In the high Cascades the normal brood size is five, and in the Great Basin females usually have 10 offspring. Larger females have larger litters. Newborn average about 22 mm SVL and 0.65 g. At least two full growing seasons are required before maturity. Males mature at smaller size than females; males at about 40 and females at 45 mm SVL in the Cascades of Oregon.

After the spring mating season, adult females and subadults are more active than adult males. During summer, peak activity occurs between 0800 and 1100 hrs. Midday heat is avoided by burrowing into the substrate. A minor peak of activity occurs in the afternoon from about 1630 to 1730 hrs. Evenings, nights, and early mornings are spent dormant under the surface. Males are not territorial, but adult females occupy largely exclusive feeding territories.

The diet varies considerably from place to place, but it normally includes a high proportion of ants. Beetles, bugs, and caterpillars are among the other prey of Short-horned Lizards. Predators of this species are thought to include Longnose Leopard Lizards, and Steller's Jays, Northern Shrikes, and other birds. Golden-mantled Ground Squirrels and Yellow Pine Chipmunks have been seen carrying and feeding on dead Short-horned Lizards in the Oregon Cascades, but it is not known whether these squirrels killed the lizards. In the Cascades, Short-horned Lizards were observed jumping stiff-legged and open-mouthed at investigating Yellow Pine Chipmunks. In terraria this bluffing behavior is accompanied by hissing and biting.

REMARKS. The subspecies of Short-horned Lizards are poorly defined, and probably lack reality. In the Pacific Northwest, radical life history differences occur between populations of *Phrynosoma douglassi douglassi* separated by only a few kilometers. Clearly, the systematics of this species needs attention.

REFERENCES. Dumas (1964), Pianka and Parker (1975).

DESERT HORNED LIZARD
PHRYNOSOMA PLATYRHINOS GIRARD

42. Desert Horned Lizard *(Phrynosoma platyrhinos)*, Harney Co., Oregon.

The Desert Horned Lizard is larger (up to 95 mm SVL) than the Short-horned Lizard and has much longer horns (much longer than wide at the base) on the back of the head. Unlike the Short-horned Lizard, which lacks ventral spotting, the Desert Horned Lizard has scattered black spots on the belly and undersurfaces of the tail and limbs, especially the thighs. The dorsum is more vividly colored than in the Short-horned Lizard. The dorsal ground color is gray, buffy tan, or even reddish. There is a pair of large dark blotches dorsolaterally on the neck and about four pairs of large dark blotches on the back. The tail has dark bands dorsally, and the hind limbs may be banded dorsally. Usually, there is a light, narrow, vertebral stripe. The ventral ground color is white, grayish on the throat.

HABITAT. The Desert Horned Lizard is found at lower elevations (up to 1,980 m) and latitudes than the Short-horned Lizard. The two species seldom are found together, the Desert Horned Lizard being less cold-adapted than the Short-horned Lizard. *Phrynosoma platyrhinos* is a lizard of open, flat, or gently rolling deserts. Sagebrush and other low desert shrubs are typical of their habitat. The species rarely occurs in areas with trees. Hardpan, sandy, and rocky soils are utilized. They occasionally climb on to small rocks to bask, but they are most often found on loose sandy soil.

VARIATION. Two subspecies are recognized, but only one, the Northern Desert Horned Lizard, *Phrynosoma platyrhinos platyrhinos,*

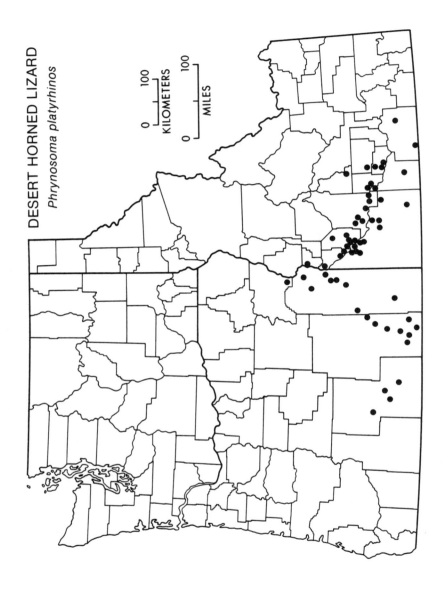

DESERT HORNED LIZARD
Phrynosoma platyrhinos

KILOMETERS
0   100

MILES
0   100

occurs in the Pacific Northwest. Variation has not been studied carefully in our region, but no conspicuous variation is evident. Individuals usually match the color of the soil and rock of the area in which they live.

LIFE HISTORY. The Desert Horned Lizard emerges from hibernation in late March to early April. Mating occurs from mid-April to early June, depending on place and year. Unlike the ovoviviparous Short-horned Lizard, the Desert Horned Lizard is oviparous. Eggs are deposited in mid-June, several centimeters deep in loose sandy soil. The oblong eggs have white flexible shells and measure about 10.5 by 17.5 mm. The normal clutch size is eight (2 to 16), and there is only a weak correlation between clutch size and female body size. Incubation lasts 50 to 60 days. Hatchlings usually appear in August, and they average 27.5 mm SVL and 1.0 g at hatching. Growth is rapid, and both sexes mature at about 22 months of age. Males mature at 68 and females at 70 mm SVL. The largest males are about 92 and the largest females about 95 mm SVL.

During the hot part of the summer, activity occurs between 0630 and 1100 hrs. In the North, they spend their nights buried a few centimeters under the soil. Like all horned lizards they burrow by lateral undulation or "shuffling" of the body. They emerge head first in the morning, before the soil begins to warm up. In the South, the Desert Horned Lizard may be active during warm nights.

The food of the Desert Horned Lizard is 35 to 65% ants and 20 to 50% beetles. They also eat spiders, crickets, grasshoppers, flies, butterflies, and various insect larvae. They are "sit-and-wait" or "ambush" predators, often feeding along ant trails or at ant mounds.

Desert Horned Lizards are well camouflaged. Their first line of defense is to sit still to avoid detection. When disturbed they generally run for the cover of a bush and will dodge around the stem of the bush rather than be chased into the open. When handled roughly they may feign death or move the head in such a manner as to jab with the long sharp horns. Prairie Falcons, Loggerhead Shrikes, Longnose Leopard Lizards, and Striped Whipsnakes are known to eat Desert Horned Lizards.

REMARKS. This species is poorly studied in the Pacific Northwest. The limits of its range and details of its life history especially need attention in this region. Early records for this species from Ft. Walla Walla, Walla Walla Co., Washington and from Sandpoint, Bonner Co., Idaho are based on specimens in the U.S. National Museum. The Washington record is probably an error in bookkeeping, and the Idaho record certainly is an error. The environment at Sandpoint is wrong for horned lizards, and records at the U.S. National Museum indicate that other desert species were collected the next day by the same person in Owyhee Co., Idaho. It would not have been possible for the collector to travel the 960 km between Sandpoint and Owyhee Co. in one day, considering the mode of transport available in the 1890s when the specimens were collected.

REFERENCES. Dumas (1964), Pianka and Parker (1975), Tanner and Krogh (1973).

SPINY LIZARDS
GENUS *SCELOPORUS*

Sceloporus is strictly a Central and North American genus, ranging from Panama northward to north-central Washington. It is the most diverse iguanid genus in North America with 16 species found in Canada and the United States. Only two species occur in the Pacific Northwest.

Spiny lizards ("blue bellies" or "swifts") have rounded elongate bodies and long tails. Their dorsal scales are rather uniform in size, strongly overlapping, centrally keeled, and posteriorly pointed. The latter feature gives them a spiny appearance and feel. They usually have a bluish throat and blue patches on each side of the belly, which are much brighter in males. The blue patches may be absent in females. Males have wider tail bases, a pair of enlarged post-cloacal scales, more obvious femoral pores, and are slightly smaller than females. *Sceloporus* is distinguished from some similar iguanid genera (e. g., *Uta*) by lacking a gular fold.

Members of this genus are strongly diurnal, basking lizards that occupy a broad range of terrestrial and arboreal habitats, but there are no burrowing species. They are usually the most conspicuous and abundant lizards, often seen on fences, wood piles, rocks, and sides of abandoned buildings. Most are egg layers, but a few are ovoviviparous.

Children in the Northwest and elsewhere often are taught that lizards with blue coloration, as occurs in many species of *Sceloporus* and in the Western Skink, are poisonous and to be avoided. This is, of course, not true.

SAGEBRUSH LIZARD
SCELOPORUS GRACIOSUS
BAIRD AND GIRARD

43. Sagebrush Lizard *(Sceloporus graciosus)*, Harney Co., Oregon.

This is the smaller of our two species of *Sceloporus,* seldom exceeding 60 mm SVL. The tail is about 1.3 times as long as the SVL. Aside from its smaller size, it differs from the Western Fence Lizard by having small granular scales on the posterior surfaces of the thighs instead of larger keeled scales; by the absence of yellow on the posterior surfaces of the limbs; and by lacking the solid blue patches on the throat. The Sagebrush Lizard also has smaller, less spiny, and more numerous dorsal scales than the Western Fence Lizard. In the Pacific Northwest, the Sagebrush Lizard is most likely to be confused with the Side-blotched Lizard, *Uta stansburiana*, which is similar in size, color, and habitat. The two are seldom found together, however, as *U. stansburiana* usually occurs at lower elevations than *Sceloporus graciosus*. *U. stansburiana* has a large dark spot behind the fore limb and a gular fold, which was not present in *S. graciosus.*

Sagebrush Lizards are gray to brown above, usually with a wide, middorsal, light-colored band and a pair of narrow, dorsolateral, light stripes. In some populations individuals have a rusty red suffusion of color on the sides of the neck and body. Ventral surfaces are white with a blue belly-patch on each side (faint or absent in females) and blue mottling on the throat (faint or absent in females). The rusty red or orange on the sides of the neck and body is brighter in females,

233

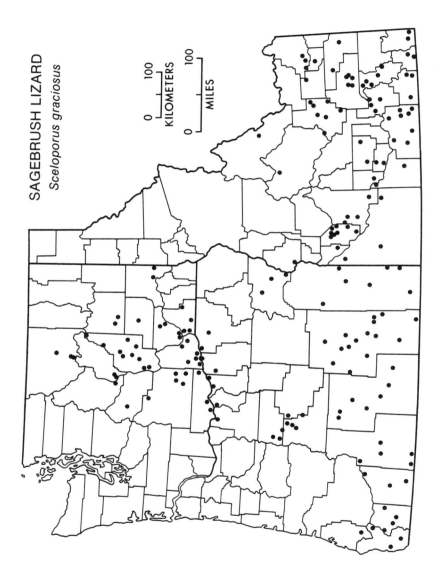

SAGEBRUSH LIZARD
Sceloporus graciosus

especially during the latter part of the active season. Males grow to larger size than females, but the sexual difference in mean SVL of mature individuals is only 1 to 4 mm.

HABITAT. The Sagebrush Lizard is usually the commonest lizard of the sagebrush plains. It also occurs in open forests of juniper, ponderosa pine, and lodgepole pine that have open brushy understories. In our region it is seldom found above 1,700 m, but in the Southwest it occurs up to 3,200 m. These lizards are ground dwellers and are usually first seen scurrying between bushes where they take cover. They seldom climb except to escape, but in some areas they climb onto low boulders. We have occasionally seen them resting on the larger branches of sagebrush but never more than a few cm above ground level.

VARIATION. Three subspecies of *Sceloporus graciosus* are currently recognized, but the only one, the Northern Sagebrush Lizard, *S.g. graciosus,* occurs in the Pacific Northwest. Variation within our area has not been studied carefully. Casual observation suggests that individuals from the eastern slopes of the Cascades in Oregon on volcanic ash substrate are larger and more brightly colored than those from the sagebrush plains to the east.

LIFE HISTORY. The Sagebrush Lizard is active from about early April to late September, with some slight yearly and geographic variation in timing. The reproductive season lasts from early May to late June or early July. In June, females deposit 2 to 7, usually 4, eggs with tough, white, leathery shells. Larger females tend to have larger clutches. The eggs average 7.5 by 12.0 mm in size, weigh about 0.25 g freshly laid, and are buried a few centimeters deep in loose soil, usually at the base of a shrub. In Utah and farther south, females lay a second clutch of eggs late in the reproductive season. There is some evidence that females produce two clutches in the Pacific Northwest as well, but because of the shorter active season in these higher latitudes they may be single-clutched in some places or during some years with particularly short growing seasons. Field work on this problem is needed. Eggs hatch about two months after they are deposited. Hatchlings first appear in mid-August; they weigh about 0.5 g and measure about 25 mm SVL. In Utah, males grow slightly faster than females, and both sexes mature in about 22 months at 50 mm SVL.

Sagebrush Lizards eat beetles, flies, butterflies, caterpillars, ants, wasps, spiders, ticks, mites, aphids, scorpions, and a wide variety of other arthropods.

When disturbed, Sagebrush Lizards run quickly for the cover of a bush. They try to hide in rodent burrows, in crevices, and under surface litter. Striped Whipsnakes are known to prey on them, and other snakes, such as Night Snakes, and predatory birds and lizards are likely to eat them. Like most iguanids, Sagebrush Lizards readily lose their tails when seized. In some areas as high as 30% of the mature females and 50% of mature males have broken or regenerating tails. This suggests that males suffer higher predation than females, a possibility that is further suggested by the high mature female to mature male sex ratio in some populations.

REMARKS. Although this is one of our commonest lizards, it has received very little attention from herpetologists. Because of its high density in some areas and broad geographic range, the species offers great opportunity for comparative and experimental life history studies.

REFERENCES. Fitch (1970), Goldberg (1975), Mueller and Moore (1969), Stebbins (1944, 1948), Stebbins and Robinson (1946), Tinkle (1973).

WESTERN FENCE LIZARD
SCELOPORUS OCCIDENTALIS
BAIRD AND GIRARD

44. Western Fence Lizard *(Sceloporus occidentalis)*, Harney Co., Oregon.

These lizards grow to a maximum size of about 88 mm SVL with tails nearly 1.5 times longer than the SVL. They are the only lizards in the Pacific Northwest with large, spiny, dorsal scales and keeled scales on the posterior surfaces of the thighs. The dorsum is brown to gray to almost black with triangular or crescentric dark blotches usually in two dorsolateral rows. The ventral coloration is grayish white with black dots. A large blue belly-patch is present on each side, and the throat has either two blue patches joined at midline or a single blue patch. The posterior surfaces of the limbs are yellow to orange with a thin black line or irregular row of black spots. Males are darker and more brightly colored than females. The dorsal blotches of males are edged posteriorly with blue or green and there may be blue or green spots along the sides of males. Males have black borders around the throat- and belly-patches. Females have fainter blue throat- and belly-patches, which are occasionally lacking. Because females are lighter dorsally, their dark dorsal blotches are usually more vivid. Young are colored like females.

HABITAT. Western Fence Lizards occur in a variety of habitats from sea level up to 2,750 m. Usually there is a vertical component to their environment, such as large boulders, trees, fence rows, sides of old buildings, or log piles. They live in rocky canyons and talus slopes of both deserts and wooded areas. Dense humid forests are avoided, and they are absent from the low, flat, desert valleys.

VARIATION. Only two of the six recognized subspecies occur in the Pacific Northwest: (1) the Northwestern Fence Lizard, *Sceloporus occidentalis occidentalis,* and (2) the Great Basin Fence Lizard, *S. o. longipes.* The former subspecies has a smaller body size (less than 75 mm SVL) than the latter (less than 95 mm SVL). Adult males of *S. o. occidentalis* generally have two blue gular spots laterally that are fused medially; whereas adult males of *S. o. longipes* usually have a single blue gular-patch. *S. o. occidentalis* occurs in the Cascades, Klamath, and Coast Mountains, and in the Willamette-Puget Trough of western Oregon and Washington. *S. o. longipes* occurs east of the eastern slopes of the Cascade Mountains.

LIFE HISTORY. The duration of the warm season active period of the Western Fence Lizard depends on local climatic conditions, being longer in coastal areas where climates are milder and shorter in the interior where the climate is harsher. They may emerge from winter sleep as early as late February and seek hibernacula as early as October.

Males emerge from hibernation a few days earlier than females. Courtship and mating occur from late April to early June. Egg laying

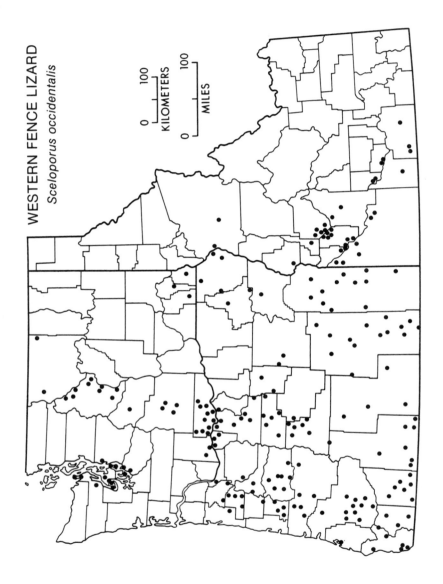

WESTERN FENCE LIZARD
Sceloporus occidentalis

KILOMETERS

0   100

MILES

0   100

occurs from early June to early July. Eggs (8 by 14 mm) have white leathery shells, and are buried in loose soil. Clutch size ranges from 3 to 17 eggs (usually about 8) with larger females depositing more eggs. Females are thought to deposit only a single clutch each season in the Northwest. Eggs hatch after about two months, normally in August. Hatchlings measure about 28 mm SVL and weigh about 0.65 g. Individuals breed for the first time during the spring of their second year at 65 to 70 mm SVL.

Western Fence Lizards feed mainly on insects, (especially beetles, flies, caterpillars, and ants) and spiders. In southeastern Oregon, 39 stomachs of the Western Fence Lizard contained 52.1% crickets and grasshoppers, 18.1% beetles, and 10.6% hymenopterans. They are in turn fed upon by predatory birds and snakes, especially Striped Whipsnakes where they occur together. Shrews occasionally feed on dormant Western Fence Lizards in talus banks. These lizards readily lose their tails to predators, and as many as 20% of the individuals may have regenerating tails.

Western Fence Lizards normally are active from shortly after sunrise until dusk, but we have seen them active at night when it is warm. They usually bask in the open sun in the morning, but move to shade during midday. Adults may appear almost black when observed basking on rocks but they lighten considerably when disturbed. They have the habit of running to the opposite side of their perches (rock or tree) when approached. Further disturbance usually drives them to the safety of a crevice or burrow.

REFERENCES. Fitch (1940b), Linn (1970), Tanner and Hopkin (1972), Whitaker and Maser (1981).

SIDE-BLOTCHED LIZARDS
GENUS *UTA*

Side-blotched lizards are small, ground-dwelling, egg-laying iguanids with small, uniform, non-spiny, dorsal scales and a transverse gular fold. The genus is restricted to western North America from central Washington south to northern Mexico, Baja California, and the islands near Baja California. There are six species of *Uta* but only one occurs in the Pacific Northwest.

SIDE-BLOTCHED LIZARD
UTA STANSBURIANA
BAIRD AND GIRARD

45. Side-blotched Lizard *(Uta stansburiana)*, Deschutes Co., Oregon.

Side-blotched Lizards (or utas) grow to a maximum size of 55 mm SVL with tails 1.2 to 1.5 times longer than the SVL. They are the only small desert lizards in our area with small, uniform, smooth, dorsal scales; a distinct, granular, gular fold; and a large bluish-black blotch behind each fore limb (the side blotch is faint in a few individuals, and it is absent in rare cases). The dorsal ground color is gray to brown with darker blotches and speckling. Females and young may have dorsal stripes. Adult males are more brightly colored than adult females and young. Males have tiny, blue, flecks dorsally and rusty orange suffusions on the throat, fore limbs, and sides of the body and tail. Females have lighter less extensive orange suffusions. The venter is grayish white. Aside from brighter color, males differ from females in their larger size, enlarged post-cloacal scales, and swollen tail bases.

240

HABITAT. The habitat of the Side-blotched Lizard varies from flat deserts to rocky canyons in arid to semi-arid regions with juniper-sage type vegetation. They may be found on sand, rocky soil, desert pavement, and bouldery slopes. Despite the usual claim that they are ground-dwellers, they are abundant on the vertical cliff faces of some of our rocky desert canyons. They seldom climb trees or bushes, however. They prefer open areas with few or no trees. Like many of our egg-laying reptiles, they are restricted to lower elevations in the Pacific Northwest than in the Southwest. In the Southwest they range up to 2,750 m; in the Northwest their elevational range is about 150 to 1,825 m. At the extreme northern limit of their range in Washington, they do not occur above 460 m. Apparently, growing seasons are too short for *Uta* above this elevation at these high latitudes.

VARIATION. Five subspecies are recognized, but only one, the Northern Side-blotched Lizard *(Uta stansburiana stansburiana)* occurs in the Pacific Northwest. Variation in the Northwest has not been studied adequately. Casual observations indicate that individuals from flat deserts are less brightly colored than those from rocky canyons, and sexual differences in coloration are greater in the latter habitats. We have little confidence in the current subspecific classification of *U. stansburiana* as applied to Northwestern populations.

LIFE HISTORY. In central Oregon and south-central Washington, Side-blotched Lizards are sporadically active as early as late March and as late as early November. The active season normally lasts 150 days. Courtship and mating occur in April through June. Females deposit one or two clutches from April to the end of June. Females deposit 2 to 5, usually 3 eggs per clutch. Early clutches are usually larger than late clutches, and larger females usually deposit more eggs than smaller females. The white leathery eggs, measuring 6.5 by 11.0 mm, are buried in sandy soil. They hatch in about 61 days, with hatchlings appearing in the population in late July or early August. Hatchlings measure 22 mm SVL and grow at a rate of about 0.2 mm SVL/ day. Most individuals mature in 10 months, but late hatching individuals do not mature until they are 20 to 22 months old. In some Texas populations, utas normally live for only about one year, but in Oregon their life expectancy is somewhat longer. In Oregon, mature males range in size from 40 to 55 and mature females from 41 to 49 mm SVL.

Utas are strictly diurnal. They are active from 0800 to about 1230 hrs, inactive from 1230 to 1520 hrs, and active again from 1530 to 1830 hrs on hot sunny days. They crawl onto cold rocks in the morning with their backs oriented to catch the rays of the sun. After they have

241

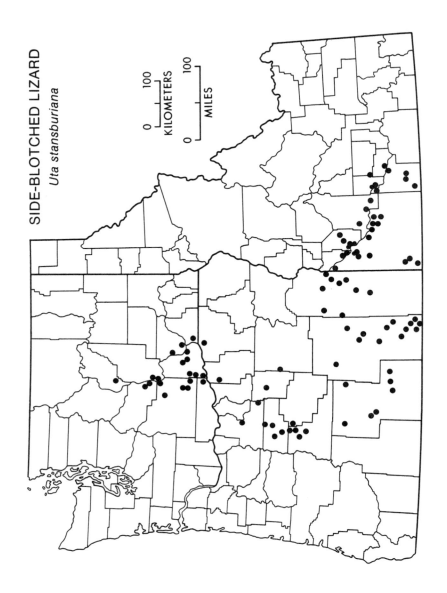

SIDE-BLOTCHED LIZARD
Uta stansburiana

KILOMETERS
0   100

MILES
0   100

warmed up, they feed and engage in head-bob and push-up displays and chases with competitors and potential mates. They occasionally leap into the air to catch flying insects.

The food of Side-blotched Lizards is the usual variety of arthropods, mainly insects. Beetles, flies, ants, caterpillars, and small grasshoppers are among the most important prey. Side-blotched Lizards are usually the most abundant lizard where they occur. Their most important predators are Night Snakes, Striped Whipsnakes, and predatory birds. They readily lose their tails to predators, and as many as 37.5% of mature males and 35.3% of mature females may have broken and regenerating tails.

Winter mortality of Side-blotched Lizards may be high in the North. As many as 567 dead utas were found in a single hibernaculum, in Deschutes Co., Oregon.

REFERENCES. Nussbaum and Diller (1976), Parker and Pianka (1975), Rickard (1967, 1968), Tanner and Hopkin (1972), Tinkle (1967).

SKINKS
FAMILY SCINCIDAE

This is a large and widespread family of lizards with about 85 genera and 1,030 species. The family is cosmopolitan with its greatest diversity in Australia, Indonesia, southwestern Pacific Islands, southeastern Asia, and Africa. The family is less diverse in the New World. Members of this family lack femoral pores, have bony plates (osteoderms) on the head and body, and most species have cylindrical bodies with smooth cycloid scales of nearly uniform size all around the body. Scales on the top of the head are enlarged. Most species readily lose their tails, which are regenerated, and there is a tendency in this family toward limb reduction and complete limb loss associated with fossorial (burrowing) habits. Many species are live bearers.

In the U.S. and Canada, there are three genera and 15 species of skinks, none of which is limbless or live bearing. A single genus and species occurs in the Northwest.

SKINKS
GENUS *EUMECES*

The genus *Eumeces* with about 45 species is found in both the New and Old Worlds. Thirteen of the 15 U.S. and Canadian species of skinks belong to this genus. Some *Eumeces* are live bearers (none in the U.S. and Canada) and others brood eggs in hidden nests. They are secretive, diurnal, carnivorous lizards with nervous behavior. Juveniles typically have brightly colored tails.

WESTERN SKINK
EUMECES SKILTONIANUS
(BAIRD AND GIRARD)

These are small shiny lizards that are attractively patterned with longitudinal stripes and often with bright blue tails, especially in the young and subadults. Western Skinks seldom exceed 83 mm SVL, and their tails are 1.5 to 2.0 times the body length.

They usually have 24 or 26 rows of smooth dorsal scales at midbody. There are usually seven upper labials and six lower labials. The adpressed limbs touch or overlap in nearly all individuals.

The color pattern consists of a middorsal dark stripe and a dorsolateral dark stripe on each side; between the dark stripes and below the dorsolateral dark stripe are two light stripes on each side. The light stripes are white to cream colored and the dark stripes are chocolate to olive brown. The striped pattern extends from the head onto the base of the tail. The chin and belly are light gray and may be mottled with bluish or greenish. The bright blue of the tail fades to blue gray or brownish gray in large individuals.

Males develop reddish coloration on the chin and sides of the head during the breeding season; otherwise the sexes are similar.

HABITAT. Western Skinks may be found in a variety of habitats, including desert canyons, open woodlands, and forests up to about 2,150 m elevation. Rocky habitats with some moisture are preferred. They can be found in rotting logs and under surface litter, and especially like to hide under large flat stones covering cool, moist earth.

VARIATION. The two subspecies in the Northwest are distinguished by color pattern. *Eumeces skiltonianus skiltonianus,* the Western Skink, has black or very dark edges on the middorsal dark

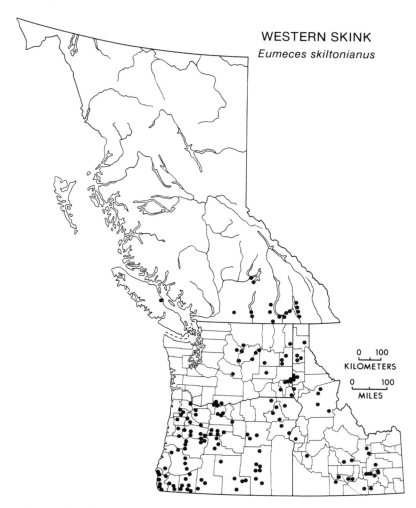

WESTERN SKINK
Eumeces skiltonianus

0   100
KILOMETERS

0   100
MILES

stripe and a thin dark line below the lower light stripe. The dorsolateral light stripe is less than one-half the width of the dorsal stripe. This is the only subspecies found in British Columbia and Washington; it occurs throughout the Oregon portion of the species range, except for extreme southeastern Malheur Co. Populations north of the Salmon River in Idaho also are assignable to this subspecies.

Eumeces skiltonianus utahensis, the Great Basin Skink, does not have darker edges on the middorsal stripe, and the light dorsolateral stripes are more than one-half the width of the middorsal dark stripe.

This subspecies occurs in Idaho south of the Salmon River and in extreme southeastern Malheur Co., Oregon.

LIFE HISTORY. The life history of the Western Skink is poorly known, especially in the Northwest. Like most skinks, they are diurnal and secretive, moving about with rapid jerky movements. They are good burrowers, and the adults may construct burrows up to 50 cm long.

In Utah, Western Skinks mate in May or June and deposit eggs in July. The eggs hatch in August. Females deposit 2 to 6 eggs in burrows or in cavities under stones that are excavated by the adults. The female remains with the eggs until they hatch and even remains with the hatchlings until they disperse from the nest. Brooding females will attack predators that threaten their broods and will repair disturbed nests.

When discovered under a stone, these lizards often escape quickly by burrowing in the loose soil or leaf litter. When grabbed, the tail is usually damaged or lost. It is thought that the bright blue color of the tail serves to attract predators away from the vital parts of the body. A freshly autotomized tail jumps and wiggles for several minutes, perhaps attracting the attention of the predator away from the escaping lizard.

The food of the Western Skink consists of small arthropods, including crickets, beetles, moths, grasshoppers, and flies. They often stalk their prey, striking with catlike speed.

REFERENCES. Tanner (1943, 1957).

TEGUS, RUNNERS, AND WHIPTAILS
FAMILY TEIIDAE

The family Teiidae is restricted to the New World, being distributed from the United States southward to Argentina. There are 38 genera and about 200 species in the family, but only one genus occurs in the United States. The family is not represented in Canada.

Teiids are ecologically diverse. Many species are very fast, active, diurnal lizards; most are terrestrial; a few are arboreal or semiarboreal; a few are skink-like and semifossorial; and two genera are semiaquatic. Teiids are primarily insectivores, but some species specialize on mollusks and have specialized molariform teeth for crushing the shells. A few are herbivorous. All are oviparous, and the family has numerous parthenogenetic (all female) species. A species from Trinidad has photophores or reflective devices.

WHIPTAILS AND RACERUNNERS
GENUS *CNEMIDOPHORUS*

Cnemidophorus is a wide-ranging genus with numerous unisexual and bisexual species found from the United States southward to southern Brazil and Bolivia. There are about 48 species of *Cnemidophorus*, many of them parthenogenetic, including some in the southwestern United States. About 16 species occur in the United States. All species of *Cnemidophorus* have granular dorsal scales and large, quadrangular, abdominal scales in 8 to 12 longitudinal rows. They have large dorsal head scales and numerous femoral pores. *Cnemidophorus* are all diurnal, active, fast lizards. There is a single bisexual species (*Cnemidophorus tigris*) occurring naturally in the Pacific Northwest. A second parthenogenetic species, the Plateau Striped Whiptail *(Cnemidophorus velox)*, has existed for at least six years at one locality in Jefferson Co., Oregon. This Oregon population probably resulted from an introduction, as the locality is several hundred kilometers to the northwest of other populations of *C. velox*. We have not included an account for this latter species.

WESTERN WHIPTAIL
CNEMIDOPHORUS TIGRIS
BAIRD AND GIRARD

46. Western Whiptail *(Cnemidophorus tigris),* Harney Co., Oregon.

The Western Whiptail in the Northwest is a dark-colored desert lizard that runs very swiftly and close to the ground. This species has small granular scales on the dorsal surface of the body, plate-like scales on the head, and keeled scales on the tail. The belly is covered

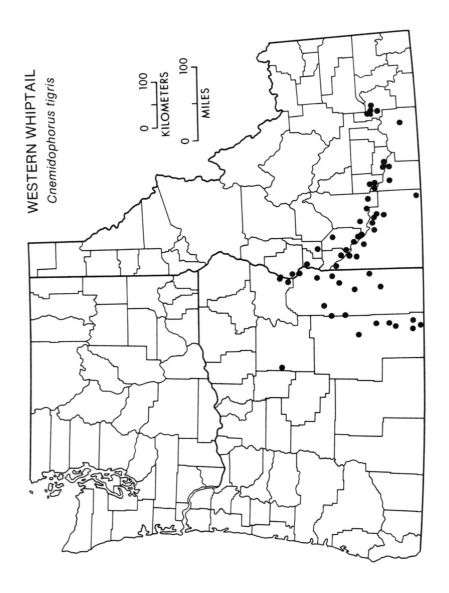

WESTERN WHIPTAIL
Cnemidophorus tigris

KILOMETERS
0   100

MILES
0   100

with smooth, large quadrangular scales arranged in eight longitudinal rows that do not overlap. There is a distinct gular fold and 19 to 23 femoral pores. Maximum SVL is 102 mm, and the round tail, if unbroken, is more than twice the length of the body. The tongue is long, thin, and forked.

The color pattern consists of four light stripes set high on the back and light spots between the stripes and along the sides. The stripes extend from the back of the head to just above the hind legs but are not evident on the tail. The dorsal ground color on the top of the head is usually olive, grading to black on the sides of the head, shoulders, front legs, and back. The front half of the body is black, covered with irregular gray spots which turn to tan or light brown at midbody. The posterior half of the body, hind legs, and tail are nearly covered with brown spots, which become so dense on the tail as to make the tail appear brown, spotted with black. The dorsal stripes are most distinct in juveniles and are faded but generally visible in adults. The ventral surfaces are light colored (blue, gray or tan) and heavily marked with black spots, which are more numerous anteriorly. The tail of juveniles is bluish.

HABITAT. The habitat requirements of the Western Whiptail, which ranges widely throughout the western United States and Mexico, are geographically variable. In the Northwest it is primarily found in desert areas with dense bushy vegetation, although it sometimes ranges out from these areas of dense cover into sparse vegetation. It is common in flat, sandy areas, rocky areas, and along dry washes where there is adequate cover. They frequent both loose and packed soils and utilize rodent burrows or dig their own.

VARIATION. There are six subspecies of *Cnemidophorus tigris* in the United States and about nine more in Mexico, but only one of these, the Great Basin Whiptail, *C. t. tigris,* occurs in the Northwest. Variation among Northwestern populations has not been studied.

LIFE HISTORY. When above ground, these lizards seem to be continually moving, darting from shrub to shrub, stopping now and then to paw the ground and feed. When running at full speed the tail is lifted off the ground, otherwise the tail drags along the ground making a distinctive track between foot prints. This species forages mainly during morning hours on hot days but extends its period of activity on cloudy days. They feed primarily on insect larvae and other soil arthropods, which they apparently dig up with their front feet. They also feed along the low branches of shrubs and have even been seen to break open termite galleries around dead vegetation and feed on the

249

termites that swarm to repair the break. Twenty-four Western Whiptails collected in southeastern Oregon had eaten 28.8% (by volume) lepidopterans, 27.1% crickets and grasshoppers, and 11.6% beetles.

The constantly active foraging of this species renders them subject to heavy predation pressure resulting in a high incidence of tail breakage in survivors, exceeding 50% in large adults of some populations.

Individuals in Idaho populations are larger than those in more southern areas (Nevada, Utah, and Arizona). Mating and ovulation occur during the first half of June, and eggs are deposited during late June to early July. Despite their larger size, females in Idaho produce fewer eggs (1 to 4, average 2.65) per clutch than females from southern areas, which produce as many as eight eggs per clutch. Idaho individuals also produce only a single clutch per year, whereas southern individuals often produce two clutches per year. Eggs are about 10 by 17 mm and hatch in early- to mid-August. The size at hatching is about 35 mm SVL and maturity for females is reached at about 69 mm SVL at an age of about 22 months. Males mature a few millimeters smaller and about two months earlier.

In the Northwest, these lizards become active in mid-April to May, and some individuals become inactive (aestivate) during the middle part of the summer when it is very hot and dry. They become active again during late summer and early fall, and they begin their winter hibernation usually in September.

REFERENCES. Burkholder and Walker (1973), Pianka (1970), Tanner and Jorgensen (1963), Whitaker and Maser (1981).

KEY TO THE SNAKES OF THE PACIFIC NORTHWEST

1A. Deep pit between nostril and eye (1), rattle on tip of tail ... Western Rattlesnake, *Crotalus viridis*
1B. No deep pit or rattle on tail 2

2A. No enlarged chin shields (2), blunt tail ... Rubber Boa, *Charina bottae*
2B. Two pair of enlarged chin shields (3) (Colubridae) 3

3A. Some or all dorsal scales keeled (4) 4
3B. All dorsal scales smooth (5) 5

4A. Four prefrontals (6) ... Gopher Snake, *Pituophis melanoleucus*
4B. Two prefrontals (7) *(Thamnophis)* 13

5A. Anal plate entire (8) 6
5B. Anal plate divided (9) 7

6A. All or most caudals entire (8) ... Longnose Snake, *Rhinocheilus lecontei*
6B. All or most caudals divided *(Lampropeltis)* 16

7A. Spine on tip of tail 8
7B. No spine on tip of tail 9

8A. Black transverse bar on each ventral ... Sharptail Snake, *Contia tenuis*
8B. No black bar on ventrals ... Western Ground Snake, *Sonora semiannulata*

9A. Orange neck ring and venter ... Ringneck Snake, *Diadophis punctatus*
9B. No neck ring 10

10A. Eye pupil vertical ... Night Snake, *Hypsiglena torquata*
10B. Eye pupil round 11

11A. Lower preocular small, wedged between adjacent upper labials (10)
.... 12
11B. Not as above (11) ... Smooth Green Snake, *Opheodrys vernalis*

12A. Dark ground color with one white dorsolateral stripe on each side ... Striped Whipsnake, *Masticophis taeniatus*
12B. No light stripes ... Racer, *Coluber constrictor*

13A. Seven upper labials 14
13B. Eight upper labials 15

14A. 17 scale rows at midbody (12) ... Northwestern Garter Snake, *Thamnophis ordinoides*
14B. 19 scale rows at midbody ... Common Garter Snake, *Thamnophis sirtalis*

251

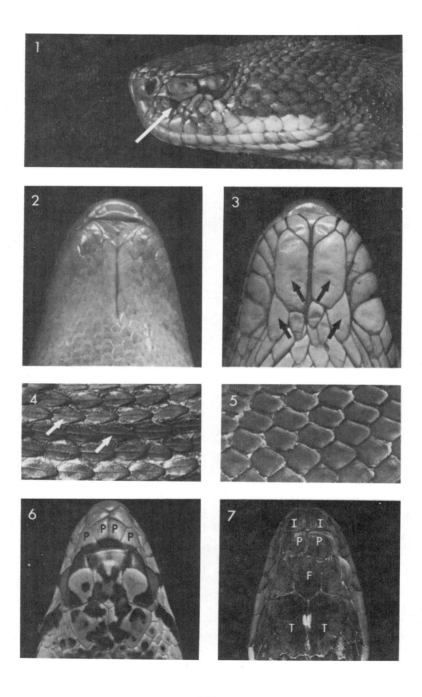

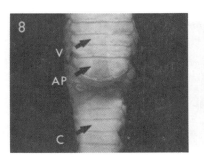

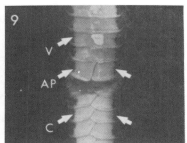

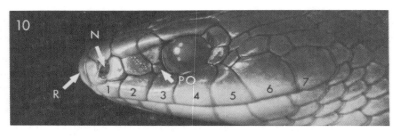

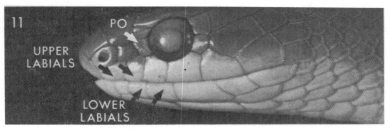

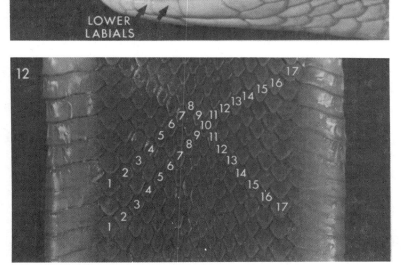

253

15A. Internasals broader than long, not tapered anteriorly (7) ... Western Terrestrial Garter Snake, *Thamnophis elegans*
15B. Internasals longer than broad, tapered ... Western Aquatic Garter Snake, *Thamnophis couchi*

16A. Snout black; banded with red, white and black ... California Mountain Kingsnake, *Lampropeltis zonata*
16B. Snout with white; no red coloration ... Common Kingsnake, *Lampropeltis getulus*

V. Key Illustration - Snakes (preceding two pages)
Figs.: (1) *Crotalus viridis,* loreal pit indicated; (2) *Charina bottae,* chin scales; (3) Colubrid chin scales; (4) Keeled dorsal scales; (5) Smooth dorsal scales; (6) *Pituophis melanoleucus* with 4 prefrontals (P); (7) *Thamnophis elegans* with 2 prefrontals (P), the internasals (I) and temporals (T) are also shown; (8) Cloacal region of snake showing ventral scales (V), entire or undivided anal plate (AP), and undivided caudal scales (C); (9) Cloacal region of snake showing ventral scales (V), divided anal plate (AP), and divided, anterior caudal scales (C); (10) *Coluber constrictor* showing rostral scale (R), external naris (N), small preocular scale (PO), and 7 supralabial scales; (11) *Opheodrys vernalis* with large preocular (PO); (12) Two methods of counting dorsal scale rows.

BOAS
FAMILY BOIDAE

Boas and pythons, species of the family Boidae, are cosmopolitan in the tropics and subtropics of the world, with fewer species in temperate zones. The family contains about 26 genera and 80 species. Boids are stout-bodied snakes with vestiges of hind legs present as spurs, which are used in courtship. Many species have well-developed heat-sensing organs, or pits, in the labial scales used partly for detecting prey, which are killed by constriction. The scales of boids are small and more variable in number than in other families of snakes that occur in the Northwest. Boids are relatively diverse, with arboreal, semiaquatic, terrestrial, and fossorial species occurring. The giants of the snake world are found in this family, with some species such as the South American Anaconda and the African Rock Python reaching total lengths of 11.4 m (37.5 feet) and 9.8 m (32.0 feet), respectively. There are authentic records of these two species killing and eating humans. There are two endemic genera in North America, each with a single species. Both are small secretive species. One, *Lichanura trivirgata* (Rosy Boa), is restricted to the Southwest, and the other, *Charina bottae* (Rubber Boa), occurs in the Northwest.

RUBBER BOAS
GENUS *CHARINA*

Charina is a monotypic genus endemic to western North America. Morphologically, the genus is defined by having a short, non-prehensile, blunt tail with fused terminal vertebrae, and by other technical details of the skull, scalation, and hemipenes. Ecologically, *Charina* are secretive, largely nocturnal, semifossorial snakes.

RUBBER BOA
CHARINA BOTTAE (BLAINVILLE)

47. Rubber Boa *(Charina bottae)*, Benton Co., Oregon.

This snake also is known as the "two-headed snake" because the tail is short and shaped like the head. Rubber Boas are seldom more than 600 mm in TL, but large females may exceed 830 mm. They are uniform in coloration dorsally with small eyes and vertical pupils. Rubber Boas never bite and are in fact so calm that a favorite trick of Dr. Kenneth Gordon was to wear one wrapped around his wrist as a bracelet while he lectured to his classes at Oregon State University. It was often well into a lecture before a student recognized his unusual accessory. The pattern of scalation is highly variable; the smooth dorsal scales are arranged in 39 to 53 rows with average counts in different areas ranging from 43.6 to 45.0. The ventrals range from 193 to 219 and caudals from 24 to 43. The ventral scales are reduced in size compared to the ventral scales of other snakes in the Northwest. There are usually 9 to 11 upper labials. There are no enlarged chin shields as seen in other snakes in the region.

The coloration is uniformly olive green, yellow brown, or dark brown dorsally, grading on the lower body scales to the lighter yellowish ventral coloration. The venter may be mottled with brown, orange, or black. Young may be tan or pink, both dorsally and ventrally.

Both males and females have anal spurs, which are rudiments of hind limbs. These are larger in males and are used by the male to stroke the female during mating. The spurs of males are hooked downward whereas those of females project straight to the rear.

256

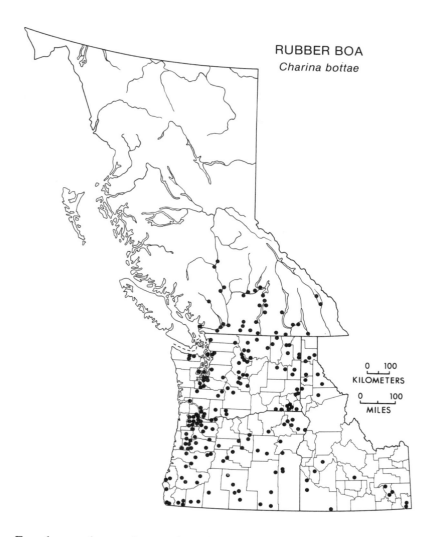

0   100
KILOMETERS

0   100
MILES

Females are larger than males, with males averaging about 470 and females about 552 mm TL. Adult males have longer tails than adult females of equivalent sizes.

HABITAT. Rubber Boas are successful in many habitats, including deserts, foothills with open vegetation, and heavily forested, montane environments. They occur from sea level up to 3,050 m elevation. They seldom are collected but can be quite common in certain areas under the correct conditions. In the Coast Mountains and foothills of western Oregon they are common in clearings where a

257

48. Rubber Boa *(Charina bottae),* Benton Co., Oregon.

forest has been cut and can be found there in rotting stumps or logs during the spring or early summer rains. They are sometimes found under flat rocks at the foot of talus slopes in desert canyons. Occasionally they are found crawling fully exposed on the surface, usually during the night or the morning hours of warm, humid, overcast days.

VARIATION. No subspecies are now recognized.

LIFE HISTORY. Rubber Boas are active from mid-March to early November in the Willamette Valley, with peak activity from April through June. A copulating pair was taken on 3 May under a piece of tin near Corvallis, Oregon. Courtship normally occurs from late April through early May, but the time will vary with local conditions. Rubber Boas give birth to small numbers of young; litter size ranges from 2 to 8. The young are normally born in September, although births as late as November have been reported. Newborn weigh 7 to 8 g and are 215 to 225 mm TL. Near Corvallis, Oregon, males are mature at sizes greater than 450 and females at sizes greater than 545 mm TL.

Rubber Boas apparently feed almost entirely on young mice and shrews, but they have also been reported to eat lizards, snakes, and small birds. They constrict their prey prior to swallowing them. In the laboratory most individuals will feed on newborn mice. They often constrict one or two young mice while they are swallowing another. If introduced into a large aquarium where a female mouse has a nest and litter the boa will crawl into the nest and eat the young while pushing the female mouse away with its tail. The body is often coiled with the tail elevated; the snake "strikes" at the mouse with the tail from this posture. The vertebrae of the tail are telescoped onto each other forming a bony club. As the snake eats the young mice the mother mouse chews on the tail and body of the snake. This results in heavily scarred tails in one-half of male and two-thirds of female Rubber Boas.

Rubber boas will also coil the body tightly with the tail elevated in response to predator attack and release a potent musk from the anal glands.

REFERENCES. Hoyer (1974), Hudson (1957), Nussbaum and Hoyer (1974), Svihla (1943).

COLUBRID SNAKES
FAMILY COLUBRIDAE

About 68% of the world's snakes belong to this family, which includes about 295 genera and 1,550 species. There are about 92 colubrid species in the United States and Canada, and 15 of 17 snake species in the Northwest belong to this family. Most colubrids in our area are nonvenomous, but a few have weak venoms that are probably not dangerous to humans. Venomous colubrids have short fixed fangs (sometimes grooved) in the rear of the mouth. Colubrids are quite variable in form and habits. Northwestern species include aquatic, terrestrial, burrowing, and semi-arboreal forms. Some constrict prey, others do not, and food habits are often specialized. There are two subfamilies in the United States: Natricinae and Colubrinae.

SUBFAMILY COLUBRINAE

This is a very diverse group of snakes, represented in the United States and Canada by 31 genera and 61 species. In the Northwest there are 10 genera and 11 species. This subfamily is typically divided into groups of genera with similar characteristics. These groups are not necessarily indicative of evolutionary lineages. There are five of these groups in the Northwest: Burrower Group; Side-grooved Rear-fanged Group; Front-grooved Rear-fanged Group; Constrictor Group; and Diurnal Group.

The Burrower Group is represented by the genera *Diadophis, Contia,* and *Rhinocheilus.* These are small nocturnal snakes with smooth scales and heads modified for burrowing. The Longnose Snake, *Rhinocheilus,* is apparently intermediate between the burrower and constrictor group but does not constrict prey.

The Side-grooved Rear-fanged Group is represented only by *Sonora* in the Northwest. These are small nocturnal snakes with smooth scales and a head modified for burrowing. They are distinguished from the burrowing group by the presence of enlarged teeth on the rear of the maxillae that are grooved on the sides.

The Front-grooved Rear-fanged Group is represented only by *Hypsiglena* in the Northwest. Members of this group have venomous saliva and enlarged teeth in the rear of the mouth. The most advanced members of this group such as Lyre Snakes, *Trimorphodon*, are the most venomous and have deeply-grooved rear teeth.

The Constrictor Group is represented by *Lampropeltis* and *Pituophis* in the Northwest. These are large heavy-bodied snakes that kill their prey by constriction.

The Diurnal Group is represented by *Opheodrys, Coluber,* and *Masticophis* in the Northwest. Members of this group are active during the day, are very fast, have excellent vision, and have long tails. These are probably the most advanced members of this family in the Northwest.

RACER
COLUBER CONSTRICTOR LINNAEUS

The Racer is an alert diurnal snake with relatively large eyes. The adults (60 to 120 cm TL) are unpatterned, and the juveniles are blotched.

Adults are uniformly olive or grayish olive dorsally. The throat, lower labials, and lower portion of the upper labials are white. The ventral surface is yellowish; yellow green in some individuals, yellowish white in others. Hatchlings have brown blotches. As the young snakes grow they become unicolored, progressing from the tail forward. Yearlings, and often two-year-olds, are blotched anteriorly and unicolored posteriorly.

Racers in the Northwest are characterized by smooth (unkeeled) dorsal scales arranged in 17 rows on the fore- and mid-body and in 15 rows on the rear body. The lower preocular is small and wedged between upper labials. There are eight upper labials, nine lower labials, and a divided anal scale.

HABITAT. They are present in a wide variety of habitats, including meadows, sagebrush flats, forest edges, and fence rows. In the Northwest, Racers are generally absent from dense forests and high mountains.

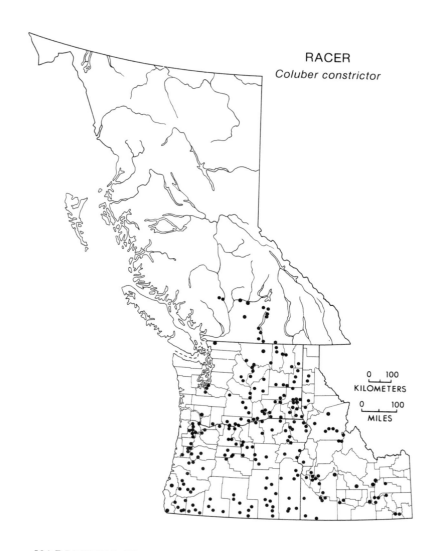

RACER

Coluber constrictor

0   100
KILOMETERS
0   100
MILES

VARIATION. There are 11 subspecies recognized in the United States but only the Western Yellowbelly Racer, *Coluber constrictor mormon,* occurs in the Northwest. This species is quite variable in other regions with different subspecies having black, blue, gray, or even blotched coloration. Some other subspecies are much larger (up to 191 cm TL) than *C. c. mormon.* In the Northwest, local variation has not been studied carefully, but Racers in eastern Oregon and southern Idaho have yellowish bellies, whereas white venters are more common in western Oregon.

LIFE HISTORY. Racers hibernate in distinct hibernacula or dens, often with other species such as *Crotalus viridis, Masticophis taeniatus,* and *Pituophis melanoleucus.* At one den site in northern Utah, about half of the Racers did not survive the winter, and the survivors had lost an average of 19.0% of their body weight. In the same area, Racers emerge from dens in late April to early May and disperse some distance before mating, usually in mid-May. They disperse a maximum of 1.8 km from the den during the summer. The average home range size is 0.38 hectares. Most Racers (more than 90%) return to the same den (in October) year after year, and some individuals occupy the same home range in successive summers. Racers displaced by humans (up to 300 m displacement) showed some ability to return to their home den.

Coluber constrictor mormon is known to deposit 3 to 6 eggs with a rough granular texture (eastern subspecies may deposit up to 24 eggs). The eggs, usually laid in early July, are deposited 5 to 7 cm below the surface in stable rock talus or abandoned mammal burrows. In 1968, we discovered 93 eggs of this species in a talus slope along with the eggs of *Elgaria multicarinata, Diadophis punctatus, Contia tenuis,* and *Pituophis melanoleucus.* A total of 345 reptile eggs, deposited by an estimated 51 females, were found in 14 m^2 of a south-facing talus slope. This remarkable concentration of reptile eggs was no doubt caused by habitat destruction in the area reducing the number of suitable sites for egg deposition. Most of the Racer eggs measured 19 to 21 by 30 to 42 mm, but some were nearly round and others were very elongate. Eggs of this species hatch in mid- to late-August; hatchlings weigh 4 to 5 g and are 215 to 220 mm TL.

Young Racers eat crickets and grasshoppers and probably other insects. The adults eat insects, young mice, and smaller reptiles. In the desert regions of the Northwest, they are especially prone to eating lizards. Racers hunt visually and can be observed in nature gliding through the grass with the head held high off the ground. They are able to detect crickets at least 50 cm away and are no doubt able to see larger prey at much greater distances.

Racers are aggressive when cornered or captured and remain aggressive in captivity. They seldom calm down in captivity unless placed in a large terrarium with hiding places. If properly housed and not handled they feed readily on crickets or smaller reptiles.

REMARKS. The locality record for this species at Sumas, Whatcom Co., Washington needs to be confirmed.

REFERENCES. Brodie et al. (1969), W.S. Brown and Parker (1976), Hirth (1966), Parker and Brown (1973).

SHARPTAIL SNAKE
CONTIA TENUIS (BAIRD AND GIRARD)

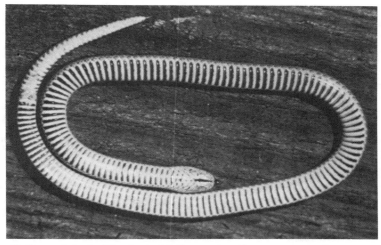

49. Sharptail Snake *(Contia tenuis),* Benton Co., Oregon; ventral color pattern.

This is a diminutive secretive snake with adults usually less than 30 cm (the record is 37 cm) in TL. Sharptail Snakes have a wide reddish-brown stripe bordered on either side by narrow, dorsolateral, red stripes extending from the neck to the tip of the tail. The head is darker brown than the dorsal stripe. The sides of the body and head are gray. In old adults the pattern is obscured and becomes darker.

The most distinctive characteristic of Sharptail Snakes is the black and white barred ventral surface. The anterior 1/3 of each ventral scale is black and the rear 2/3 is white to light gray. The caudal scales are not barred. There are 15 rows of smooth dorsal scales, 147 to 186 ventrals, 27 to 57 caudals, 7 upper labials, and 7 lower labials. The anal scale is divided, and the scales on the tip of the tail form a spine.

HABITAT. Sharptail Snakes usually are found in moist rotting logs or stable talus slopes, often near streams or in other damp habitats. They frequent the edges of coniferous or open hardwood forests. In the Northwest, they are restricted to relatively low elevations, but are found as high as 1,700 m in California. They are very spotty in distribution but can be common locally.

VARIATION. No subspecies are recognized, but the northern-most populations from Washington and British Columbia are known

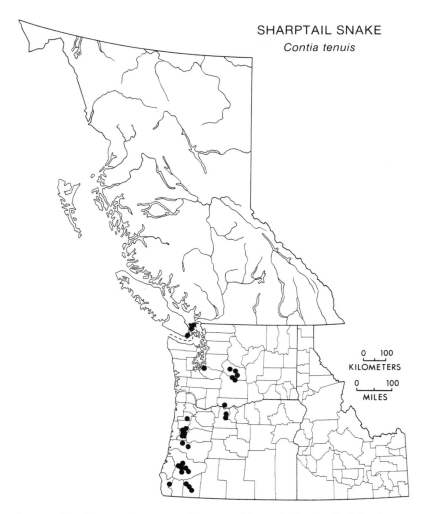

SHARPTAIL SNAKE
Contia tenuis

0   100
KILOMETERS

0   100
MILES

from only a few specimens, and geographic variation in the Northwest needs to be studied.

LIFE HISTORY. The eggs of *Contia tenuis* are laid in late June or early July. A full term egg discovered in October near Corvallis, Oregon was 7 by 28 mm and weighed 0.84 grams. Six hatchlings weighed 0.4 to 0.6 g and measured 89 to 104 mm TL. Clutches of 2, 3, 4, 8, and 9 eggs have been found in rock outcrops and in grass roots from 7 to 15 cm underground. The clutches of 8 and 9 were undoubtedly deposited by two or more females. Each female produces 3 to 5 eggs.

The period of activity may extend from late February to November in the Willamette Valley, but they are most commonly seen from late March through early June in that area. There is a second minor peak of surface activity in late September to November. Their period of surface activity thus coincides with the cooler wetter portions of the growing season. They are active at lower temperatures (10° to 17° C) than most reptiles and care must be taken to prevent captive individuals from overheating and dying.

Apparently Sharptail Snakes eat small slugs exclusively. This habit is made possible by the relatively long sharp teeth of this species.

When picked up, Sharptail Snakes thrash from side to side, and, if confined, they press the tail spine against one's skin. This is a startling experience for a collector and presumably would also startle a small predator that had seized the snake.

REMARKS. There is a published record for Sharptail Snakes at Chase, British Columbia. We suspect the record is erroneous and have not indicated it on the range map.

REFERENCES. Brodie et al. (1969), Cook (1960), Zweifel (1954).

RINGNECK SNAKE
DIADOPHIS PUNCTATUS (LINNAEUS)

This small (less than 55 TL cm in the Northwest), attractive snake has a slate-green back with a bright orange ventral surface and normally has a bright orange neck band 1 1/2 to 2 scales wide. The orange ventral coloration grades into brilliant red on the underside of the tail. The ventral coloration extends 1 1/2 to 2 scale rows onto the side of the snake and onto the upper labial scales. The head tends to be darker than the rest of the body. The orange belly is flecked with black, which is especially dense on the chin and throat. The scales are smooth except for ridges on the dorsal scales above the vent in males. The scalation is variable geographically.

HABITAT. Ringnecks are most common in wooded (oak-pine) regions, but they also occur in open, grassy or brushy areas and in relatively open, rocky canyons. They are found under rocks and rotting logs and in talus.

VARIATION. There are 12 subspecies currently recognized in the United States; many of these were described as distinct species and then synonymized. Only two subspecies occur in the Northwest: the Northwestern Ringneck Snake, *Diadophis punctatus occidentalis*, and the Regal Ringneck Snake, *D.p. regalis*. The subspecies in Oregon,

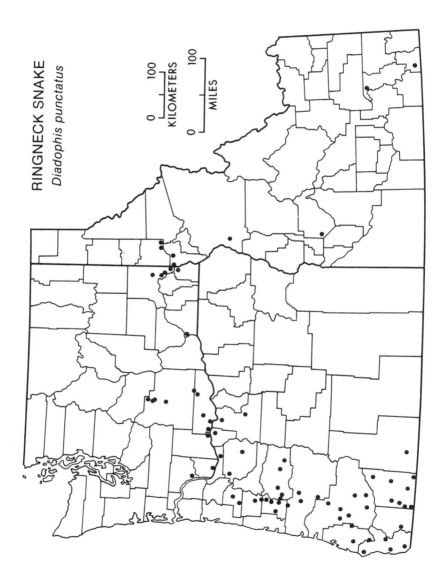

RINGNECK SNAKE
Diadophis punctatus

50. Ringneck Snake *(Diadophis punctatus)*, Benton Co., Oregon.

Washington, and northwestern Idaho is *D. p. occidentalis*. It is characterized by 182 to 210 ventrals, 55 to 67 caudals, 7 upper labials, 8 lower labials, 15 dorsal scale rows, and 11 to 12 maxillary teeth. The subspecies in southeastern Idaho is *D. p. regalis*. It is larger than *D. p. occidentalis* and has more ventrals, caudals, and dorsal scale rows (17). *D. p. regalis* usually lacks a neck ring, but is otherwise similar in coloration to the western form.

LIFE HISTORY. Repeated courtship was observed in a captive pair collected 4 May in Nez Perce Co., Idaho. The male rubbed his closed mouth up and down the sides of the female until he encountered the female's neck ring, at which time he bit the female's neck (on the ring) and aligned the lower part of his body with that of the female. The female's neck ring appeared to serve as a releaser for the biting behavior of the male, but this is not certain.

Ringneck Snakes deposit about three eggs per year in early July in stabilized talus or in rotting logs. The eggs are 23 to 30 mm long and 9 to 13 mm wide (these are measurements of hatched eggs, which are perhaps wider than unhatched eggs). Thirteen recently-hatched individuals caught 26 September near Corvallis, Oregon weighed 1.3 to 2.9 g (mean= 2.0) and measured 139 to 172 mm (mean = 188.8)

TL. There is evidence that females reproduce annually in northern Utah.

In northern Utah, Ringnecks departed from a den in May and returned in late September to early October. In the Northwest, Ringnecks are surface active from March to November, varying somewhat from year to year and by locality.

When uncovered in the field, Ringnecks often assume a characteristic posture with the head under the body and the tail coiled tightly and held with the bright red ventral surface up.

Ringnecks feed primarily on salamanders and lizards but may also eat insects, frogs, earthworms, and smaller snakes. The last two maxillary teeth on each side are enlarged and separated from the others by a gap. These teeth are not grooved or hollow, but their presence and the feeding behavior of Ringnecks suggest that they are venomous. We have observed that Ringnecks chew up and down the body of salamander *(Plethodon)* prey, then release the salamander and crawl to the head where they start to swallow. Salamanders bitten in this manner, which takes several minutes, appear to be paralyzed. When first captured Ringnecks often salivate heavily but have not attempted to bite. Many people in western Oregon believe that Ringnecks are poisonous if eaten by cats and dogs, but there are no data to support this belief. A Ringneck Snake swallowed by a Rubber Boa was regurgitated the next day, and there was no indication of digestive action. All of this and the tail display suggest that the Ringneck is venomous, although it is not believed to be dangerous to man.

REFERENCES. Blanchard (1942), Brodie et al. (1969), Parker and Brown (1974).

NIGHT SNAKE
HYPSIGLENA TORQUATA (GUENTHER)

51. Night Snake *(Hypsiglena torquata),* Deschutes Co., Oregon; photo by K.M. Walker.

This is a small (to about 46 cm TL in the Northwest), rear-fanged, mildly venomous snake. It has dark blotches on a light ground color and in this characteristic resembles young Gopher Snakes. It can be distinguished easily from Gopher Snakes by its smooth scales and the vertical pupil of the eye. Night Snakes have 21 rows of smooth dorsal scales that are reduced to 15 near the vent region. There are 177 to 204 ventrals, 44 to 66 caudals, 8 upper labials, and 10 lower labials. The head is distinctly wider than the neck and the temporal regions are swollen. The rear upper teeth are enlarged as fangs.

The dorsal ground color is white or buff, but the dorsum is covered with tiny brown or black dots giving a tan, gray, or olive appearance. The color pattern is of dark brown blotches over the lighter ground color. There are two rows of large dark brown spots down the back, one on each side of the middorsal line. These spots tend to merge posteriorly into small saddles. There are rows of smaller dark brown spots along the sides. The head is dusky brown with a dark brown line from the nostril through the eye to the angle of the jaw. This dark line is accentuated by the white upper labials. There are large dark brown

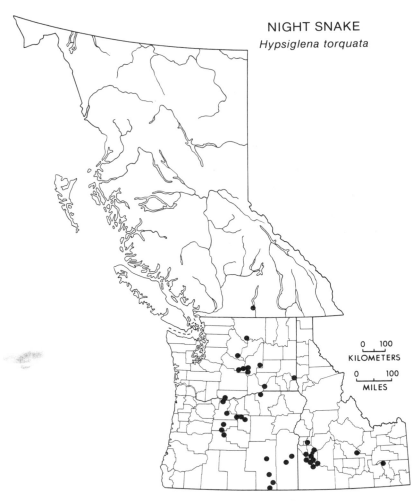

NIGHT SNAKE
Hypsiglena torquata

0   100
KILOMETERS
0   100
MILES

blotches at the side and rear of the head and a large median spot on the neck. The median spot is widest posteriorly and in some individuals joins with the lateral neck spots to form a wide dark collar. The belly is white or buff, almost pearly in life, and unmarked by dark pigmentation. In southeastern Idaho, adult females are much larger (max SVL = 525 mm; max weight = 50 g) than adult males (400 mm; 20 g).

HABITAT. In the Northwest, Night Snakes are restricted to arid regions, usually in the vicinity of rocky outcrops, up to about 1,700 m elevation. They can sometimes be captured by tethering a small lizard such as a Side-blotched Lizard near a rocky outcrop in the evening and

270

returning early the next morning to find that a Night Snake has swallowed the lizard. Otherwise they can be collected by turning rocks on hillsides, or by driving slowly along roads during warm summer nights and spotting them in the beams of the headlights.

VARIATION. There are six subspecies recognized in the United States but only one, the Desert Night Snake, *Hypsiglena torquata deserticola,* occurs in the Northwest. There are no data on interpopulational variation in the Northwest.

LIFE HISTORY. Night Snakes are active from about late April until late October. They are primarily nocturnal or crepuscular; we have never seen one abroad during the daytime. Limited observations suggest that eggs are deposited in late June or early July in the Northwest. There is no other information available concerning Night Snake reproduction in our area. In the Southwest, eggs average 10.1 by 27.6 mm and weigh an average of 1.94 g. The shells are white with a rough granular surface. Females deposit 3 to 9 (usually 4) eggs. The incubation period is about two months. Arizona hatchlings ranged in size from 133 to 192 mm TL and weighed 0.66 to 2.30 g.

Their diet consists primarily of lizards and occasionally anurans which they subdue with toxic saliva before swallowing. One of us watched a captive Night Snake seize a Side-blotched Lizard by its body just in front of the lizard's hind legs. Although there was no apparent chewing action, the lizard was dead in 10 minutes.

When annoyed, Night Snakes flatten and coil the body tightly with the head on top. From this position they strike repeatedly in the direction of the disturbance. This appears to be a bluff as they do not attempt to bite.

REFERENCES. Clark and Lieb (1973), Diller and Wallace (1981).

COMMON KINGSNAKE
LAMPROPELTIS GETULUS (LINNAEUS)

52. Common Kingsnake *(Lampropeltis getulus)*, Josephine Co., Oregon.

This snake is recognized easily by its black and white banded pattern. It is a large (to about 100 cm TL in our area) snake that rarely is seen in the Northwest. The snout and sides of the head are white with black edges on most scales. The top of the head and neck are black, sometimes with small white spots. They have 23 rows of smooth dorsal scales, 7 upper labials, 9 lower labials, an entire anal, 206 to 254 ventrals, and 41 to 62 rows of caudals.

HABITAT. This species is widespread in the southern United States in many kinds of habitats, up to about 1,650 m elevation. In the Northwest, it occurs only in Douglas, Jackson, and Josephine Cos., Oregon, where it is found in the more mesic river valleys. Most specimens have been found in areas of thick vegetation along streams.

VARIATION. There are seven subspecies in the United States. Only one subspecies, the California Kingsnake, *Lampropeltis getulus californiae*, occurs in the Northwest. In the southern portion of its range, this subspecies is either black and white or brown and white (the white is often yellowish); in southern California it may be either banded or striped. In Oregon all known individuals are black and white banded with the black bands widest on the back and narrowest on the lower sides.

LIFE HISTORY. No information is available on reproduction in our area, but southern members of this subspecies deposit 2 to 12 (usually 9) eggs. In other areas, mating has been observed from mid-March to early June, and egg-laying usually occurs in July. The incubation period is about 70 days. Eggs average about 24 by 50 mm, and hatchlings are about 245 to 290 mm SVL. These snakes are usually aggressive when first encountered, striking and vibrating their tails, but they usually quickly become gentle in captivity. They feed primarily on lizards and other snakes, including snakes as large as themselves. Less common prey include rodents, birds, and bird eggs.

REFERENCES. Fitch (1949).

53. Common Kingsnake *(Lampropeltis getulus),* Siskiyou Co., California; eating a mouse; photo by R.W. Van Devender.

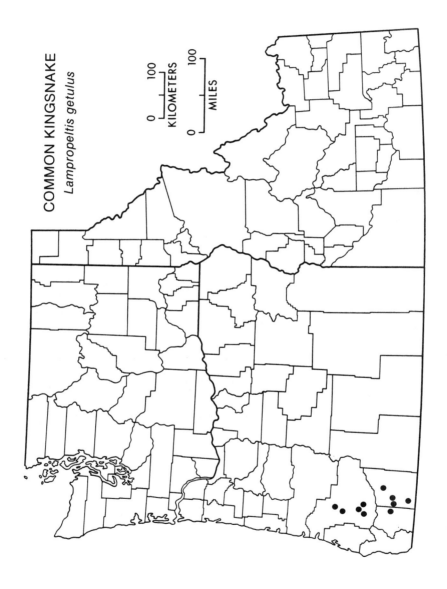

COMMON KINGSNAKE
Lampropeltis getulus

KILOMETERS
0 — 100

MILES
0 — 100

CALIFORNIA MOUNTAIN KINGSNAKE
LAMPROPELTIS ZONATA
(LOCKINGTON EX BLAINVILLE)

This is unquestionably the most attractive snake in the Northwest, having a bright pattern of red, white, and black bands. Because of their color, they are known locally as "Coral King Snakes." Adults seldom exceed 75 cm in TL but large individuals may reach 100 cm.

They have 23 rows of smooth dorsal scales, an undivided anal plate, 7 upper labials, 9 lower labials, 194 to 227 ventrals, and 46 to 62 caudals. The snout is black, sometimes with red flecking but never with white markings. There is a white collar on the back of the head followed by a second black band, followed by a regular series of red, black, white, black, and red bands. The white bands do not widen greatly toward the belly. The red bands are widest on the lower sides and are narrowest or even broken by black middorsally. The pattern of bands is broken on the venter. While poorly known, this species is common in certain restricted areas.

HABITAT. California Mountain Kingsnakes occur in oak and pine forests and on chaparral slopes up to 2,750 m elevation. They may be found under and inside of rotting logs, and they are sometimes found under rocks.

VARIATION. Individuals in the Northwest are supposed intergrades between the Saint Helena Mountain Kingsnake, *Lampropeltis zonata zonata* and the Sierra Mountain Kingsnake, *L. z. multicincta*. For this species, the zone of intergradation is as great or greater than the range of the recognized subspecies. The systematic relationships of this species should be reexamined. Specimens from the Washington population need to be studied, and there is believed to be a population near Maupin, Wasco Co., Oregon, although no specimens from there have been seen by us.

LIFE HISTORY. Females are known to deposit 3 to 8 eggs, and the incubation period is about 63 days. There is little other information available on their life history. The bright banded coloration is thought to be mimetic of the color pattern of coral snakes. Although coral snakes are not found in the Northwest it is possible for migratory birds to encounter them in Mexico, Central America, and South America, learn to avoid them there and continue to avoid snakes with similar color patterns when they migrate north for the summer. In this way the California Mountain Kingsnake may be protected by its resemblance to coral snakes that live in other regions.

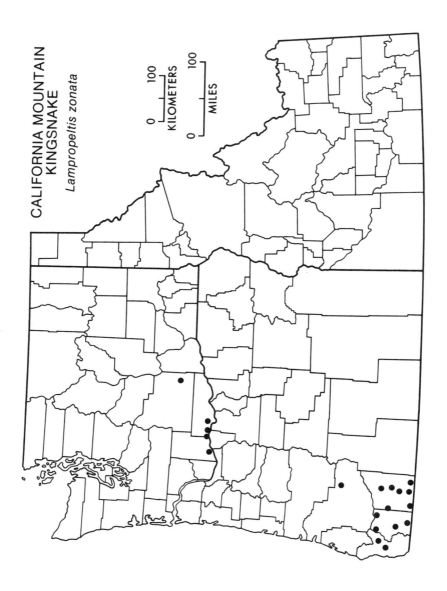

CALIFORNIA MOUNTAIN
KINGSNAKE

Lampropeltis zonata

0   100
KILOMETERS

0   100
MILES

These snakes eat lizards, snakes, mice, and nestling birds.
REFERENCES. Stebbins (1954-General Literature).

STRIPED WHIPSNAKE
MASTICOPHIS TAENIATUS (HALLOWELL)

This is an alert, long (up to 183 cm TL), slender snake that has large eyes, a long tail, and dark and light stripes the length of the body. Striped Whipsnakes are characterized by 15 dorsal scale rows and an elongate, bellshaped frontal. As in the Racer, a small lower preocular is wedged between the 3rd and 4th upper labials. There are 188 to 214 ventrals, 122 to 160 caudals, and a divided anal scale.

The plates on the top of the head are white-edged, and the upper and lower labials are white with black blotches. The middorsal area is black or gray-brown and often has a bluish or olive sheen. On each side there is a series of light and dark stripes. The white or buff colored dorsolateral stripe is bisected by a thin, broken, black line. Below this prominent dorsolateral stripe, there is a dark stripe, followed by another light stripe, which is again bisected by a thin, often broken, black line. These stripes run together on the rear body and tail. The chin and throat are white but speckled with black or brown. The ventral color changes gradually from white on the anterior body, to buffy at midbody, to pink or orange on the undersurface of the tail. Males and females are about the same size, and there is very little difference in tail length between the two sexes.

HABITAT. In our area, this species occurs in grasslands, sagebrush flats, and dry rocky canyons, up to about 1,540 m elevation.

VARIATION. Four subspecies occur in the United States but only one, The Desert Striped Whipsnake, *Masticophis taeniatus taeniatus*, occurs in the Northwest.

LIFE HISTORY. Very little information is available on the Striped Whipsnake in the Pacific Northwest. However, excellent studies have been done just to the south in northern Utah. In that area, Striped Whipsnakes den communally, usually with other species such as *Coluber constrictor, Crotalus viridis,* and *Pituophis melanoleucus.* After spending 149 to 250 days hibernating, Striped Whipsnakes emerge from their dens from late March to late May. About 95% of the adults and 26% of the juveniles survive the hibernation period, according to one study. In another study, 61% of the snakes survived the winter, and the survivors had lost an average of 9.4% of their initial

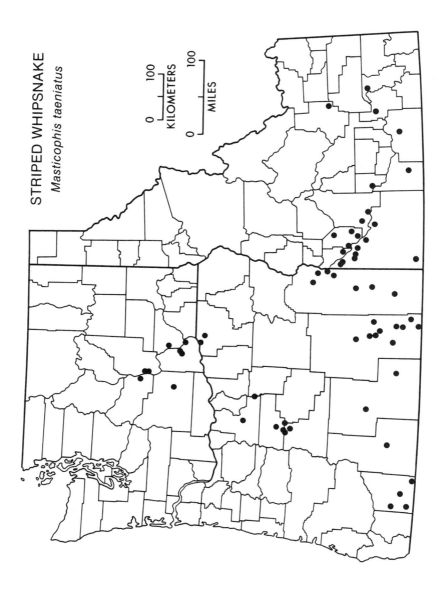

STRIPED WHIPSNAKE
Masticophis taeniatus

body weight. The snakes emerge from the dens over a period of 30 to 45 days. Males emerge first and are highly active in searching for mates. We observed male combat in this species in May near a den in southeastern Oregon, and combat was also observed in the spring by biologists in northern Utah.

Mating occurs in late April and May at the same time the eggs are yolking. Ovulation occurs in June, and oviposition occurs in late June or early July. Females shed their skin about eight days before oviposition. Eggs are usually deposited in abandoned burrows of small mammals, as much as 34 cm below the surface. Nest sites are often communal, and other species (*Coluber constrictor* and *Pituophis melanoleucus*) may share the nest site with the whipsnakes. Females produce 3 to 10 (mean = 6.6) eggs that have a rough granular surface, with larger females producing more eggs. The incubation period is 50 to 57 days, and hatching occurs from late August to early September. Hatchlings average 39.6 cm TL and 7.3 g. Hatchlings shed their skin for the first time about nine days after hatching. Growth is rapid for the first three years and then slows considerably. Males mature in about one year at 60 cm SVL, and females mature in two to three years at 71 cm SVL. Five and six-year-old Striped Whipsnakes are common, and there is evidence that some individuals live 10 to 20 years. Whipsnakes return to their dens in September to October.

Striped Whipsnakes eat primarily lizards and snakes but also feed on small mammals, young birds and even insects. While hunting, the head is held high off the ground. These snakes also often hunt or bask in the branches of bushes or small trees. They apparently have keen eyesight and are difficult to approach. When they become aware of the presence of a person (and perhaps predators) they orient the head in that direction observing the approach. When the person comes within 15 to 20 m the snake streaks away. The stripes along the snake's body make it especially difficult to judge its speed, and in many cases the snake is gone before the would-be collector is aware that the snake is moving rapidly.

REFERENCES. Bennion and Parker (1976), Hirth (1966), Parker and Brown (1973, 1980).

SMOOTH GREEN SNAKE
OPHEODRYS VERNALIS (HARLAN)

This is a small (adults 30 to 45 cm TL), slender, bright green snake. It has 15 rows of smooth dorsal scales, and the eye touches the fourth upper labial; there is no lower preocular wedged between the upper labials as in *Coluber constrictor* and *Masticophis taeniatus*. The Smooth Green Snake has 7 upper labials, a divided anal, and a long slender tail; males have 125 to 141 ventrals and females have 139 to 154 ventrals. The dorsal surface is bright green, the upper labials are yellowish, and the lower labials and the chin and neck are white. The ventral surface is yellowish, becoming bright yellow on the underside of the tail.

HABITAT. Smooth Green Snakes usually are found in damp meadows bordering streams or lakes. They also occur in drier rocky areas, but usually only if there is some grass or similarly dense vegetation present. They are found in both lowland and montane environments. They are difficult to find in their natural environment because of their green color, which blends perfectly with the vegetation, and because of their secretive behavior.

VARIATION. Two subspecies are recognized, but only one, the Western Smooth Green Snake, *Opheodrys vernalis blanchardi*, is likely to occur in our area.

LIFE HISTORY. Nothing is known about the biology of this species in Idaho, but in other areas (and presumably here also) they are diurnal predators on insects and spiders. In the laboratory they feed readily on crickets. Both spring and autumn mating has been observed in this species. In late summer the female deposits 3 to 12 (usually 7) eggs. The eggs of the Smooth Green Snake are long and slender (8 to 18 mm wide by 19 to 34 mm long) and have a very thin white shell. Eggs are retained in the oviducts for a variable (depending on locality) length of time, and the young are nearly full term when the eggs finally are laid, normally in August in Michigan. The young can be seen readily through the egg shells of freshly deposited eggs. The young emerge from the eggs within a few days (4 to 23 days in northern Michigan) after the eggs are laid. Newly-hatched individuals vary in size from 101 to 166 mm TL, although total lengths of 114 to 131 are more common.

REMARKS. This species is known in the Northwest from reliable sight records in extreme southeastern Idaho (Bear Lake Co.). Voucher specimens are needed to verify its presence in the Northwest, and any new information on this species in our area would be welcomed.

REFERENCES. Blanchard (1933).

GOPHER SNAKE
PITUOPHIS MELANOLEUCUS (DAUDIN)

54. Gopher Snake *(Pituophis melanoleucus deserticola),* Lake Co., Oregon.

This is a large (to about 180 cm TL in the Northwest, but up to 275 cm in southern parts of the range) heavy-bodied snake that is locally very common in the Northwest. Gopher Snakes are also known as "Bullsnakes," and contrary to common belief, they do not hybridize with rattlesnakes.

Gopher Snakes have dark brown or black blotches on a tan or light brown background. They have a row of dorsal blotches flanked on each side by a row of lateral blotches. There is a characteristic dark crescent passing between the eyes and down to the angle of the jaw on each side. The rostral scale is large, and the dorsal scales are keeled except for several lower rows on each side. The anal plate is entire, there are usually 8 (7 to 10) upper labials, and 12 to 13 lower labials. Males have relatively longer tails than females.

HABITAT. It occurs in a great variety of habitats including prairies, coniferous forests, and deserts. It is generally absent from dense forests and high mountains in the Northwest and seems to be most common in semi-arid brushy areas adjacent to farms.

VARIATION. Of the ten subspecies in the United States and Canada, two occur in our area, and they intergrade widely through central Oregon. The Pacific Gopher Snake, *Pituophis melanoleucus*

281

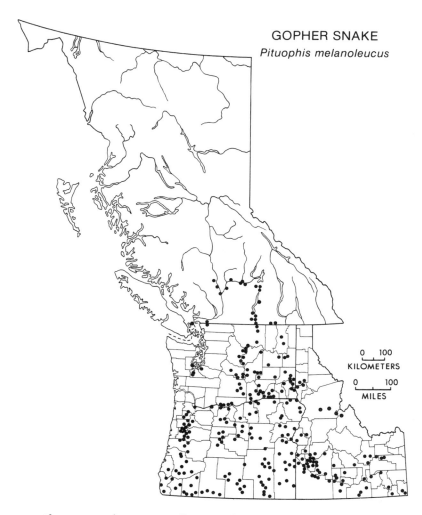

GOPHER SNAKE
Pituophis melanoleucus

0   100
KILOMETERS

0   100
MILES

catenifer, occurs in western Oregon. It has dorsal blotches that are usually brown and separated. The areas between the lateral blotches are often grayish. Dorsal scale rows are 29 to 33, usually 31. There are 56 to 93 dorsal blotches on the body and 14 to 30 on the tail. Males have 207 to 230 ventrals and 59 to 79 caudals; females have 200 to 230 ventrals and 53 to 78 caudals.

Except in western Oregon, the subspecies in the Northwest is the Great Basin Gopher Snake, *Pituophis melanoleucus deserticola*, which often has black, anterior, dorsal blotches that are connected, and in which the anterior lateral blotches form lines on the sides of the neck.

Dorsal scale rows are 29 to 37, usually 31 or 33. There are 46 to 66 dorsal blotches on the body and 12 to 21 on the tail. Males have 224 to 252 ventrals and 58 to 72 caudals; females have 223 to 263 ventrals and 50 to 67 caudals.

Snakes in the zone of intergradation usually resemble *P. m. deserticola* in blotching and *P.m. catenifer* in scalation.

LIFE HISTORY. Gopher Snakes near Corvallis, Oregon *(Pituophis melanoleucus catenifer)* deposit from 3 to 9 eggs, which are smooth in texture. Twenty-five eggs measured 27 to 31 mm in diameter by 47 to 74 mm in length. The eggs are deposited in cavities in stable talus. Forty-eight hatchlings weighed 11.9 to 22.4 g and were 253 to 303 mm in SVL and 287 to 364 mm in TL. Hatchlings had 2 to 4 cubic centimeters of yolk remaining in the body cavity. Hatchlings emerge in late September or October and probably overwinter in the talus slope. The large amount of yolk remaining at hatching may provide the necessary energy to survive the winter, as it is unlikely that they feed before spring. Hatchlings we have observed bite or strike at any object brought near them but refuse to feed. The hatchlings will strike aggressively while they are only partially out of the egg.

In northern Utah, Gopher Snakes *(Pituophis melanoleucus deserticola)* spend 179 to 250 days in winter dens, usually with other species (see Striped Whipsnake account). In one study, 89% of the adults and 29% of the juveniles survived the period of winter hibernation. Survivors lost about 4.8% of their initial body weight. They emerge later than the Striped Whipsnakes over a period of about 29 to 48 days during late April to late May. The males emerge before the females. Males of this subspecies have been observed in "combat" during the mating season, in April and May. Yolking of eggs also occurs in April and May. Ovulation occurs in June, and oviposition occurs in late June to early July. Females shed about six days before laying their eggs. Females deposit 4 to 15 (mean = 8.4) eggs, the larger females producing more eggs. Nest sites are often abandoned mammal burrows on south-facing slopes, which lack perennial vegetation. Nests are frequently communal with other Gopher Snakes and other species. The eggs are placed close together in the nests, with eggs often touching. There is some evidence that females use the same nest site in successive years. The incubation period is 50 to 59 days, and the hatchlings average 38.6 cm SVL and 13.4 g. Hatchlings shed for the first time about 16 days after hatching. Growth is rapid through the first three years and then slows. Males become sexually mature at one or two years and females at three to five years of age. Males mature at about 70 and females at about 75 cm SVL. Males are the larger sex in this

55. Gopher Snake *(Pituophis melanoleucus catenifer)*, Benton Co., Oregon; newly-hatched individual.

56. Gopher Snake *(Pituophis melanoleucus catenifer)*, Benton Co., Oregon; eggs and hatchling.

northern Utah population.

In southwestern Idaho, Gopher Snakes are active in the morning and again in the late afternoon at body temperature of about 30° C. The life history in this area is similar to that reported for Utah, but males and females are about the same size and fewer eggs are laid (mean = 6.9). In the Idaho study, density of Gopher Snakes was estimated at 1.3 snakes per hectare.

Gopher Snakes are generally day-active, but they are also active during warm nights. They are largely terrestrial, but they are good climbers and sometimes search for prey in bushes and trees. The primary prey is rodents, but they occasionally eat rabbits and birds, and juveniles also eat lizards. We once encountered a Gopher Snake about to devour young robins in a nest about four m above the ground on a juniper branch. This occurred in complete darkness (about 2100 hr); we were drawn to the scene by the cries of the parent birds. Gopher Snakes are eaten frequently by birds of prey such as the Red-tailed Hawk.

Gopher Snakes have an impressive aggressive display when encountered. "When approached it may puff up, hiss loudly, strike vigorously. The tip of the tail may be rapidly vibrated, and if this is done in dry leaves the resulting sound is not unlike the whir of a rattlesnake." (Gordon, 1939). It has also been suggested that the color pattern of Gopher Snakes is mimetic of that of the Western Rattlesnake.

REFERENCES. Brodie et al. (1969), Diller (1981), Ferguson et al. (1956), R.M. Hansen (1950), Kardong (1980), Parker and Brown (1980), Shaw (1951), Woodbury (1941).

LONGNOSE SNAKE
RHINOCHEILUS LECONTEI
BAIRD AND GIRARD

57. Longnose Snake *(Rhinocheilus lecontei),* Kern Co., California.

In our area, this curiously colored snake is known only from the Snake River Canyon of southwestern Idaho. It is a relatively slender snake usually less than 70 cm in TL (the record is 104 cm) with dark blotches and red, orange, yellow, and white coloration between the blotches. The Longnose Snake is characterized by a long pointed snout with a large rostral scale recurved over the top of the snout. The lower jaw is shorter than the upper jaw, an adaptation for burrowing. There are 23 rows of smooth dorsal scales, 8 upper labials, 9 lower labials, 181 to 218 ventrals and an undivided anal plate. The caudals (41 to 61) are unique among the colubrid snakes of our area in being arranged in a single row anteriorly on the tail; they may be divided posteriorly. Adult males are somewhat larger than adult females. The largest female in a sample of 11 from southwestern Idaho measured 660 mm SVL; eight of 22 males from the same area exceeded this size, the largest being 725 mm SVL.

The color pattern is variable but is usually as follows: snout and sides of head cream, marked with black; back of head black or brown, marked with yellow or white; back with large black or brown dorsal blotches containing some scales with cream-colored centers; spaces between blotches are narrower than the blotches and may be red, orange, yellow, or white; the lower sides and belly are cream or white, often marbled with dark pigment.

HABITAT. Longnose Snakes inhabit deserts, prairies, and dry rocky canyons. As they spend their inactive daylight periods deep underground, they are seldom collected by turning surface objects. Their true abundance is best revealed by using drift fences and funnel traps in likely habitat. Their abundance is also indicated by the frequency of their remains in nests of predatory birds.

VARIATION. Only two subspecies occur in the United States; the Western Longnose Snake, *Rhinocheilus lecontei lecontei,* is found in our area.

LIFE HISTORY. These snakes are largely nocturnal or crepuscular and burrow rapidly into sand or loose soil when disturbed. This burrowing is accomplished by rapid lateral undulations of the body. They often lie with the body covered with sand and the head exposed. They feed largely on lizards, but they also take small mice. They are eaten commonly by hawks in the Birds of Prey Natural Area of southwestern Idaho. Like the Gopher Snake, they may vibrate their tails when disturbed. Females deposit 5 to 8 eggs in areas outside of the Northwest, but nothing is known about their life history in the Northwest. In the Southwest, eggs are laid during the first part of July, and the eggs hatch in late August. The hatchlings range in size from 202 to 220 mm TL.

REMARKS. It would not be surprising to find this snake in other areas of southwestern Idaho or in southern Harney and Malheur Cos., Oregon.

REFERENCES. Diller and Wallace (1981), Klauber (1941).

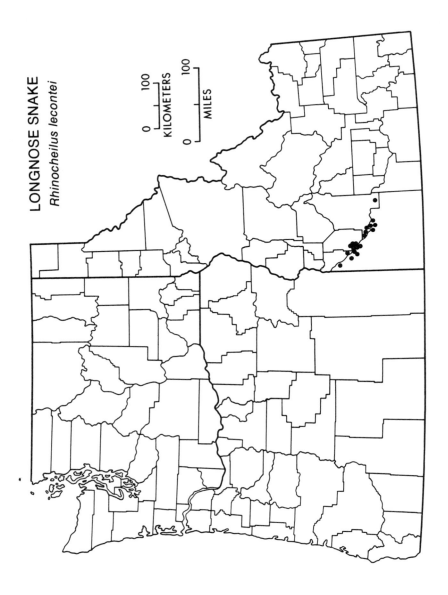

LONGNOSE SNAKE
Rhinocheilus lecontei

KILOMETERS
0   100

MILES
0   100

WESTERN GROUND SNAKE
SONORA SEMIANNULATA
BAIRD AND GIRARD

The Western Ground Snake is a small (maximum TL is 48 cm but most are smaller) secretive snake that is active at night. The snout is rounded and projects beyond the lower jaw. Western Ground Snakes have 15 rows of smooth dorsal scales. The scales along the sides of the body have light-colored edges. There are 149 to 185 ventral scales, 40 to 60 caudal scales, and 7 upper labials. The tail is short and tipped with a spine. In southwestern Idaho, they come in two color patterns of nearly equal frequency. One is orange and black banded, the other unbanded.

Banded individuals have 25 to 50 black crossbands, few, if any, of which meet on the belly. The spaces between the bands are orange on top of the back, and this orange grades into light olive or buff on the lower sides.

Unbanded individuals may have a broad (about seven scale rows wide) pinkish or reddish stripe which is not sharply set off from the gray, olive, or tan sides. Other unbanded individuals are uniform olive, gray, reddish, or tan in coloration. A few unbanded individuals have a single black saddle behind the head.

Among 14 females from southwestern Idaho, the largest measures 305 mm SVL; five males, among a sample of 19 from the same area, exceed this size, the largest measuring 335 mm SVL.

HABITAT. This species occurs in desert or prairie regions with sandy soil. Individuals can be found under surface objects or in clumps of grass roots, but "drift-fencing" is the best way to collect them.

VARIATION. Until recently there were five subspecies recognized in the United States. The subspecies in the Northwest was the Great Basin Ground Snake, *Sonora semiannulata isozona.* Currently, no subspecies are recognized, and *Sonora episcopa* also has been synonymized with *Sonora semiannulata.* The study leading to this systematic change did not include specimens from throughout the range of *Sonora,* and the taxonomy of this species is therefore uncertain.

LIFE HISTORY. There is no information on the life history of this species in the Northwest, but in other parts of its range females deposit an average of four eggs. Ground snakes have shallow grooves on the outer sides of their rear teeth, and may, therefore, be mildly venomous. They are not known to bite humans.

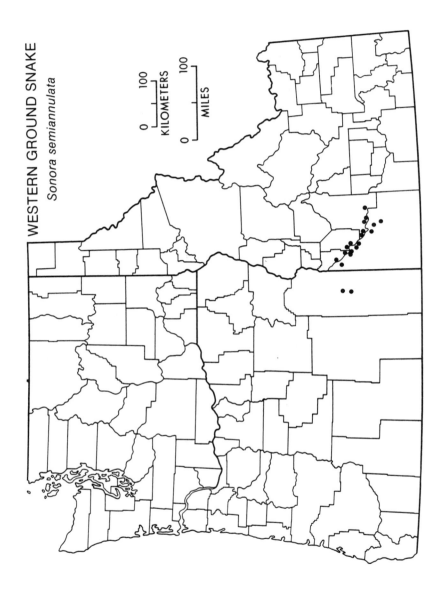

WESTERN GROUND SNAKE
Sonora semiannulata

0   100
KILOMETERS

0   100
MILES

Small arthropods such as spiders and centipedes make up the prey of Western Ground Snakes. Raptorial birds occasionally prey on them.

REFERENCES. Diller and Wallace (1981), Frost and Van Devender (1979).

NATRICINE SNAKES
SUBFAMILY NATRICINAE

These are probably the most successful of all snakes as indicated by abundance of individuals. All North American members of this family give birth to fully developed young. Only one genus, *Thamnophis,* occurs in the Northwest.

There are 22 known species of *Thamnophis,* or garter snakes, 13 in the United States and Canada, and four in the Northwest. They all have keeled dorsal scales and generally are found in or around water. In the Northwest the species are best distinguished by the number of various scales and color pattern. The systematic relationships within and between species of garter snakes in the Northwest are poorly understood.

WESTERN AQUATIC GARTER SNAKE
THAMNOPHIS COUCHI (KENNICOTT)

58. Western Aquatic Garter Snake *(Thamnophis couchi),* Josephine Co., Oregon.

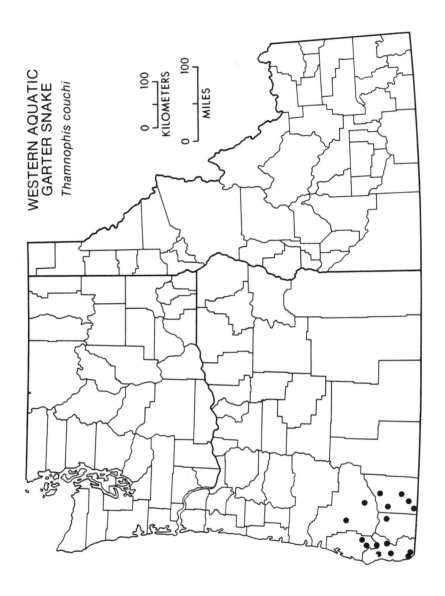

WESTERN AQUATIC
GARTER SNAKE
Thamnophis couchi

KILOMETERS

MILES

This is a large (to 84 cm TL) gray garter snake with a narrow head and a pointed snout. In our area it has 21 rows of keeled dorsal scales, 8 upper labials (the 6th and 7th are not enlarged as in *Thamnophis elegans*), 10 lower labials, 154 to 171 ventrals, and 74 to 94 caudals. The internasal scales are longer than wide and pointed anteriorly. The ground color is pale gray with two rows of alternating black spots on each side; these spots are often fused in large individuals. The dorsal stripe is usually lacking or diffused into the ground color, but, when present, is narrow and dull yellow and often confined to the neck region. The lateral stripe, when present, is faint and blends into the ventral coloration. The upper labials are pale gray to white with black on the posterior margins. The ventral surface is white to gray and usually unmarked with dark pigment. The rear body and tail are pinkish or purple.

HABITAT. This is the most aquatic snake in the Northwest. In southwestern Oregon, it is never far from permanent water, mainly streams and rivers at relatively low elevations. In northern California, is occurs up to 1,525 m.

VARIATION. There are six subspecies in the United States but only one ranges as far north as southern Oregon. This is the Oregon Garter Snake, *Thamnophis couchi hydrophilus*.

LIFE HISTORY. These snakes generally restrict their activity to streams where they are found basking on boulders along the banks and in mid-stream. When approached, they escape by diving into the water and hiding under rocks or in exposed tree roots. This behavior makes the Western Aquatic Garter Snake the most difficult garter snake to collect. This species is not found along streams without exposed boulders and heavy riparian vegetation.

Females are larger than males. Mature males range in size from 330 to 580 and mature females from 350 and 610 mm SVL. Mating has been observed in April in California. Seven to twenty-five young are born in August. The smallest reported individual, apparently a newborn, measured 213 mm TL.

Thamnophis couchi feed in the water on fish, tadpoles, frogs, and salamander larvae. More than one-half of their food is fishes, including sculpins and trout up to 2.4 cm in length. The rest of the prey are largely *Rana boylei* tadpoles and adults and *Dicamptodon ensatus* larvae.

REFERENCES. Fitch (1936, 1940a, 1941a).

WESTERN TERRESTRIAL GARTER SNAKE
THAMNOPHIS ELEGANS
(BAIRD AND GIRARD)

59. Western Terrestrial Garter Snake *(Thamnophis elegans),* Oregon.

This is a large geographically variable garter snake, that despite its common name, is largely aquatic in some regions. The four subspecies occupy different habitats and have different food habits.

Thamnophis elegans has internasal scales that are broader than long and not pointed anteriorly, 19 to 23 rows of keeled dorsal scales, 146 to 185 ventrals, 67 to 101 caudals, 8 upper labials, and 10 lower labials. The sixth and seventh upper labials are enlarged.

VARIATION. All four of the U.S. and Canadian subspecies occur in the Northwest.

The Klamath Garter Snake, *Thamnophis elegans biscutatus,* is the largest (often more than 90 cm TL, up to 107 cm) and most heavy-bodied subspecies. It usually has 23, sometimes 21, dorsal scale rows. This subspecies is found in water or on boulders along or in water. When alarmed they escape into water and hide under boulders. They apparently capture prey only in water, eating fish, leeches, lampreys, tadpoles, toads, and frogs. The dorsal coloration is brown, black, or gray with a yellow to brown, uneven dorsal stripe. The upper labials are olive gray, and the belly is gray, suffused with black toward the rear. The range of this subspecies in the Northwest is a small area in southcentral Oregon, mainly southern Klamath and Lake Cos.

The Mountain Garter Snake, *Thamnophis elegans elegans,* occurs near water or in damp meadows, but it is neither found in water, nor does it escape into water when disturbed. It feeds entirely terrestrially, eating slugs, toads, frogs, lizards, and mice. Adults are normally about 61 cm TL and have 21 (sometimes 19) dorsal scale rows. The middorsal stripe is bright yellow or orange, broad, and sharp edged. The lateral stripes are fairly distinct and yellow or buff colored. The dorsal coloration is black or dark brown with light flecks. Because of the dark ground color, the two alternating rows of dorsolateral black spots are evident only when the body is expanded. The upper labials are pale gray or tan, and the posterior ones are marked with black wedges. The belly is light gray, and rarely marked with black. This subspecies lacks the bright red markings of *T. e. terrestris.* In our area, *T. e. elegans* occurs only in southwestern Oregon, in the Klamath-Siskiyou and Cascade Mountains and nearby valleys, but it does not reach the coast in the Klamath Mountains.

The Coast Garter Snake, *Thamnophis elegans terrestris,* is similar to *T. e. elegans* in habitat requirements, and it also feeds terrestrially. It eats slugs, young mice, lizards, and salamanders. They usually have 19, rarely 21, dorsal scale rows and sometimes have 7 rather than 8 upper labials. There are almost no available data on adult size, but one mature male measured 585 mm TL. They are reddish brown or olive brown with two dorsolateral rows of alternating black spots. The middorsal stripe is broad, straight edged, and bright yellow. The lateral stripe is olive yellow with red flecking. There are also red flecks on the sides and belly. The chin is cream colored and the venter pale green or blue. This subspecies barely enters the Northwest in the extreme southwestern, coastal Klamath Mountains of Curry and western Josephine Cos., Oregon.

The Wandering Garter Snake, *Thamnophis elegans vagrans,* is found near marshes or other water and feeds on land and in the water. Recorded prey include fish, tadpoles, slugs, snails, earthworms, mice, lizards, frogs, birds, and salamanders. On Mitlenatch Island in the northern Strait of Georgia, British Columbia, these snakes feed on some marine and seashore invertebrates and fishes, as well as on young of sea birds. Saliva of this subspecies has been reported to be mildly poisonous, and presumably is used to subdue struggling prey. This subspecies usually has 21 rows of dorsal scales and sometimes grows to 97 cm TL. The dorsal color is usually brownish or dark gray and the upper labials are similar to the ground color, not lighter as in the other subspecies. There are melanistic individuals in western Washington, eastern Oregon and perhaps elsewhere in the range. The dorsal stripe is dull yellow or brown, narrow, and uneven because it is

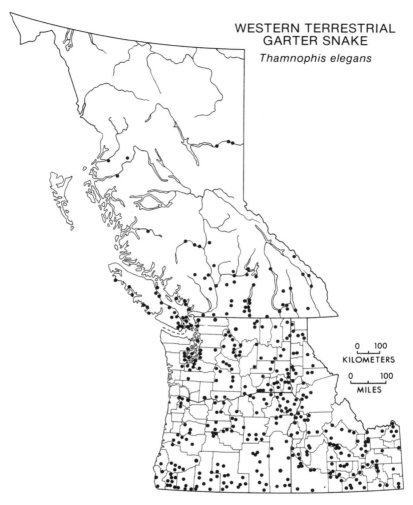

WESTERN TERRESTRIAL
GARTER SNAKE
Thamnophis elegans

0   100
KILOMETERS
0   100
MILES

invaded by the upper of the two alternating rows of black spots. In some individuals there is no dorsal stripe, in others the dorsal stripe is broken by invading black spots. The belly is gray with black flecking concentrated along the midventral line. This is the most wide-ranging subspecies, being the only subspecies of *T. elegans* in British Columbia, Washington, and Idaho. This subspecies also occurs in most of eastern Oregon. In Idaho, it has been recorded at elevations as high as 2,500 m.

LIFE HISTORY. *Thamnophis elegans* give live birth to 4 to 19 young. *T. e. vagrans* has larger litters than the other subspecies, but the body size-litter size relationships have not been studied adequately. Newborn range in size from 167 to 213 mm TL. Young are usually born in late July or early August. Females grow to a maximum size of 974 and males to 715 mm TL. One curious difference between aquatic and terrestrial subspecies is the fact that the terrestrial subspecies have swollen upper labial scales caused by enlarged salivary glands.

On Vancouver Island, *Thamnophis elegans* eats different prey than the other two species of garter snakes *(T. ordinoides* and *T. sirtalis)* on the island, but has preferred body temperature different from only one *(T. sirtalis)* of the two.

REMARKS. The systematic relationships between the subspecies of *Thamnophis elegans* and between this species and *T. couchi* need further investigation. For such a common species, there is remarkably little known about its life history.

REFERENCES. Campbell (1969), Fitch (1941a, 1949), Fox (1951), Gregory (1978), Gregory and Duncan McIntosh (1980), Hebard (1950, 1951a), Vest (1982).

NORTHWESTERN GARTER SNAKE
THAMNOPHIS ORDINOIDES
(BAIRD AND GIRARD)

This is a small-headed entirely terrestrial garter snake that seldom exceeds 600 mm TL, although a specimen 850 mm long has been reported. This species is by far the most variable snake in the Northwest, but it can be distinguished from the other garter snakes by its small head, 17 scale rows, and 7 upper labials.

Thamnophis ordinoides is characterized by 17 (rarely 19) rows of keeled dorsal scales, 7 upper labials, and 8 or 9 lower labials. Males have 137 to 162 ventrals and 56 to 82 caudals; females have 134 to 159 ventrals and 49 to 72 caudals. The color pattern may be striped, spotted, unmarked, or a combination of stripes and spots. A dorsal stripe is usually well-developed but can be faint, broken, or absent. The color of the dorsal stripe can be red, orange, yellow, blue, or white. The lateral stripe, when present, is usually pale yellow. The ground color can be gray, olive, brown, black, or bluish. Dark spots, when present, are usually black and arranged in two alternating rows on each dorsolateral surface. The sides also are often flecked with white. The upper labials are usually the same color as the ventral surfaces which may be yellow, light olive, or gray. The belly is often boldly marked with black or red. Red is a more common color in the southern parts of the

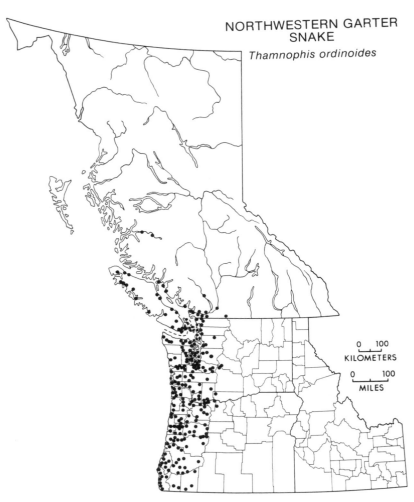

NORTHWESTERN GARTER
SNAKE

Thamnophis ordinoides

0   100
KILOMETERS
0   100
MILES

species range.

HABITAT. *Thamnophis ordinoides* is found in meadows and along the edges of forests and thick brushy areas, from sea level to about 1,370 m. They apparently spend most of their time in thickets and talus slopes, occasionally entering open areas to bask.

VARIATION. There are no subspecies recognized.

LIFE HISTORY. Northwestern Garter Snakes generally are active from about mid-March to late October, although they are infrequently seen during the winter months as well at lowland sites when the weather permits. During the winter, they hibernate in talus banks

298

or in cracks in fissured rock. Mating occurs during the spring (mid-March through April) and less commonly in the fall. Females ovulate in May, and the young are born from late July to mid-August. Litter size ranges from 3 to 20, but litters of 8 to 12 are more common. Newborn range in size from 150 to 190 mm TL. There is evidence that larger females produce more and larger young in the Willamette Valley, but no such relationship was found near Puget Sound. In the Willamette Valley, apparently only about 78% of the adult females reproduce each year, and only 67% of the mature females in the Puget Sound area reproduce in a given year. It is thought that males grow to adult size in one year, but that females mature at two years of age. Mature males range in size from 420 to 670 mm TL, whereas mature females range from 308 to 850 mm TL. Males have relatively longer tails than females.

The primary food of both young and adults is small slugs, but they also eat earthworms and small salamanders. Predators of this species are largely unknown, but a Spotted Owl killed and partially ate an adult *Thamnophis ordinoides* in the Oregon Cascades.

REFERENCES. Fitch (1940a), Gregory (1978), Gregory and Duncan McIntosh (1980), Hebard (1950, 1951a, 1951b), G.R. Stewart (1965, 1968).

COMMON GARTER SNAKE
THAMNOPHIS SIRTALIS
(LINNAEUS)

This is a large (to 132 cm TL), heavy-bodied garter snake that throughout most of our area has some red coloration along the sides of the body and seven upper labials. *Thamnophis sirtalis* is characterized by 19 rows of keeled dorsal scales, 7 upper labials, 10 lower labials, an average of 163 to 165 ventrals in males and 158 to 159 in females, and an average of 81 to 86 caudals in males and 72 to 79 in females. In the Northwest, a dorsal stripe is present but variably expressed, and the lateral stripes are similarly variable.

HABITAT. This species is most common in wet meadows and along water courses, but it can be found far from water in open valleys and in deep coniferous forests. It ranges in elevation from sea level up to about 2,450 m. It is very common in some areas. We once caught more than 150 of these snakes in an hour along the Willamette River in Linn Co., Oregon.

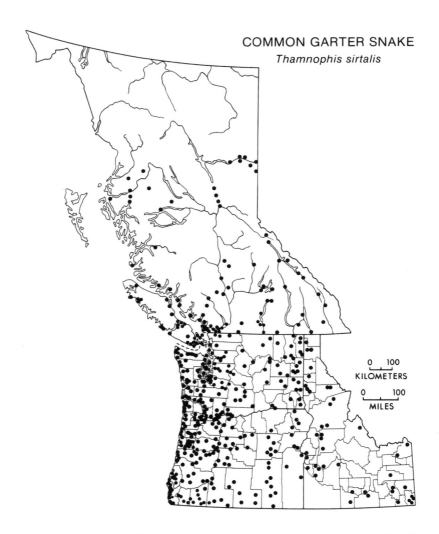

COMMON GARTER SNAKE
Thamnophis sirtalis

0   100
KILOMETERS

0   100
MILES

VARIATION. This is the most wide-ranging snake in North America, being found throughout the United States (except the southwestern deserts), the southern half of Canada, and even into Alaska. This species is highly variable geographically. Of the 12 subspecies in the United States and Canada four occur in the Northwest.

The Red-spotted Garter Snake, *Thamnophis sirtalis concinnus*, is found in northwestern Oregon, and barely into southwestern Washington in southern Cowlitz and Clark Cos. It is most typical in the Willamette Valley. The top and sides of the head are red, often

300

very bright red. The dorsal stripe of yellow to bright yellow green is wide, as in *T. s. fitchi*. The body is black with a series of large red blotches down both sides; the red blotches in this subspecies are as wide or wider than the black spaces between blotches. The lateral stripes are usually absent, but narrow irregular pale cream stripes may be present. The chin is white, and the throat pale green or blue. The belly becomes progressively darker posteriorly, eventually becoming bluish black, marked with black suffusions.

The Valley Garter Snake, *Thamnophis sirtalis fitchi*, is the most wide-ranging subspecies in the Northwest, occurring throughout Idaho, the eastern two-thirds of Oregon and Washington, the southern one-third of Oregon, and most of British Columbia (except Vancouver Island; the extreme, southwestern, coastal region adjacent to Vancouver Island; and extreme eastern British Columbia). The top of the head is black or dark gray and the upper labials are buff or yellow, sometimes with a reddish wash on the posteriormost labials. The body is black with a row of small red blotches on the lower one-half of the body. These red blotches are in contact with the lateral stripe and sometimes the two intermingle. The dorsal stripe is bright yellow and straight-edged occupying the middorsal scale row and one half of each adjacent scale row. The lateral stripes are buff or yellow and occupy the second and lower half of the third scale rows. The lower labials and chin are cream colored, and the belly is yellow-green or yellow-blue without black markings.

The Red-sided Garter Snake, *Thamnophis sirtalis parietalis*, is a subspecies that occurs mainly in the Great Plains. It barely enters the Northwest in extreme eastern British Columbia along the Alberta border. This form is dark olive to almost black dorsally with a yellow, even-edged, middorsal stripe that covers the middorsal scale row and an additional ½ scale on each side of it. The dorsal stripe is continuous from head to tail tip. There is a lateral stripe on each side, about two scales wide (the second and third scale rows) and of an orange-yellow color with reddish suffusion. The areas between the dorsolateral scales are red, and when the skin is stretched the red color becomes more obvious, often forming reddish bars. There is a series of black spots along each side between the stripes. The top of the head is olive, and the venter is olive to dull green, with a small black spot on either end of each ventral scale. This form has 19 dorsal scale rows and seven upper labials.

The Puget Sound Garter Snake, *Thamnophis sirtalis pickeringi*, is a melanistic form found west of the Cascades in Washington, on Vancouver Island, and on the southwestern mainland coast of British

Columbia adjacent to Vancouver Island. The top of the head and body are black, and the upper labials are pale green with black wedges on the posterior margins. The greenish dorsal stripe is one scale row wide, narrow, and uneven. The greenish lateral stripe, located on the second scale row, is broken. Red lateral blotches, when present, are confined to the skin between the scales. The chin is white, becoming light green or blue on the anterior venter and darker, even black, toward the vent and tail.

LIFE HISTORY. The active period for this species varies considerably across the Pacific Northwest, corresponding to the length of the local growing season. In the Willamette Valley, males may emerge during warm winter days to bask near their den sites, but winter basking is not possible over much of the range in the Northwest.

It is quite common to find these garter snakes mating in the open soon after they emerge in early spring. There is some mating activity in the autumn as well, at least in some areas. The females have a copulatory plug immediately after mating that fills the cloaca and prevents remating. Males do not court recently-mated females but are capable of mating with many different females each spring. Ovulation occurs in May or early June. The embryos develop within the females, and there is an exchange of nutrients and waste products between the female and her developing young. The young are born alive in late summer, from late July to mid-August in western Oregon. Normal litters are 10 to 15 but several litters between 70 and 80 have been reported, and litters as small as five are known. As is the case with the Northwestern Garter Snake, larger females produce more and larger young, at least in the Willamette Valley. In that area, only about 68% of the adult females reproduce each year. Newborn range in size from 214 to 278 mm TL. Males grow to adult size in about one year. but females require two years. In the Willamette Valley, adult males range in size from 360 to 590 and adult females from 435 to 890 mm SVL. Males have longer tails than females of the same SVL.

The newly-born snakes feed on earthworms, but adults primarily eat frogs, toads, and salamanders. Small mammals, birds, fish, and even other reptiles are occasionally taken. Adults were observed feeding on larval *Dicamptodon* and trout in streams near Mount St. Helens in the Washington Cascades. Near Blue River, Oregon, an adult was found foraging at night in a cold mountain stream, where it eventually took a small larval *Dicamptodon ensatus* from the water. This species is able to eat the highly toxic newt *Taricha granulosa;* it is 2,000 times less susceptible to the toxins of this newt than are white mice. *Thamnophis sirtalis concinnus* have been observed taking adult

302

newts from pitfall traps and appeared to congregate around this ready source of food.

Like most snakes, this species usually attempts to escape when approached, but some large individuals flatten the head and body and strike viciously. When the body is flattened the red color patches become more evident, resulting from the exposure of the skin between the scales. In addition to biting, garter snakes have especially repulsive secretions from the anal musk glands. When captured the snake writhes its body, smearing fecal material and musk over itself and its captor. When capturing a garter snake one must often choose between being bitten or smeared with feces and musk: a difficult choice.

REMARKS. The systematic relationships between the currently recognized subspecies of *Thamnophis sirtalis* are poorly understood. *T. s. fitchi* is especially variable and needs to be studied.

REFERENCES. Brodie (1968b), Devine (1975, 1977), Fitch (1941a, 1941b, 1965), Fitch and Maslin (1961), Gregory (1978), Gregory and Duncan McIntosh (1980), Hebard (1950, 1951a), G.R. Stewart (1965, 1968).

PIT VIPERS
FAMILY VIPERIDAE
SUBFAMILY CROTALINAE

The family Viperidae includes the Old World subfamily Viperinae (Old World Vipers) with 11 genera and 60 species distributed across Europe, Asia, and Africa, and the subfamily Crotalinae (Pit Vipers), which occurs both in the Old and New Worlds. About two-thirds of the crotaline species are New World, however, with seven genera and 127 species currently recognized. Members of both subfamilies have a special fang-erecting mechanism, in which the maxillary bone on each side of the upper jaw can be rotated to erect the anteriormost tooth, which is elongate, hollow, and used for injecting venom. The erecting mechanism allows the fangs of viperids to be much longer (hence more efficient delivery organs) than would be possible if they were permanently fixed in an erected position, as in other venomous snakes such as cobras and boomslangs. When not in use, the long fangs of viperids can be folded neatly out of the way.

The two subfamilies differ in that crotalines have a loreal pit organ between the eye and nostril and excavated maxillary bones for accommodating the pit organ. Some advanced crotalines have a rattle on the tail tip, which is never present in viperines.

Pit vipers are very heavy-bodied snakes with heads distinctly larger than their necks. The pit organs are infrared heat-sensing devices that are used for detecting warm-blooded prey. These snakes are largely nocturnal and have vertical eye pupils. Most members of this subfamily give birth to live young. There are 17 species in the United States and Canada belonging to three genera; *Agkistrodon* (moccasins), *Sistrurus* (pigmy rattlesnakes), and *Crotalus* (rattlesnakes). These, along with coral snakes which do not occur in the Northwest, are the only dangerously venomous snakes in the United States and Canada. Only one species of viper, the Western Rattlesnake, *Crotalus viridis,* occurs in the Northwest.

RATTLESNAKES
GENUS *CROTALUS*

The genus *Crotalus* is restricted to the New World, ranging from southern Canada southward through the Americas to northern Argentina. There are 28 species in the genus, 13 of which occur in Canada and the United States, most species occurring in the Southwest. Among snakes, only the genera *Crotalus* and *Sistrurus* are characterized by rattles on the tip of the tail. *Sistrurus* have nine large plates on top of the head, whereas *Crotalus* have smaller, more numerous, dorsal head scales, arranged asymmetrically. All species of *Crotalus* are live-bearers, most aggregate in dens for winter hibernation, and the males of most species are aggressive toward one another during the spring mating season when they often are observed in combat bouts. These bouts, or "combat dances," involve pushing and intertwining of the anterior portion of the bodies, often with the heads and necks held vertically. Larger males usually win by driving the smaller males away.

WESTERN RATTLESNAKE
CROTALUS VIRIDIS (RAFINESQUE)

60. Western Rattlesnake *(Crotalus viridus lutosus),* Harney Co., Oregon.

This is the only rattlesnake and the only dangerously venomous snake in the Northwest.

Crotalus viridis is a medium-sized rattlesnake, being much smaller than the Western Diamondback Rattlesnake *(C. atrox),* but larger than the Sidewinder *(C. cerastes),* both of which are southwestern species. The largest *C. viridis* ever taken in the Northwest was 150 cm TL, but any specimen over 122 cm is a very large animal, and 75 to 90 cm TL is the normal adult size. This rattlesnake has a wide triangular head, thin neck, heavy body, and thick, short tail which terminates in a rattle. They also have undivided anterior caudal scales, a vertically elliptical pupil, and a distinct pit in the loreal scale between the nostril and the eye. They have dark blotches on a lighter background and a dark stripe from the eye to the angle of the jaw. The three subspecies in our area have similar scale counts. There are 23 to 29 rows of dorsal scales (usually 27 in *C.v. viridis* and 25 in the others); the lower 1 to 3 scale rows may be smooth, but the others are keeled. In males there are 161 to 190 ventrals and 18 to 31 caudals; in females 170 to 196 ventrals and 15 to 25 caudals. Upper labials are 10 to 19, usually 15, and lower

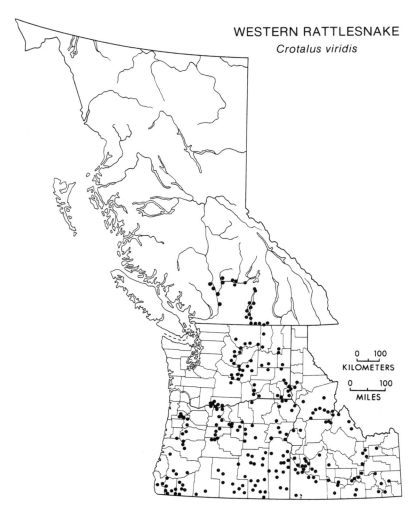

WESTERN RATTLESNAKE
Crotalus viridis

0   100
KILOMETERS
0   100
MILES

labials are 11 to 20, usually 16.

HABITAT. The Western Rattlesnake occupies many different habitats from sandy deserts to woodlands, from near sea level up to 3,350 m in California, but generally below 2,280 m in the Northwest. Residents of the Northwest believe that a number of rattlesnake species are found in their area including Sidewinders, Diamondbacks, and Timber Rattlers. This supposed diversity is because of the wide range of habitats and the variation in color of *Crotalus viridis*. They are most common near den areas, which are normally south-facing rocky slopes that are not shaded by vegetation.

VARIATION. Three of the eight subspecies of the Western Rattlesnake in the United States and Canada occur in the Northwest. The three subspecies differ mostly in color pattern, but there are zones of intergradation between subspecies and locally variable populations. The color of rattlesnakes usually resembles the substrate of the area. A desert-dwelling snake will blend with the sand and snakes living in areas with lava will be very dark.

The Great Basin Rattlesnake, *Crotalus viridis lutosus,* has less distinct markings along the side of the head than *C. v. viridis.* The light postocular band is two or more scales wide and fades into the ground color. The ground color is buff, light gray, or light brown. The 32 to 49 (average 40.2) body blotches are irregular in shape and tend to have light centers. The areas between the blotches are as wide or wider than the blotches. The lateral secondary blotches are faint or absent. This subspecies occurs in the desert regions of southern Idaho and southeastern Oregon.

The Northern Pacific Rattlesnake, *Crotalus viridis oreganus,* has head markings like *C. v. lutosus* but darker ground color (dark brown, dark gray or even black). The 20 to 41 (average 33.1) blotches have uneven edges, and the blotches are wider than the spaces between them. The secondary lateral blotches are conspicuous. The Northern Pacific Rattlesnake is the only subspecies in British Columbia and Washington. It also occurs in western and northern Oregon; and in west-central Idaho along the western half of the canyon of the Salmon River, the lower Clearwater drainage, and the Snake River Canyon in the vicinity of Hell's Canyon northward to Lewiston.

The Prairie Rattlesnake, *Crotalus viridis viridis,* has a wide distinct dark stripe from the eye to the angle of the jaw, which is bordered on either side by straight-edged light bands. The postocular white bands are 1 to 1½ scales wide. The ground color is greenish to olive brown with 33 to 57 (average 43.7) dark brown blotches. The blotches are straight-edged and surrounded with light-colored scales. Secondary blotches are present along the sides. The Prairie Rattlesnake barely enters the Northwest in east-central Idaho in the Salmon river country of Idaho, Lemhi, and Valley Cos.

LIFE HISTORY. In the deserts of the Great Basin, Western Rattlesnakes *(Crotalus viridis lutosus)* often den with other species, usually Racers, Striped Whipsnakes, and Gopher Snakes in various combinations. In northern Utah, they arrive at the dens from late September to early November, and individuals normally return to the same den each year. They hibernate for about 210 days. During the period of hibernation, they may suffer as high as 34% mortality, and the survivors will have lost 7 to 8% of their initial body weight. They emerge from the dens in late April and mate during May. During the mating season, males may be seen in combat near the dens. Only about one-half of the adult females are pregnant in a given year, suggesting that they produce young every other year. Females give birth to fully developed (and fully venomous) young in the autumn (mid-September to October). In our area, reported litter sizes range from 1 to 25, but normal litters are: *C. v. lutosus,* 6 to 9; *C. v. oreganus,* 3 to 5; and *C. v. viridis,* 9 to 12. In southwestern Idaho, the average litter size of *C. v. lutosus* is 8.3, and there is a high correlation between female size and litter size, with larger females producing larger litters. Newborn measure 242 to 270 mm TL. Males reach mature size in their second year, but females are not mature until their fourth year. As is often the case in species with male combat, males are the larger sex. Mature males in northern Utah range in size from 65 to 121 and mature females from 55 to 107 cm SVL.

Rattlesnakes are most active at night and at dusk; in cool weather they may be active during the day. Rattlesnakes primarily eat warm-blooded prey such as mice, wood rats, ground squirrels, and rabbits, which they find using the heat-sensitive lining of the loreal pit. They also have been seen climbing trees and feeding on nesting birds. They rarely take lizards and amphibians. In one study in southeastern Idaho, the diet of Western Rattlesnakes was 80% (by volume) ground squirrels, *Spermophilus townsendi.* It was estimated that the rattlesnakes annually consume 25% of the available ground squirrels.

Rattlesnakes in the Northwest are not as aggressive as in other areas, but they must be treated with respect. When cornered, the rattlesnake assumes an aggressive coil with the head raised high above the body and the neck in an S-shaped curve. It is possible for a rattlesnake to strike the full length of its body, or even further, if it strikes downhill. It is not uncommon for a rattlesnake to lie quietly and allow a person to pass within a few centimeters of it without rattling; on the other hand, some may rattle at a great distance. There are reports of hearing snakes rattle several hundred meters away. Rattles are interlocked segments of thickened skin from the terminal cone of the tail. Each shedding adds one segment to the base of the rattle. Because a snake often sheds 2 to 3 times each year, the number of segments on the rattle is not indicative of the age of the snake. There are rarely more than 10 to 12 segments on a rattle because the outer ones wear out or break and fall off.

SNAKE BITE. The fangs of rattlesnakes and other vipers are long, hollow, and erected when the mouth is opened. Rattlesnakes do not usually bite and hold on, rather they strike with a stabbing motion, inject venom and then withdraw. The venom, which primarily acts by digesting tissues, especially blood cells, is produced by large modified salivary glands. Dead rattlesnakes can bite! There are many records of people being bitten by snakes that have been cut into pieces. It is wise to treat "dead" snakes with the same care as live ones.

A survey of snake bite in the Northwest (Oregon, Washington, and Idaho) from 1950 to 1959 revealed that 49 people per year were bitten by rattlesnakes, but that only about 10 per year were hospitalized and half of these were not bitten seriously. During this ten-year-period only one person died of snake bite; during this same period of time, ten people in the Northwest are known to have died from bee or wasp stings.

REFERENCES. Diller (1981), Glissmeyer (1951), Hirth (1966), Kardong (1980), Klauber (1972), Parker and Brown (1973), Parrish (1980).

GLOSSARY

AESTIVATION — Summer dormancy to escape hot and dry periods.

AMPLEXUS — Clasping of a female by a male frog or salamander during mating.

ANTERIOR — Pertaining to the head end.

AUTOTOMY — Self amputation; the loss of the tail in salamanders and lizards.

BALANCER — Lateral growth below each eye of the early larval stages of some salamanders.

CAUDAL — Pertaining to the tail, caudal scales (caudals) of reptiles are those on the ventral surface of the tail.

CLOACA — The single chamber through which the contents of the digestive, excretory, and reproductive systems pass. Opens to the outside at the vent (cloacal opening).

DISTAL — Away from the base or point of attachment (body); the outermost parts of limbs or tail; as opposed to proximal (near).

DORSAL — Pertaining to the back (dorsum).

ECTOTHERMIC — Body temperature controlled by environment, no internal regulation.

FEMORAL PORES — A single row of skin glands located along the lower rear edge of the thigh in lizards.

GRANULAR GLANDS — In the skin of amphibians, the distasteful secretions of the glands function to repulse predators.

HEMIPENES — Paired, eversible copulatory organs in male snakes and lizards (singular, hemipenis).

IRIDOPHORES — Pigment cells producing white or metallic colors.

LATERAL — Pertaining to the side.

LONGITUDINAL — Extending lengthwise.

MAXILLARY TEETH — Teeth on the maxillary bones, located along the sides of the upper jaw.

MEDIAL — Pertaining to the middle, or toward the middle.

MELANISTIC — Color pattern obliterated by excessive number of melanophores causing the animal to appear very dark or uniformly black.

MELANOPHORES — Pigment cells causing black or dark brown coloration.

MENTAL GLAND — On the chin of adult male salamanders, serves to stimulate females during courtship.

METAMORPHOSIS — The change from larva to terrestrial adult in amphibians.

NARIS — External opening of the nasal passage (plural, nares). Internal nares (choanae) open into the mouth.

310

NEOTENY — Condition of prolonged larval period or failure to metamorphose at the normal time. Often intended to include attainment of sexual maturity in the larval form.

NOXIOUS — Distasteful or repulsive.

ORBIT — Eye socket.

OVIPAROUS — Eggs deposited; embryonic development outside of the female's body.

OVIPOSIT — To deposit eggs.

OVOVIVIPAROUS — Eggs retained in the body during development. Females give birth to young but there is no exchange of nutrients between female and young.

PAEDOGENESIS — The precocious development of sexual maturity in larval individuals.

PAROTOID GLAND — Concentration of granular glands located in the skin on the rear corners of the head of some amphibians.

PHALANGES — Bones in the fingers and toes (singular, phalange or phalanx).

POISON GLANDS — Granular glands.

POSTERIOR — Pertaining to the rear portion of the body.

PREMAXILLARY TEETH — Teeth on the premaxillary bone, located in the anterior medial portion of the upper jaw.

PROXIMAL — Near the base or point of attachment (body), as opposed to distal (away from).

SYMPATRIC — Two or more species occurring in the same area.

SVL — Snout-vent length, measured from tip of snout to anterior margin of vent.

TL — Total length, measured from tip of snout to tip of tail.

TRANSVERSE — Extending from side to side.

TYMPANUM — The membrane covering the middle ear in frogs, the ear drum.

VASA DEFERENTIA — The ducts conducting sperm away from the testes (singular, vas deferens).

VENT — Cloacal opening.

VENTRAL — Pertaining to the underside, or venter. Ventral scales (ventrals) of reptiles are those on the underside of the body.

VIVIPAROUS — Females give birth to young and provide nutrients to developing embryos.

GENERAL REFERENCES

Altig, R. G. 1970. A key to the tadpoles of continental United States and Canada. Herpetologica 26 (2): 180-207.

Anderson, O. I., and J. R. Slater. 1941. Life zone distribution of the Oregon reptiles. Occas. Pap. Dept. Biol. Coll. Puget Sound 15: 109-119.

Baxter, G. T. and M. D. Stone. 1980. Amphibians and reptiles of Wyoming. Wyoming Game and Fish Department Bull. 16, i-vi+137 pp.

Behler, J. L. and F. W. King. 1979. The Audubon Society field guide to North American reptiles and amphibians. Alfred A. Knopf, New York, 719 pp.

Bishop, S. C. 1943. Handbook of salamanders. Comstock, Ithaca, i-xiv+555 pp.

Brattstrom, B. H. 1963. A preliminary review of the thermal requirements of amphibians. Ecology 44 (2): 238-255.

Brattstrom, B. H. 1965. Body temperatures of reptiles. Amer. Midl. Nat. 73(2): 376-422.

Brodie, E. D., Jr. 1977. Salamander antipredator postures. Copeia 1977 (3): 523-535.

Brown, W. C. and J. R. Slater. 1939. The amphibians and reptiles of the islands of the state of Washington. Occas. Pap. Dept. Biol. Coll. Puget Sound 4: 6-31.

Campbell, R. W., M. G. Shepard, B. M. van der Raay and P. T. Gregory. 1982. A bibliography of Pacific Northwest Herpetology. British Columbia Prov. Mus. Heritage Record No. 14, i-vi+152 pp.

Carl, G. C. 1943. The amphibians of British Columbia. British Columbia Prov. Mus. Handbook No. 2, 62 pp.

Carl, G. C. 1968. The reptiles of British Columbia. British Columbia Prov. Mus. Handbook No. 3, 65 pp.

Carr, A. 1952. Handbook of turtles. Cornell University Press, Ithaca, i-xviii+542 pp.

Catalogue of American Amphibians and Reptiles. 1963. et seq. American Society of Ichthyologists and Herpetologists (1963-1970), Society for the Study of Amphibians and Reptiles (1971-present).

Collins, J. T., J. E. Huheey, J. L. Knight and H. M. Smith. 1978. Standard common and current scientific names for North American amphibians and reptiles. Soc. Study Amph. Rept. Misc. Publ., Herp. Circ. No. 7, i-iv+36 pp.

Cope, E. D. 1889. The Batrachia of North America. Bull. U. S. Natl. Mus. 34:1-525+86 plates.

Cope, E. D. 1900. The crocodilians, lizards, and snakes of North America. U.S. Natl. Mus. Report for the year ending June 30, 1898, Part II:151-1294+36 plates.

Dickerson, M. C. 1906. The frog book. Doubleday, Page and Co., New York, i-xviii+253 pp.

Dunn, E. R. 1926. Salamanders of the family Plethodontidae. Smith College, Fiftieth Anniversary Publ. Serv. Vol. 7, i-viii+441 pp.

Ernst, C. H. and R. W. Barbour. 1972. Turtles of the United States. University Press of Kentucky, Lexington, i-x+347 pp.

Fichter, E. and A. D. Linder. 1964. The amphibians of Idaho. Idaho State University, Pocatello, Spec. Publ., 34 pp.

Fitch, H. S. 1936. Amphibians and reptiles of the Rogue River Basin, Oregon. Amer. Midl. Nat. 17 (3):634-652.

Fitch, H. S. 1970. Reproductive cycles in lizards and snakes. Univ. Kansas Mus. Nat. Hist., Misc. Publ. 52:1-247.

Gordon, K. 1939. The Amphibia and Reptilia of Oregon. Oregon State Monographs, Studies in Zoology 1:1-82.

Green, D. M. and R. W. Campbell. The amphibians of British Columbia. British Columbia Prov. Mus. Handbook, in press.

Gregory, P. T. and R. W. Campbell. The reptiles of British Columbia. British Columbia Prov. Mus. Handbook, in press.

Leviton, A. 1972. Reptiles and amphibians of North America. Doubleday and Co., Inc., New York, 250 pp.

Linder, A. D. and E. Fichter. 1977. The amphibians and reptiles of Idaho. Idaho State University Press, Pocatello, 78 pp.

Livezey, R. L. and A. H. Wright. 1947. A synoptic key to the salientian eggs of the United States. Amer. Midl. Nat. 37(1):179-222.

Owen, R. P. 1940. A list of the reptiles of Washington. Copeia 1940(3):169-172.

Pickwell, G. 1947. Amphibians and reptiles of the Pacific States. Stanford University Press, Stanford, i-xiv+236 pp.

Pope, C. H. 1939. Turtles of the United States and Canada. Alfred A. Knopf, New York, i-xx+343 pp.

Pritchard, P. C. H. 1979. Encyclopedia of turtles. T. F. H. Publ., Inc., Neptune, New Jersey, 895 pp.

Shaw, C. E. and S. Campbell. 1974. Snakes of the American West. Alfred A. Knopf, New York, i-xii+332 pp.

Slater, J. R. 1941. The distribution of amphibians and reptiles in Idaho. Occas. Pap. Dept. Biol. Coll. Puget Sound 14:78-109.

Slater, J. R. 1955. Distribution of Washington amphibians. Occas. Pap. Dept. Biol. Coll. Puget Sound 16:122-154.

Slater, J. R. 1963a. A key to the adult reptiles of Washington State. Occas. Pap. Dept. Biol. Univ. Puget Sound 23:209-211.

Slater, J. R. 1963b. Distribution of Washington reptiles. Occas. Pap. Dept. Biol. Univ. Puget Sound 24:212-232.

Slater, J. R. 1964. County records of amphibians for Washington. Occas. Pap. Dept. Biol. Univ. Puget Sound 26:237-242.

Slater, J. R. and W. C. Brown. 1941. Island records of amphibians and reptiles for Washington. Occas. Pap. Dept. Biol. Coll. Puget Sound 13:74-77.

Slevin, J. R. 1928. The amphibians of western North America. Occas. Pap. Calif. Acad. Sci. 16:1-152.

Slevin, J. R. 1934. A handbook of reptiles and amphibians of the Pacific states including certain eastern species. Calif. Acad. Sci. Spec. Publ., 73 pp.

Smith, H.M. 1946. Handbook of lizards. Cornell University Press, Ithaca, i-xxi+557 pp.

Smith, H.M. 1978. Amphibians of North America. Golden Press, New York, 160 pp.

Smith, H. M. and E. D. Brodie, Jr. 1982. Reptiles of North America. Golden Press, New York, 240 pp.

Stebbins, R.C. 1951. Amphibians of western North America. Univ. Calif. Press, Berkeley, i-xviii+539 pp.

Stebbins, R. C. 1954. Amphibians and reptiles of western North America. McGraw-Hill, New York, i-xxiv+536 pp.

Stebbins, R. C. 1966. A field guide to western reptiles and amphibians. Houghton Mifflin Co., Boston, i-xiv+279 pp.

Storer, T. I. 1925. A synopsis of the Amphibia of California. Univ. Calif. Publ. Zool. 27:1-342.

Storm, R. M. 1966. Amphibians and reptiles. Northwest Science 40(4):138-141.

Tanner, W. W. 1941. The reptiles and amphibians of Idaho No. I. Great Basin Naturalist 2(2):87-97.

Van Denburgh, J. 1897. The reptiles of the Pacific Coast and Great Basin: an account of the species known to inhabit Oregon, Washington, Idaho, and Nevada. Occas. Pap. Calif. Acad. Sci. 5:1-236.

Van Denburgh, J. 1912. Notes on some reptiles and amphibians from Oregon, Idaho, and Utah. Proc. Calif. Acad. Sci. (Fourth Series) 3:155-160.

Van Denburgh, J. 1922. The reptiles of western North America - an account of the species known to inhabit California and Oregon, Washington, Idaho, Utah, Nevada, Arizona, British Columbia, Sonora and Lower California. Vol. 1 - Lizards and Vol. 2 - Snakes and Turtles. Occas. Pap. Calif. Acad. Sci. 10, 1028 pp.

Wake, D. B. 1966. Comparative osteology and evolution of the lungless salamanders, family Plethodontidae. Mem. So. Calif. Acad. Sci. 4:1-111.

Wright, A. H. and A. A. Wright. 1949. Handbook of frogs. Cornell University Press, Ithaca, i-xii+640 pp.

Wright, A. H. and A. A. Wright. 1957. Handbook of snakes. Cornell University Press, Ithaca, Vols. I and II, i-xx,i-x+1105 pp.

Zim, H. S. and H. M. Smith. 1953. Reptiles and amphibians, a guide to familiar American species. Golden Press, New York, 157 pp.

LITERATURE CITED

Allan, D. M. 1973. Some relationships of vocalization to behavior in the Pacific treefrog, *Hyla regilla*. Herpetologica 29(4):366-371.

Altig, R. G. and E. D. Brodie, Jr. 1968. Albinistic and cyanistic frogs from Oregon. Wasmann J. Biol. 26(2):241-242.

Altig, R. G. and E. D. Brodie, Jr. 1971. Foods of *Plethodon larselli, Plethodon dunni* and *Ensatina eschscholtzi* in the Columbia River Gorge, Multnomah County, Oregon. Amer. Midl. Nat. 85(1):226-228.

Altig, R. G. and E. D. Brodie, Jr. 1972. Laboratory behavior of *Ascaphus truei* tadpoles. J. Herpetology 6(1):21-24.

Alvarado, R. H. 1967. The significance of grouping water conservation in *Ambystoma*. Copeia 1967(3):667-668.

Anderson, J. D. 1967. A comparison of the life histories of coastal and montane populations of *Ambystoma macrodactylum* in California. Amer. Midl. Nat. 77(2):323-355.

Anderson, J. D. 1968. A comparison of the food habits of *Ambystoma macrodactylum sigillatum, Ambystoma macrodactylum croceum.* and *Ambystoma tigrinum califoriense.* Herpetologica 24(4): 273-284.

Antonelli, A. L, R. A. Nussbaum and S. D. Smith. 1972. Comparative food habits of four species of stream-dwelling vertebrates *(Dicamptodon ensatus, D. copei, Cottus tenius, Salmo gairdneri).* Northwest Science 46(4):277-289.

Axtell, R. W. 1972. Hybridization between western collared lizards with a proposed taxonomic rearrangement. Copeia 1972(4):707-727.

Bennion, R. S. and W. S. Parker. 1976. Field observations on courtship and aggressive behavior in desert striped whipsnakes, *Masticophis t. taeniatus.* Herpetologica 32(1):30-35.

Black, J. R. and R. M. Storm. 1970. Notes on the herpetology of Grant Co., Oregon. Great Basin Naturalist 30(1):9-12.

Blanchard, F. N. 1933. Eggs and young of the smooth green snake, *Liopeltis vernalis* (Harlan). Pap. Mich. Acad. Sci., Arts and Lett. 17:493-508.

Blanchard, F. N. 1942. The ring-neck snakes, genus *Diadophis.* Bull. Chicago Acad. Sci. 7(1):1-44.

Bragg, A. N. 1965. Gnomes of the night. University of Pennsylvania Press, Philadelphia, 127 pp.

Brame, A. H., Jr. and K. F. Murray. 1968. Three new slender salamanders *(Batrachoseps)* with a discussion of relationships and speciation within the genus. Bull. Los Angeles Nat. Hist. Mus. 4:1-35.

Breckenridge, W. J. 1944. Reptiles and amphibians of Minnesota. Univ. Minnesota Press, Minneapolis, i-xiv+202 pp.

Briggs, J. 1978. An asymptotic growth model allowing seasonal variation in growth rates, with application to a population of the Cascade frog, *Rana cascadae* (Amphibia, Anura, Ranidae). J. Herpetology 12(4):559-564.

Briggs, J. L. and R. M. Storm. 1970. Growth and population structure of the Cascade frog *Rana cascadae* Slater. Herpetologica 26(3):283-300.

Brodie, E. D., Jr. 1968a. Observations on the mental hedonic gland-clusters of western salamanders of the genus *Plethodon*. Herpetologica 24(3):248-250.

Brodie, E. D., Jr. 1968b. Investigations on the skin toxin of the adult rough-skinned newt, *Taricha granulosa*. Copeia 1968(2):307-313.

Brodie, E. D., Jr. 1970. Western salamanders of the genus *Plethodon:* systematics and geographic variation. Herpetologica 26(4):468-516.

Brodie, E.D., Jr. 1982. Toxic salamanders. J. Amer. Med. Assoc. 247(10): 1408.

Brodie, E. D., Jr. and L. S. Gibson. 1969. Defensive behavior and skin glands of the northwestern salamander, *Ambystoma gracile*. Herpetologica 25(3):187-194.

Brodie, E. D., Jr., J. L. Hensel, Jr. and J. A. Johnson. 1974a. Toxicity of the urodele amphibians *Taricha, Notophthalmus, Cynops,* and *Paramesotriton* (Salamandridae). Copeia 1974(2):506-511.

Brodie, E. D., Jr., J. A. Johnson and C. K. Dodd, Jr. 1974b. Immobility as a defensive behavior in salamanders. Herpetologica 30(1):79-85.

Brodie, E. D., Jr., R. A. Nussbaum and R. M. Storm. 1969. An egg-laying aggregation of five species of Oregon reptiles. Herpetologica 25(3):223-227.

Brown, H. A. 1975. Reproduction and development of the red-legged frog, *Rana aurora*, in northwestern Washington. Northwest Science 49(4):241-252.

Brown, H. A. 1976. The time-temperature relation of embryonic development in the northwestern salamander, *Ambystoma gracile*. Can. J. Zool. 54(4):552-558.

Brown, R. E. 1972. Size variation and food habits of larval bullfrogs, *Rana catesbeiana* Shaw, in western Oregon. Ph.D. Thesis, Oregon State University, Corvallis, 83 pp.

Brown, W. S. and W. S. Parker. 1976. Movement ecology of *Coluber constrictor* near communal hibernacula. Copeia 1976(2):225-242.

Burkholder, G. L. and J. M. Walker. 1973. Habitat and reproduction of the desert whiptail lizard. *Cnemidophorus tigris* Baird and Girard in southwestern Idaho at the northern part of its range. Herpetologica 29(1):76-83.

Burns, D. M. 1962. The taxonomic status of the salamander *Plethodon vandykei larselli*. Copeia 1962(1): 177-181.

Bury, R. B. 1973. Western *Plethodon:* systematics and biogeographic relationships of the *elongatus* group. Hiss News-Journal 1(2):56-57.

Bury, R. B. and J. H. Wolfheim. 1973. Aggression in free-living pond turtles *(Clemmys marmorata)*. Bioscience 23(11):659-662.

Bury, R. B., J. H. Wolfheim and R. A. Luchenbach. 1979. Agonistic behavior in free-living painted turtles *(Chrysemys picta belli).* Biol. Behav. 4:227-239.

Calef, G. W. 1973a. Natural mortality of tadpoles in a population of *Rana aurora.* Ecology 54(4):741-758.

Calef, G. W. 1973b. Spatial distribution and "effective" breeding population of red-legged frogs *(Rana aurora)* in Marion Lake, British Columbia. Can. Field-Nat. 87(3):279-284.

Campbell, R. W. 1969. Notes on some foods of the wandering garter snake on Mitlenatch Island, British Columbia. Syesis 2(½):183-187.

Chandler, A. C. 1918. The western newt or water dog, *Notophthalmus torosus,* a natural enemy of mosquitoes. Oregon Agric. Coll. Exp. Sta. Bull. 152:1-24.

Christiansen, J. L. and E. O. Moll. 1973. Latitudinal reproductive variation within a single subspecies of painted turtle, *Chrysemys picta bellii.* Herpetologica 29(2):152-163.

Clark, D. R. and C. S. Lieb. 1973. Notes on reproduction in the night snake *(Hypsiglena torquata).* Southwest Nat. 18(2):248-252.

Coates, M. L., E. Benedict and C. L. Stephens. 1970. An unusual aggregation of the newt *Taricha granulosa granulosa.* Copeia 1970(1):176-178.

Cook, S. F., Jr. 1960. On the occurrence and life history of *Contia tenuis.* Herpetologica 16(3):163-173.

Davis, W. C. and V. C. Twitty. 1964. Courtship behavior and reproductive isolation in species of *Taricha* (Amphibia, Caudata). Copeia 1964(4):601-610.

Detling, L. E. 1968. Historical background of the flora of the Pacific Northwest. Bull. Mus. Nat. Hist. Univ. Oregon 13:1-57.

Devine, M. C. 1975. Copulatory plugs in snakes: enforced chastity. Science 187(4179):844-845.

Devine, M. C. 1977. Copulatory plugs, restricted mating opportunities and reproductive competition among male garter snakes. Nature 267(5609):345-346.

Dickman, M. 1968. The effect of grazing by tadpoles on the structure of a periphyton community. Ecology 49(6):1188-1190.

Diller, L. V. 1981. Comparative ecology of Great Basin rattlesnakes *(Crotalus viridis lutosus)* and Great Basin gopher snakes *(Pituophis melanoleucus deserticola)* and their impact on small mammal populations in the Snake River Birds of Prey Natural Area. Ph.D. Dissertation, University of Idaho, Moscow, i-xi+89 pp.

Diller, L. V. and R. L. Wallace. 1981. Additional distribution records and abundance of three species of snakes in southwestern Idaho. Great Basin Naturalist 41(1):154-157.

Dorsch, A. J. 1967. Aggregational behavior in the boreal toad, *Bufo boreas boreas* Baird and Girard. M.S. Thesis, Oregon State University, Corvallis, 61 pp.

Dumas, P. C. 1955. Eggs of the salamander *Plethodon dunni* in nature. Copeia 1955(1):65.

Dumas, P. C. 1956. The ecological relations of sympatry in *Plethodon dunni* and *Plethodon vehiculum*. Ecology 37(3):484-495.

Dumas, P. C. 1964. Species-pair allopatry in the genera *Rana* and *Phrynosoma*. Ecology 45(1):178-181.

Dumas, P. C. 1966. Studies of the *Rana* species complex in the Pacific Northwest. Copeia 1966(1):60-74.

Dunlap, D. G. 1955. Inter- and intraspecific variation in Oregon frogs of the genus *Rana*. Amer. Midl. Nat. 54(2):314-331.

Dunlap, D. G. and R. M. Storm. 1951. The Cascade frog in Oregon. Copeia 1951(1):81.

Dunn, E. R. 1940. The races of *Ambystoma tigrinum*. Copeia 1940(3):154-162.

Eagleson, G. W. 1976. A comparison of the life histories and growth patterns of populations of the salamander *Ambystoma gracile* (Baird) from permanent low-altitude and montane lakes. Cn. J. Zool. 54(12):2098-2111.

Efford, I. E. and J. A. Mathias. 1969. A comparison of two salamander populations in Marion Lake, British Columbia. Copeia 1969(4):723-736.

Efford, I. E. and K. Tsumura. 1973. A comparison of the food of salamanders and fish in Marion Lake, British Columbia. Trans. Amer. Fish. Soc. 102(1):33-47.

Emlen, S. T. 1968. Territoriality in the bullfrog, *Rana catesbeiana*. Copeia 1968(2):240-243.

Evenden, F. G., Jr. 1946. Notes on the herpetology of Elmore County, Idaho. Copeia 1946(4):256-257.

Evenden, F. G., Jr. 1948. Distribution of the turtles of western Oregon. Herpetologica 4(6):201-204.

Fairchild, L. 1981. Mate selection and behavioral thermoregulation in Fowler's toads. Science 212:950-951.

Feder, J. H., G. Z. Wurst and D. B. Wake. 1978. Genetic variation in western salamanders of the genus *Plethodon*, and the status of *Plethodon gordoni*. Herpetologica 34(1):64-69.

Feldman, M. 1982. Notes on reproduction in *Clemmys marmorata*. Herpetological Review 13(1):10-11.

Ferguson, D.E. 1961. The geographic variation of *Ambystoma macrodactylum* Baird, with the description of two new subspecies. Amer. Midl. Nat. 65(2):311-338.

Ferguson, D. E., K. E. Payne and R. M. Storm. 1956. The geographic distribution of the subspecies of *Pituophis catenifer* Blainville in Oregon. Copeia 1956(4):255-257.

Fitch, H. S. 1940a. A biogeographical study of the *ordinoides* Artenkreis of garter snakes (genus *Thamnophis*). Univ. Calif. Publ. Zool. 44(1):1-150.

318

Fitch, H. S. 1940b. A field study of the growth and behavior of the fence lizard. Univ. Calif. Publ. Zool. 44(2): 151-172.

Fitch, H. S. 1941a. The feeding habits of California garter snakes. Calif. Fish and Game 27(2):2-32.

Fitch, H. S. 1941b. Geographic variation in garter snakes of the species *Thamnophis sirtalis* in the Pacific Coast region of North America. Amer. Midl. Nat. 26(3):570-592.

Fitch, H. S. 1949. Study of snake populations in central California. Amer. Midl Nat. 41(3):513-579.

Fitch, H. S. 1965. An ecological study of the garter snake, *Thamnophis sirtalis*. Univ. Kansas Publ. Mus. Nat. Hist. 15(10):493-564.

Fitch, H. S. and T. P. Maslin. 1961. Occurrence of the garter snake, *Thamnophis sirtalis* in the Great Plains and Rocky Mountains. Univ. Kansas Publ. Mus. Nat. Hist. 13(5):289-308.

Formanowicz, D. R., Jr. and E. D. Brodie, Jr. 1979. Palatablility and antipredator behavior of selected *Rana* to the shrew *Blarina*. Amer. Midl. Nat. 101(2):456-458.

Formanowicz, D. R., Jr. and E. D. Brodie, Jr. 1982. Relative palatabliities of members of a larval amphibian community. Copeia 1982(1):91-97.

Fox, W. 1951. Relationships among the garter snakes of the *Thamnophis elegans* Rassenkreis. Univ. Calif. Publ. Zool. 50(5):485-530.

Frost, D. R. and T. R. Van Devender. 1979. The relationship of the groundsnakes *Sonora semiannulata* and *S. episcopa* (Serpentes: Colubridae). Occas. Pap. Mus. Zool. Louisiana State Univ. 52:1-9.

Gibbons, J. W. 1968. Population structure and survivorship in the painted turtle, *Chrysemys picta*. Copeia 1968(2):260-268.

Glissmeyer, H. R. 1951. Egg production of the Great Basin rattlesnake. Herpetologica 7(1):24-27.

Goldberg, S. R. 1972. Reproduction in the southern alligator lizard *Gerrhonotus multicarinatus*. Herpetologica 28(3):267-273.

Goldberg, S. 1975. Reproduction in the sagebrush lizard, *S. graciosus*. Amer. Midl. Nat. 93(1):177-187.

Graf, W. 1939. The distribution and habits of amphibia and reptiles in Lincoln, Benton, and Linn Counties. M. S. Thesis, Oregon State University, Corvallis, 93 pp.

Gregory, P. T. 1978. Feeding habits and diet overlap of three species of garter snakes (*Thamnophis*) on Vancouver Island. Can. J. Zool. 56(9):1967-1974.

Gregory, P. T. 1979. Predator avoidance behavior of the red-legged frog (*Rana aurora*). Herpetologica 35(2):175-184.

Gregory, P. T. and A. G. Duncan McIntosh. 1980. Thermal niche overlap in garter snakes (*Thamnophis*) on Vancouver Island. Can. J. Zool. 58(3):351-355.

Haertel, J. D. 1970. Experimental hybridization between *Rana pretiosa* and *Rana cascadae*. Herpetologica 26(4):436-446.

319

Hanlin, H. G., J. J. Beatty and S. W. Hanlin. 1979. A nest site of the western red-backed salamander *Plethodon vehiculum* (Cooper). J. Herpetology 13(2):214-216.

Hansen, H. P. 1947. Postglacial forest succession, climate, and chronology in the Pacific Northwest. Trans. Amer. Philos. Soc. 37(1):1-130.

Hansen, R. M. 1950. Sexual behavior in two male gopher snakes. Herpetologica 6(5):120.

Heatwole, H. 1961. Habitat selection and activity of the wood frog, *Rana sylvatica* Le Conte. Amer. Midl. Nat. 66(2):301-313.

Hebard, W. B. 1950. Relationships and variation in the garter snakes, genus *Thamnophis* of the Puget Sound region of Washington state. Herpetologica 6(4):97-101.

Hebard, W. B. 1951a. Notes on the ecology of garter snakes in the Puget Sound region. Herpetologica 7(2):61-62.

Hebard, W. B. 1951b. Notes on the life history of the Puget Sound garter snake, *Thamnophis ordinoides*. Herpetologica 7(4): 177-179.

Henderson, B. A. 1973. The specialized feeding behavior of *Ambystoma gracile* in Marion Lake, British Columbia. Can. Field Nat. 87(2):151-154.

Hendrickson, J. R. 1954. Ecology and systematics of salamanders of the genus *Batrachoseps*. Univ. Calif. Publ. Zool. 54(1):1-46.

Herreid, C. F., II. and S. Kinney. 1966. Survival of Alaskan woodfrog *(Rana sylvatica)* larvae. Ecology 47(6):1039-1040.

Herreid, C. F., II. and S. Kinney. 1967. Temperature and development of the wood frog, *Rana sylvatica* in Alaska. Ecology 48(4):579-590.

Heusser, C. J. 1960. Late-Pleistocene environments of North Pacific North America. Amer. Geog. Soc. Spec. Publ. 35, 308 pp.

Heusser, C. J. 1965. A Pleistocene phytogeographical sketch of the Pacific Northwest and Alaska. *In:* Wright, H. E. and D. G. Frey (eds.), The Quaternary of the United States. Princeton University Press, Princeton, pp. 469-483.

Highton, R. and A. Larson. 1979. The genetic relationships of the salamanders of the genus *Plethodon*. Syst. Zool. 28(4):579-599.

Hirth, H. F. 1966. Weight changes and mortality of three species of snakes during hibernation. Herpetologica 22(1):8-12.

Howard, R.D. 1978a. The influence of male-defended oviposition sites on early embryo mortality in bullfrogs. Ecology 59(4):789-798.

Howard, R. D. 1978b. The evolution of mating strategies in bullfrogs, *Rana catesbeiana*. Evolution 32(4):850-871.

Howard, R. D. 1980. Mating behavior and mating success in woodfrogs, *Rana sylvatica*. Anim. Behav. 28(3):705-716.

Hoyer, R. F. 1974. Description of a rubber boa *(Charina bottae)* population from western Oregon. Herpetologica 30(3):275-283.

Hubbard, M. E. 1903. Correlated protective devices in some California salamanders. Univ. Calif. Publ. Zool. 1(4):157-170.

Hudson, G. E. 1957. Late parturition in the rubber snake. Copeia 1957(1):51-52.

Ingram, W. and W. W. Tanner. 1971. A taxonomic study of *Crotaphytus collaris* between the Rio Grande and Colorado rivers. Brigham Young Univ. Sci. Bull., Biol. Ser. 13(2):1-29.

Jameson, D. L. 1956. Growth, dispersal and survival of the Pacific tree frog. Copeia 1956(1):25-29.

Jameson, D. L. 1957. Population structure and homing responses in the Pacific tree frog. Copeia 1957(3):221-228.

Jameson, D. L., J. P. Mackey and R. C. Richmond. 1966. The systematics of the Pacific tree frog, *Hyla regilla*. Proc. Calif. Acad. Sci., Fourth Series 33(19):551-619.

Johnson, J. A. and E. D. Brodie, Jr. 1975. The selective advantage of the defensive posture of the newt *Taricha granulosa*. Amer. Midl. Nat. 93(1):139-148.

Johnson, O. 1965. Early development, embryonic temperature tolerance and rate of development in *Rana pretiosa luteiventris* Thompson. Ph.D. Thesis. Oregon State University, Corvallis, 74 pp.

Jorgensen, C. D., A. M. Orton and W. W. Tanner. 1963. Voice of the leopard lizard *Crotaphytus wislizeni* Baird and Girard. Proc. Utah Acad. Sci. Arts Lett. 40(1):115-116.

Kardong, K. V. 1980. Gopher snakes and rattlesnakes: presumptive Batesian mimicry. Northwest Science 54(1):1-4.

Kessel, B. 1965. Breeding dates of *Rana sylvatica* at College, Alaska. Ecology 46(1-2):206-207.

Kezer, J. and D. S. Farner. 1955. Life history patterns of the salamander *Ambystoma macrodactylum* in the high Cascade Mountains of southern Oregon. Copeia 1955(2):127-131.

Klauber, L. M. 1941. The long-nosed snakes of the genus *Rhinocheilus*. Tran. San Diego Soc. Nat. Hist. 9(29):289-332.

Klauber, L. M. 1972. Rattlesnakes. Vols. 1 and 2, 2nd Ed., University of Calif. Press, Berkeley and Los Angeles, 1533 pp.

Knudsen, J. W. 1960. The courtship and egg mass of *Ambystoma gracile* and *Ambystoma macrodactylum*. Copeia 1960(1):44-46.

Landreth, H. F. and D. E. Ferguson. 1967. Newt orientation by sun compass. Nature 215:516-518.

Licht, L. E. 1969a. Observations on the courtship behavior of *Ambystoma gracile*. Herpetologica 25(1):49-52.

Licht, L. E. 1969b. Comparative breeding behavior of the red-legged frog *(Rana aurora aurora)* and the western spotted frog *(Rana pretiosa pretiosa)* in southwestern British Columbia. Can. J. Zool. 47(6):1287-1299.

Licht, L. E. 1969c. Unusual aspects of anuran sexual behavior as seen in the red-legged frog, *Rana aurora aurora*. Can. J. Zool. 47(4):505-509.

Licht, L. E. 1971. Breeding habits and embryonic thermal requirements of the frogs, *Rana aurora aurora* and *Rana pretiosa pretiosa*, in the Pacific Northwest. Ecology 52(1):116-124.

Licht, L. E. 1973. Behavior and sound production by the northwestern salamander, *Ambystoma gracile.* Can. J. Zool. 51(10):1055-1056.

Licht, L. E. 1974. Survival of embryos, tadpoles, and adults of the frogs *Rana aurora aurora* and *Rana pretiosa pretiosa* sympatric in southwestern British Columbia. Can. J. Zool. 52(5):613-627.

Licht, L. E. 1975a. Growth and food of larval *Ambystoma gracile* from a lowland population in southwestern British Columbia. Can. J. Zool. 53(11):1716-1722.

Licht, L. E. 1975b. Comparative life history features of the western spotted frog, *Rana pretiosa,* from low- and high-elevation populations. Can. J. Zool. 53(9):1254-1257.

Licht, P., M. E. Feder and S. Bledsoe. 1975. Salinity tolerance and osmoregulation in the salamander *Batrachoseps.* J. Comp. Physiol. 102:123-134.

Linn, P. H. 1970. A study of two populations of *Sceloporus occidentalis* (Iguanidae) in Oregon. Oregon State Univ., Dept. Zool., Unpubl. Master's Thesis, 26 pp.

Livezey, R. L. 1959. The egg mass and larvae of *Plethodon elongatus* Van Denburgh. Herpetologica 15(1):41-42.

Logier, E. B. S. 1932. Some accounts of the amphibians and reptiles of British Columbia. Trans. Royal Can. Inst. 18, 2(53):311-336.

Lynch. J. F. 1981. Patterns of ontogenetic and geographic variation in the black salamander, *Aneides flavipunctatus* (Caudata: Plethodontidae). Smithsonian Contr. Zool. 324, i-iv+53pp.

MacGinitie, H. D. 1958. Climate since the late Cretaceous. *In:* Hubbs, C. L. (ed.), Zoogeography. Amer. Assoc. Adv. Sci. Publ. 51, pp. 61-79.

Mahmoud, I. Y. 1968. Nesting behavior in the western painted turtle, *Chrysemys picta belli.* Herpetologica 24(2):158-162.

Maiorana, V. C. 1976. Size and environmental predictability for salamanders. Evolution 30(3):599-613.

Maiorana, V. C. 1977. Tail autotomy, functional conflicts and their resolution by a salamander. Nature 265:533-535.

Martof, B. S. 1953a. Territoriality in the green frog, *Rana clamitans.* Ecology 34(1):165-174.

Martof, B. S. 1953b. Home range and movements of the green frog, *Rana clamitans.* Ecology 34(3):529-543.

Martof, B. S. 1956. Growth and development of the green frog, *Rana clamitans,* under natural conditions. Amer. Midl. Nat. 55(1):101-117.

Martof, B. S. and R. L. Humphries. 1959. Geographic variation in the wood frog, *Rana sylvatica.* Amer. Midl. Nat. 61(2):350-389.

322

Maslin, T. P. 1939. Egg-laying of the slender salamander *(Batrachoseps attenuatus)*. Copeia 1939(4):209-212.

Maslin, T.P. 1950. The production of sound in caudate Amphibia. Univ. Colorado Stud. Biol. 1:29-45.

McCoy, C. J. 1967. Natural history notes on *Crotaphytus wislizeni* (Reptilia; Iguanidae). Amer. Midl. Nat. 77(1):138-146.

McKenzie, D. S. and R. M. Storm. 1970. Patterns of habitat selection in the clouded salamander, *Aneides ferreus* (Cope). Herpetologica 26(4):450-454.

McKenzie, D. S. and R. M. Storm. 1971. Ontogenetic color patterns of the clouded salamander, *Aneides ferreus* (Cope). Herpetologica 27(2):142-147.

Metter, D. E. 1961. Water levels as an environmental factor in the breeding season of *Bufo boreas boreas* (Baird and Girard). Copeia 1961(4):488.

Metter, D. E. 1964a. A morphological and ecological comparison of two populations of the tailed frog, *Ascaphus truei* Stejneger. Copeia 1964(1):181-195.

Metter, D. E. 1964b. On breeding and sperm retention in *Ascaphus*. Copeia 1964(4):710-711.

Metter, D. E. 1967. Variation in the ribbed frog *Ascaphus truei* Stejneger. Copeia 1967(3):634-649.

Montanucci, R. R., R. W. Axtell and H. C. Dessauer. 1975. Evolutionary divergence among collared lizards *(Crotaphytus)*, with comments on the status of *Gambelia*. Herpetologica 31(3):336-347.

Moore, J. A. 1949. Geographic variation of adaptive characters in *Rana pipiens* Schreber. Evolution 3(1):1-24.

Morris, R. L. and W. W. Tanner. 1969. The ecology of the western spotted frog, *Rana pretiosa pretiosa* Baird and Girard, a life history study. Great Basin Naturalist 29(2):45-81.

Moyle, P. B. 1973. Effects of introduced bullfrogs, *Rana catesbeiana*, on the native frogs of the San Joaquin Valley, California. Copeia 1973(1):18-22.

Mueller, C. F. and R. E. Moore. 1969. Growth of the sagebrush lizard, *Sceloporus graciosus*, in Yellowstone National Park. Herpetologica 25(1):35-38.

Myers, G. S. and T. P. Maslin. 1948. The California plethodont salamander, *Aneides flavipunctatus* (Strauch), with description of a new subspecies and notes on other western *Aneides*. Proc. Biol. Soc. Wash. 61:127-135.

Neish, I. C. 1971. Comparison of size, structure, and distributional patterns of two salamander populations in Marion Lake, British Columbia. J. Fish. Res. Bd. Canada 28(1):49-58.

Noble, G. K. 1925. An outline of the relation of ontogeny to phylogeny within the Amphibia II. Amer. Mus. Novit. 166:1-10.

Nussbaum, R. A. 1969a. Nests and eggs of the Pacific giant salamander, *Dicamptodon ensatus* (Eschscholtz). Herpetologica 25(4):257-262.

Nussbaum, R. A. 1969b. A nest site of the Olympic salamander, *Rhyacotriton olympicus* (Gaige). Herpetologica 25(4):277-278.

Nussbaum, R. A. 1970. *Dicamptodon copei,* n. sp., from the Pacific Northwest, U.S.A. (Amphibia: Caudata: Ambystomatidae). Copeia 1970(3):506-514.

Nussbaum, R. A. 1976. Geographic variation and systematics of salamanders of the genus *Dicamptodon* Strauch (Ambystomatidae). Misc. Publ. Mus. Zool. Univ. Michigan 149:1-94.

Nussbaum, R. A. and E. D. Brodie, Jr. 1971. The taxonomic status of the rough-skinned newt, *Taricha granulosa* (Skilton), in the Rocky Mountains. Herpetologica 27(3):260-270.

Nussbaum, R. A. and G. W. Clothier. 1973. Population structure, growth, and size of larval *Dicamptodon ensatus* (Eschscholtz). Northwest Science 47(4):218-227.

Nussbaum, R. A. and L. V. Diller. 1976. The life history of the side-blotched lizard, *Uta stansburiana* Baird and Girard, in north-central Oregon. Northwest Science 50(4):243-260.

Nussbaum, R. A. and R. F. Hoyer. 1974. Geographic variation and the validity of subspecies in the rubber boa, *Charina bottae* (Blainville). Northwest Science 48(4): 219-229.

Nussbaum, R. A. and C. Maser. 1969. Observations of *Sorex palustris* preying on *Dicamptodon ensatus.* The Murrelet 50(2):23.

Nussbaum, R. A. and C. K. Tait. 1977. Aspects of the life history and ecology of the Olympic salamander, *Rhyacotriton olympicus* (Gaige). Amer. Midl. Nat. 98(1):176-199.

O'Hara, R. K. 1981. Habitat selection behavior in three species of anuran larvae: environmental cues, ontogeny, and adaptive significance. Ph.D. Thesis, Oregon State University, Corvallis, 146 pp.

O'Hara, R. K. and A. R. Blaustein. 1981. An investigation of sibling recognition in *Rana cascadae* tadpoles. Animal Behavior 29(4):1121-1126.

Oliver, M. G. and H. M. McCurdy. 1974. Migration, overwintering, and reproductive patterns of *Taricha granulosa* on southern Vancouver Island. Can. J. Zool. 52(4):541-545.

Pace, A. E. 1974. Systematic and biological studies of the leopard frogs *(Rana pipiens* Complex) of the United States. Misc. Publ. Mus. Zool., Univ. Michigan 148:1-140.

Pack, H. J. 1920. Eggs of the swamp tree frog. Copeia 1920(77):7.

Parker, W. S. and W. S. Brown. 1973. Species composition and population changes in two complexes of snake hibernacula in northern Utah. Herpetologica 29(4):319-326.

Parker, W. S. and W. S. Brown. 1974. Notes on the ecology of regal ringneck snakes *(Diadophis punctatus regalis)* in northern Utah. J. Herpetology 8(3):260-262.

Parker, W. S. and W. S. Brown. 1980. Comparative ecology of two colubrid snakes, *Masticophis t. taeniatus* and *Pituophis melanoleucus deserticola* in northern Utah. Milwaukee Pub. Mus.. Publ. Biol. and Geol. No. 7, i-viii+104 pp.

Parker, W. S. and E. R. Pianka. 1975. Comparative ecology of populations of the lizard *Uta stansburiana.* Copeia 1975(4):615-632.

Parker, W. S. and E. R. Pianka. 1976. Ecological observations on the leopard lizard *(Crotaphytus wislizeni)* in different parts of its range. Herpetologica 32(1):95-114.

Parrish, H. M. 1980. Poisonous snake bites in the United States. Vantage Press, New York, i-xii+469 pp.

Peabody, F. E. 1954. Trackways of an ambystomid salamander from the Paleocene of Montana. J. Paleont. 28(1):79-83.

Peacock, R. L. and R. A. Nussbaum. 1973. Reproductive biology and population structure of the western red-backed salamander, *Plethodon vehiculum* (Cooper). J. Herpetology 7(3):215-224.

Pettus, D. and G. M. Angleton. 1967. Comparative reproductive biology of montane and piedmont chorus frogs. Evolution 21(3):500-507.

Pianka, E. R. 1970. Comparative autecology of the lizard *Cnemidophorus tigris* in different parts of its geographic range. Ecology 51(4):703-720.

Pianka, E. R. and W. S. Parker. 1975. Ecology of horned lizards: a review with special reference to *Phrynosoma platyrhinos.* Copeia 1975(1):141-162.

Pimentel, R. A. 1959a. Positive embryo-maternal size correlation in the northern alligator lizard, *Gerrhonotus coeruleus principis.* Herpetologica 15(1):6-8.

Pimentel, R. A. 1959b. Seasonal variation in the morphology of the rough-skinned newt, *Taricha torosa granulosa,* with discussion of the systematics of the *granulosa* group. Herpetologica 15(1):8-13.

Pimentel, R. A. 1960. Inter- and intrahabitat movements of the rough skinned newt, *Taricha torosa granulosa* (Skilton). Amer. Midl. Nat. 63(2):470-496.

Ray, C. 1958, Vital limits and rates of desiccation in salamanders. Ecology 39(1):75-83.

Remington, D. C. 1968. Suture-zones of hybrid interaction between recently joined biotas. *In:* Dobzhansky, T., M. K. Hecht and W. C. Steere (eds.). Evolutionary Biology, Vol. 2, Meredith Corporation, New York, pp. 321-428.

Resnick, L. E. and D. L. Jameson. 1963. Color polymorphism in Pacific tree frogs. Science 142(3595):1081-1083.

Rickard, W. H. 1967. Onset of winter dormancy in lizards and beetles. Northwest Science 41(2):92-95.

Rickard, W. H. 1968. Field observations on the altitudinal distribution of the side-blotched lizard. Northwest Science 42(4):161-164.

Riemer, W. J. 1958. Variation and systematic relationships within the salamander genus *Taricha.* Univ. Calif. Publ. Zool. 56(3):301-390.

Rose, F. L. and D. Armentrout. 1976. Adaptive strategies of *Ambystoma tigrinum* Green inhabiting the Llano Estacado of West Texas. J. Anim. Ecol. 45(3):713-729.

Ryan, M. J. 1980. The reproductive behavior of the bullfrog *(Rana catesbeiana)*. Copeia 1980(1):108-114.

Samallow, P. B. 1979. Dynamics of enzyme polymorphism in a natural population of the boreal toad, *Bufo boreas boreas* Baird and Girard: evidence of natural selection via differential mortality in early life history stages. Ph.D. Thesis, Oregon State University, Corvallis, 182 pp.

Samallow, P. B. 1980. Selective mortality and reproduction in a natural population of *Bufo boreas*. Evolution 34(1):18-39.

Sanborn, S. R. and R. B. Loomis. 1979. Systematics and behavior of collared lizards *(Crotaphytus, Iguanidae)* in southern California. Herpetologica 35(2):101-106.

Schaub, D. L. and J. H. Larsen. 1978. The reproductive ecology of the Pacific treefrog *(Hyla regilla)*. Herpetologica 34(4): 409-416.

Schmid, W. D. 1982. Survival of frogs in low temperature. Science 215:697-698.

Seeliger, L. M. 1945. Variation in the Pacific mud turtle. Copeia 1945(3):150-159.

Shaw, C. E. 1951. Male combat in American colubrid snakes with remarks on combat in other colubrid and elapid snakes. Herpetologica 7(4):149-168.

Slater, J. R. 1939. Description and life history of a new *Rana* from Washington. Herpetologica 1(6):145-149.

Slater, J. R. 1962. Variations and new range of *Clemmys marmorata*. Occas. Pap. Dept. Biol. Univ. Puget Sound 20:204-205.

Smith, N. M. and W. W. Tanner. 1972. Two new subspecies of *Crotaphytus* (Sauria; Iguanidae). Great Basin Naturalist 32(1):25-34.

Smith, N. M. and W. W. Tanner. 1974. A taxonomic study of the western collared lizards, *Crotaphytus collaris* and *Crotaphytus insularis*. Brigham Young Univ. Sci. Bull., Biol. Ser. 19(4):1-29.

Snyder, R. C. 1956. Comparative features of the life histories of *Ambystoma gracile* (Baird) from populations at low and high altitudes. Copeia 1956(1):41-50.

Snyder, W. F. and D. L. Jameson. 1965. Multivariate geographic variation of mating call in populations of the Pacific tree frog. Copeia 1965(2):129-142.

Sprules, W. G. 1974. Environmental factors and the incidence of neoteny in *Ambystoma gracile* (Baird) (Amphibia: Caudata). Can. J. Zool. 52(12):1545-1552.

Stebbins, R. C. 1944. Field notes on a lizard, the mountain swift, with special reference to territorial behavior. Ecology 25(2):233-245.

Stebbins, R. C. 1948. Additional observations on home ranges and longevity in the lizard *Sceloporus graciosus*. Copeia 1948(1):20-22.

Stebbins, R. C. 1949a. Observations on laying, development, and hatching of the eggs of *Batrachoseps wrighti*. Copeia 1949(3):161-168.

Stebbins, R. C. 1949b. Speciation in salamanders of the plethodontid genus *Ensatina*. Univ. Calif. Publ. Zool. 48(6):377-526.

Stebbins, R. C. 1949c. Courtship of the plethodontid salamander *Ensatina eschscholtzii*. Copeia 1949(4):274-281.

Stebbins, R. C. 1954. Natural history of the salamanders of the plethodontid genus *Ensatina*. Univ. Calif. Publ. Zool. 54(2):47-124.

Stebbins, R. C. and C. H. Lowe, Jr. 1949. The systematic status of *Plethopsis* with a discussion of speciation in the genus *Batrachoseps*. Copeia 1949(2):116-129.

Stebbins, R. C. and C. H. Lowe, Jr. 1951. Subspecific differentiation in the Olympic salamander *Rhyacotriton olympicus*. Univ. Calif. Publ. Zool. 50(4):465-484.

Stebbins, R. C. and H. B. Robinson. 1946. Further analysis of a population of the lizard *Sceloporus graciosus gracilis*. Univ. Calif. Publ. Zool. 48(3):149-168.

Stelmock. J. J. and A. S. Harestad. 1979. Food habits and life history of the clouded salamander *(Aneides ferreus)* on northern Vancouver Island, British Columbia. Syesis 12:71-75.

Stewart, G. R. 1965. Thermal ecology of the garter snakes *Thamnophis sirtalis concinnus* (Hallowell) and *Thamnophis ordinoides* (Baird and Girard). Herpetologica 21(2):81-102.

Stewart, G. R. 1968. Some observations on the natural history of two Oregon garter snakes (genus *Thamnophis*). J. Herpetology 2(3-4):71-86.

Stewart, J. R. 1979. The balance between number and size of young in the live bearing lizard *Gerrhonotus coeruleus*. Herpetologica 35(4):342-350.

Storer, T. I. 1930. Notes on the range and life-history of the Pacific fresh-water turtle, *Clemmys marmorata*. Univ. Calif. Publ. Zool. 35(5):429-441.

Storm, R. M. 1947. Eggs and young of *Aneides ferreus*. Herpetologica 4(2):60-62.

Storm, R. M. 1960. Notes on the breeding biology of the red-legged frog *(Rana aurora aurora)*. Herpetologica 16(4):251-259.

Storm, R. M. and A. R. Aller. 1947. Food habits of *Aneides ferreus*. Herpetologica 4(2):59-60.

Storm, R. M. and R. A. Pimentel. 1954. A method for studying amphibian breeding populations. Herpetologica 10(3):161-166.

Svihla, A. 1935. Notes on the western spotted frog, *Rana pretiosa pretiosa*. Copeia 1935(3):119-122.

Svihla, A. 1943. Notes on young rubber snakes. Copeia 1942(2):128.

Svihla, A. 1953. Diurnal retreats of the spade-foot toad *Scaphiopus hammondi*. Copeia 1953(3):186.

Sype, W. E. 1975. Breeding habits, embryonic thermal requirements and embryonic and larval development of the Cascade frog, *Rana cascadae* Slater. Ph.D. Thesis, Oregon State University, Corvallis, 113 pp.

Tanner, W. W. 1943. Notes on the life history of *Eumeces skiltonianus skiltonianus*. Great Basin Naturalist 4(3-4):81-88.

Tanner, W. W. 1953. Notes on the life history of *Plethopsis wrighti* Bishop. Herpetologica 9(3):139-140.

Tanner, W. W. 1957. A taxonomic and ecological study of the western skink *(Eumeces skiltonianus)*. Great Basin Naturalist 17(3-4):59-94.

Tanner, W. W. and B. H. Banta. 1977. The systematics of *Crotaphytus wislizeni*, the leopard lizards. Part III. The leopard lizards of the Great Basin and adjoining areas, with a description of a new subspecies from the Lahontan Basin. Great Basin Naturalist 37(2):225-240.

Tanner, W. W. and J. M. Hopkin. 1972. Ecology of *Sceloporus occidentalis longipes* Baird and *Uta stansburiana stansburiana* Baird and Girard on Rainier Mesa, Nevada Test Site, Nye County, Nevada. Brigham Young Univ. Sci. Bull., Biol. Ser. 15(4):139.

Tanner, W. W. and C. D. Jorgensen. 1963. Reptiles of the Nevada Test Site. Brigham Young Univ. Sci. Bull., Biol. Ser. 3(3):131.

Tanner, W. W. and J. E. Krogh. 1973. Ecology of *Phrynosoma platyrhinos* at the Nevada Test Site, Nye County, Nevada. Herpetologica 29(4):327-342.

Tanner, W. W. and J. E. Krogh. 1974. Ecology of the leopard lizard, *Crotaphytus wislizeni* at the Nevada Test Site, Nye County, Nevada. Herpetologica 30(1):63-72.

Thorson, T. and A. Svihla. 1943. Correlation of the habits of amphibians with their ability to survive the loss of body water. Ecology 24(3):374-381.

Tihen, J. A. 1949. The genera of gerrhonotine lizards. Amer. Midl. Nat. 41(3):580-601.

Tihen, J. A. 1974. Two new North American Miocene salamandrids. J. Herpetology 8(3):211-218.

Tinkle, D. W. 1967. The life and demography of the side-blotched lizard, *Uta stansburiana*. Misc. Publ. Mus. Zool. Univ. Michigan 132:1-182.

Tinkle, D. W. 1973. A population analysis of the sagebrush lizard, *Sceloporus graciosus* in southern Utah. Copeia 1973(2):284-296.

Tinkle, D. W., J. D. Congdon and P. C. Rosen. 1981. Nesting frequency and success; implications for the demography of painted turtles. Ecology 62(6):1426-1432.

Turner, F. B. 1958. Life-history of the western spotted frog in Yellowstone National Park. Herpetologica 14(2):96-100.

Turner, F. B. 1959. An analysis of the feeding habits of *Rana p. pretiosa* in Yellowstone Park, Wyoming. Amer. Midl. Nat. 61(2):403-413.

Turner, F. B. 1960. Population structure and dynamics of the western spotted frog, *Rana p. pretiosa* Baird and Girard, in Yellowstone Park, Wyoming. Ecol. Monogr. 30(3):251-278.

Turner, F. B., J. R. Lannom, P. Medica and G. A. Hoddenbach. 1969. Density and composition of fenced populations of leopard lizards (*Crotaphytus wislizenii*) in southern Nevada. Herpetologica 25(4):247-257.

Twitty, V. C. 1942. The species of California *Triturus*. Copeia 1942(2):65-76.

Twitty, V. C. 1966. Of scientists and salamanders. W. H. Freeman, San Francisco, i-x+178 pp.

Van Denburgh, J. 1895. Notes on the habits and distribution of *Autodax iecanus*. Proc. Calif. Acad. Sci., Ser. 2, 5:776-778.

van Frank, R. 1955. *Paleotaricha oligocenica,* new genus and species, an Oligocene salamander from Oregon. Breviora 45:1-12.

Vest, D. 1982. The toxic Duvernoy's secretion of the wandering garter snake (*Thamnophis elegans vagrans*). Toxicon, in press.

Vitt, L. J. 1973. Reproductive biology of the anguid lizard, *Gerrhonotus coeruleus principis*. Herpetologica 29(2):176-184.

Vitt, L. J. 1974. Reproductive effort and energy comparisons of adults, eggs, and neonates of *Gerrhonotus coeruleus principis*. J. Herpetology 8(2):165-168.

Waddick, J. W. and H. M. Smith. 1974. The significance of scale characters in evaluation of the lizard genera *Gerrhonotus, Elgaria,* and *Barisia.* Great Basin Naturalist 34(4):257-266.

Wells, K. D. 1976. Multiple egg clutches in the green frog (*Rana clamitans*). Herpetologica 32(1):85-87.

Wells, K. D. 1977. Territoriality and male mating success in the green frog (*Rana clamitans*). Ecology 58(4):750-762.

Wells, K. D. 1978. Territoriality in the green frog (*Rana clamitans*): vocalizations and agonistic behavior. Anim. Behav. 26(4):1051-1063.

Werntz, J. G. 1969. Spring mating of *Ascaphus*. J. Herpetology 3(3-4):167-169.

Wever, E. G., M-C. Hepp-Reymond and J. A. Vernon. 1966. Vocalization and hearing in the leopard lizard. Proc. Natl. Acad. Sci. 55:98-106.

Whitaker, J. O. and C. Maser. 1981. Food habits of seven species of lizards from Malheur County, southern Oregon. Northwest Science 55(3):202-208.

White, R. L. 1977. Prey selection by the rough skinned newt (*Taricha granulosa*) in two pond types. Northwest Science 51(2):114-118.

Whitney, C. L. 1980. The role of the "encounter" call in spacing of Pacific tree frogs, *Hyla regilla*. Can. J. Zool. 58(1):75-78.

Whitney, C. L. and J. R. Krebs. 1975a. Mate selection in Pacific tree frogs. Nature 244(5506):325-326.

Whitney, C. L. and J. R. Krebs. 1975b. Spacing and calling in Pacific tree frogs, *Hyla regilla*. Can. J. Zool. 53(11):1519-1527.

Wiens, J. A. 1970. Effects of early experience on substrate pattern selection in *Rana aurora* tadpoles. Copeia 1970(3):543-548.

Wiens, J. A. 1972. Anuran habitat selection: early experience and substrate selection in *Rana cascadae* tadpoles. Anim. Behav. 20(22):218-220.

Wiewandt, T. A. 1969. Vocalization, aggressive behavior, and territoriality in the bullfrog, *Rana catesbeiana.* Copeia 1969(2):276-285.

Woodbury, A. M. 1941. Copulation in gopher snakes. Copeia 1941(1):54.

Woodward, B. 1982. Male persistence and mating success in Woodhouse's toad *(Bufo woodhousei).* Ecology 63(2):583-585.

Zweifel, R. G. 1954. Adaptation to feeding in the snake *Contia tenuis.* Copeia 1954(4):299-300.

Zweifel, R. G. 1955. Ecology, distribution and systematics of frogs of the *Rana boylei* group. Univ. Calif. Publ. Zool. 54(4):207-292.

INDEX

332